Infrared Spectroscopy
in
Surface Chemistry

INFRARED SPECTROSCOPY IN SURFACE CHEMISTRY

MICHAEL L. HAIR

RESEARCH & DEVELOPMENT LABORATORIES
CORNING GLASS WORKS
CORNING, NEW YORK

1967

MARCEL DEKKER, INC., New York

Preface

Shortly after accepting the invitation to write this book, a good friend commented to me that "the trouble with books is that people believe them." This statement, though made in jest, contains a great deal of truth; there exists a considerable gap in the scientific literature between books, which can be considered "fact," and papers, which may be argued about. The application of infrared spectroscopy to surface studies is comparatively recent, but it has become a unique and popular tool. Basic information about a surface interaction may be obtained in an almost routine way. The increasing activity in this field is continually adding to our understanding of the nature of surfaces and surface species, and the techniques used to obtain the infrared spectra of adsorbed species are becoming more elegant and precise. The entire subject is, therefore, in a state of flux, and throughout this text it should be remembered that although the interpretations given are true in a broad sense, they may not be correct in their exact detail. Many are based on evidence which at present is insufficient. In reviewing the data obtained to date, I have attempted to present the best interpretations available at this time. In some cases, however, the interpretations have been biased, either to present a more uniform picture or, in some cases, to conform to my own preconceived ideas. The reader is therefore encouraged to think deeply about the interpretations.

v

Today, in compiling a book on any scientific subject, the author must first decide whether to edit the contributions of a number of individual experts or to go it alone and provide an overall view of the subject as it appears to one man. Personally, I have never been very happy with books containing a series of reviews by a miscellany of authors, and I therefore preferred to present my own review of the experimental results obtained in this field. I have always felt that the nature of the atomic heterogeneity of surfaces has been ignored to a large extent by surface chemists other than those interested in catalysis. This has been partially due to the lack of a simple method for examining surfaces—a gap now filled by infrared spectroscopy. The application of this technique to the investigation of surface reactions has been largely pioneered by scientists whose primary interest is in elucidating the nature of catalytic activity. The efforts of these workers in this direction have had minimal success, but their results are of immediate and practical importance to anyone who is interested in surface phenomena.

This text, therefore, has been written primarily for myself. It contains the information that I would like to have had available in single-volume form when I first became interested in the chemistry of surfaces. The infrared method has been indispensable to my own work. I hope my readers will find the results obtained from this technique as exciting and informative as they have been to me.

The preparation of this text would not have been possible without the help of many people. In particular my thanks are due to my wife for both her patience and impatience during the writing of this book.

The management of Corning Glass Works are thanked for the facilities placed at my disposal. Several members of the staff made comments which have been incorporated in the manuscript; those of Dr. W. Hertl and Dr. M. E. Nordberg have been especially valuable. The secretarial assistance of Miss Janice Drake and Miss Mary Ellen Hurlburt and the illustrations by Mr. R. Crocker are appreciated.

Dr. R. P. Eischens (Texaco) and Dr. J. B. Peri (American Oil Company) have also made comments which have been incorporated in the manuscript, and their help is gratefully acknowledged. The several scientists who provided me with manuscripts prior to their publication are also thanked for their cooperation.

M. L. HAIR

Corning, New York
April 1967

Table of Contents

6-1. Introduction   217
6-2. Carbon Monoxide Adsorbed on Nickel and
      Nickel Oxide   218

      A. Strongly Adsorbed Carbon Monoxide   218
      B. Weakly Adsorbed Carbon Monoxide   221
      C. Effect of the Supporting Oxide   222
      D. Nickel Metal Films   225
      E. Adsorption on Nickel Oxide   227
      F. Nickel Carbonyl   227

6-3. The Nature of the Ni–SiO$_2$ Surface   228

      A. Surface Hydroxyl Groups   228
      B. Ammonia Adsorption   228
      C. HCl Adsorption   229

6-4. Carbon Monoxide Adsorption on Other
      Metals   230

      A. Carbon Monoxide on Platinum   230
      B. Carbon Monoxide on Palladium   234
      C. Carbon Monoxide on Ruthenium   234
      D. Carbon Monoxide on Iridium   235
      E. Carbon Monoxide on Rhodium   235
      F. Carbon Monoxide on Copper   236
      G. Carbon Monoxide on Iron   238

6-5. Prediction of Catalytic Activity   241

      A. Concept of Matching Vibrations   241
      B. Intermedions   243
      C. The Adsorption Process   247
      D. Prediction of Catalytic Activity   248

6-6. The Nature of Carbon Monoxide Adsorption   248
6-7. Some Miscellaneous Adsorption Studies   252

      A. Nitric Oxide on Nickel and Iron   252
      B. Nitrogen Dioxide Adsorption   254
      C. Oxygen-Containing Compounds Adsorbed on Iron   254
      D. Sulfur Compounds Adsorbed on Nickel   255
      E. Nitrogen on Nickel   257
      F. Formic Acid on Nickel (Oxide)   261
      G. Ethylene Adsorption on Metal Surfaces   262
      H. Acetylene Adsorption on Metal Surfaces   263
      I. Paraxylene on Transition Metals: Isotopic Exchange   264

      References   264

Infrared Spectroscopy
in
Surface Chemistry

1

Surface Chemistry

1-1. INTRODUCTION

The word "surface" and the area known as "surface chemistry" mean many things to many people. Mathematically, a surface can be reduced to the two-dimensional plane that separates two phases, but to the chemist it is clear that a third dimension, however small, must exist. In defining the thickness of this interfacial layer there is room for much argument, and the area of surface chemistry has embraced studies that range all the way from observations of individual atoms to macroscopic phenomena investigated with the ordinary-light microscope.

In so far as this text is concerned our primary interest will be with the atomic constitution of surfaces, and discussion will be limited to effects that are often less than one, and rarely more than two atomic layers in depth. At this level of interest microscopic techniques are of no avail to the investigator. Indirect techniques must generally be used, and it is in this area that the application of spectroscopic techniques to surface problems has had outstanding growth and success.

To understand why surface properties should be in any way different from bulk properties, it is necessary to speculate on the nature of a crystalline surface. To do this, let us consider the crystal of zinc sulfide

1

(ZnS) that is illustrated in Fig. 1-1 (*1*). In this diagram it is seen that every zinc atom is surrounded by four sulfur atoms and that every sulfur atom is in turn surrounded by four zinc atoms. The intermolecular forces are thus balanced, and a state of maximum entropy is attained. The unit cell is outlined, and the perfect crystal is obtained by a reproduction of this unit cell in three dimensions. Somewhere, however, the crystal growth must stop. No more unit cells can be added, and a surface is obtained. As soon as this crystal surface is reached, no matter where it is defined, it is clear that broken bonds must exist and, whereas all the internal atoms are completely surrounded by other atoms in a symmetrical way such that all attractive forces between the atoms are canceled out, the surface atoms are subject to an asymmetric distribution of forces and do not exist in a state of maximum entropy. The state of unsaturation or strain at this theoretical surface can be partially relieved by either of the following:

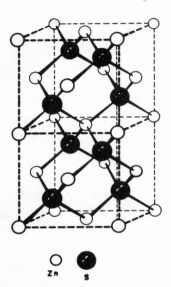

Zn ○   S ●

Fig. 1-1. Zinc sulfide crystal. Two unit cells outlined by dashed lines. [Redrawn from Reference (1), courtesy of Clarendon Press, Oxford.]

1. Rearrangement of the surface atoms so that they exist in positions, that are displaced from their regular crystallographic positions.

2. The phenomenon known as *adsorption*. In this process molecules of a foreign substance are added to the surface, thereby relieving the unsaturation and causing a decrease in the free energy of the surface.

In the latter process the change of surface free energy ΔG is related to the heat of absorption ΔH and to the change of entropy ΔS by the equation

$$\Delta G = \Delta H - T \, \Delta S \qquad (1\text{-}1)$$

in which T is the absolute temperature. From this equation it follows that the heat of adsorption is nearly always negative and thus the adsorption process is nearly always exothermic. The compound that is adsorbed is known as the *adsorbate*, and the material that provides the adsorptive properties is known as the *adsorbent*. By definition, the process of adsorption is limited to the surface of a material, bulk penetration of one material by another being known as *absorption*.

The phenomenon of adsorption can occur at all surfaces, and five types of interface can exist: gas–solid, liquid–solid, liquid–liquid, solid–solid, and gas–liquid. The gas–solid interface has probably received the most attention in the literature and is the best understood. The liquid–solid interface is now receiving much attention because of its importance in many electrochemical and biological systems, but the nature of the interface is imperfectly understood on an atomic scale, primarily because of lack of suitable techniques for investigating the adsorption phenomenon. The other interfaces have been poorly studied. This situation is likely to be reversed, however, and the current emphasis and enthusiastic research on composite materials is bound to lead to new investigations of surface interactions in efforts to explain the remarkable mechanical strength of some of these materials. It is clear that all reactions involving two phases must involve an interfacial reaction before the bulk process can occur.

The study of the gas–solid adsorption process has excited the interest of both academic and industrial scientists for many years, and the reasons are not hard to find. Industrially it is known that this phenomenon plays an essential role in the catalytic process. The ability of surfaces to selectively accelerate the rate of many chemical reactions is the basis of much of the heavy-chemical production in the world, and the sale of the catalyst materials alone is a $200,000,000-a-year business (2). The use of such materials as silica gel and charcoal as drying agents and adsorbents for dyes and noxious gases is well known and is an industry by itself.

A great deal of work has been expended in an effort to understand the atomic steps involved in the adsorption and catalytic processes, and as a result, the kinetics of many of these reactions are well understood. Up to 10 years ago, however, no technique that was sufficiently sensitive to identify adsorbed intermediates was available, and most of the kinetic data were interpreted by using reaction schemes that could be neither proved nor disproved. The application of infrared spectroscopy to surface studies, although it has not yet answered many of the questions that have been asked, has added immeasurably to our knowledge of interfacial reactions and provides positive identification of many surface species.

Spectroscopic techniques in general have probably been the most useful tool ever made available to chemists for the investigation of atoms and molecules. Thus, the study of molecular spectra gives information not only of the dimension of molecules but also of molecular vibrational, rotational, and electronic states. The earliest application of spectroscopy to the study of surface interactions was in the study of dyes adsorbed on various oxides. Color changes often took place upon adsorption, and they could be studied in the ultraviolet and visible regions of the spectrum. Since the changes in the spectrum are attributable to changes in the electronic configuration of the molecule, it was possible to obtain some information about the surface of the adsorbent. Unfortunately, much of this work was carried out on ill-defined surfaces and many of the early conclusions must be considered suspect.

The first application of infrared spectroscopy to surface studies appears to be a little-known paper by Buswell et al. (3), who discussed the spectra observed during the desorption of water from a montmorillonite surface. This was followed by a series of papers by Yaroslavskii, Terenin, and other Russian scientists on adsorption on surface hydroxyl groups (4–7). This, together with the pioneering work of Eischens on chemical adsorption and of McDonald, Sheppard, and Yates on physical adsorption, has laid the foundations for the science as it exists today. The wide acceptance of the infrared method as a technique for studying adsorbed molecules can be seen from a glance through the literature. The number of papers published each year has steadily increased since the introduction of the technique. Indeed, the infrared spectrometer is fast becoming an indispensable tool to the practicing surface chemist both as a research tool and as a routine way of checking surface purity.

The application of ultraviolet spectroscopy and magnetic resonance spectroscopy to surface studies since 1950 has been appreciable but not nearly as rapid as the application of infrared. This is undoubtedly because ultraviolet and resonance spectra are not subject to as ready interpretation as infrared spectra and both are somewhat limited in their applications.

1-2. ADSORPTION PROCESSES

From Eq. (1-1) it is seen that the adsorption process is nearly always exothermic. Many heats of adsorption have been measured. These measurements indicate that there are, in general, two distinct types of adsorption that can be differentiated. The first type, known as *physical adsorption* or *physisorption*, is a process in which the bond between the adsorbent and the adsorbate is thought to be of the van der Waals type. Because this bond is very weak, it is characterized by a low heat of adsorption, usually of the order of 2–5 cal/mole. This value is of the same order of magnitude as the heat of vaporization of the adsorbate and lends credence to the concept of a weak "physical" bonding. Physical adsorption is usually observed at low temperatures or on relatively "inert" surfaces.

The second type of adsorption that is observed is known as *chemical adsorption*, or *chemisorption*. In this case the adsorbate undergoes a strong chemical interaction with the unsaturated surface and gives rise to a high heat of adsorption, usually of the order of 15–20 kcal/mole. Chemical adsorption is often characterized by taking place at elevated temperatures and is often an activated process. It may be dissociative, nondissociative, or reactive in nature.

Exact differentiation between chemical and physical adsorption is often difficult and usually unprofitable. To the practicing chemist a physically adsorbed species is usually considered to be an adsorbed material that can be completely removed from the surface, without decomposition, by prolonged evacuation at room temperature or by heating to 120°C. This experimental choice of conditions is completely arbitrary, and the final decision is always left with the experimenter. The advent of infrared spectroscopy has led to a better means of distinguishing between the two processes.

The infrared spectrum of a molecule arises as a result of the vibrations of the atoms within the molecule; the symmetry and bond strengths of the molecule as a whole determine the number and frequency of the vibrations. When a molecule is adsorbed, it is clear that the "one-sided" surface forces must cause a change, however slight, in the symmetry of the molecule, and any quantitative measure of this change can be directly related to the nature of the adsorption. If the molecule is physically adsorbed, it is subjected only to weak intermolecular forces of the van der Waals type and thus its symmetry is only slightly perturbed from that of the gas phase. Accordingly, the infrared spectrum is altered only slightly, and small frequency shifts, usually less than 1 %, are observed. (Some Raman vibrations, normally inactive in the infrared, can become activated during the physical adsorption process, but their frequencies are only slightly altered.) During the chemisorption process, however, the symmetry of the adsorbed species is completely different from that of the gaseous molecule, the surface bond is very strong, and the adsorption may be dissociative in nature. In this case, a completely new infrared spectrum is observed and band shifts and intensities are far removed from those of the gaseous adsorbate. In view of this, Leftin and Hobson (8) have defined physical adsorption as "adsorption which leads to perturbation of the electronic or stereochemical states of the molecule but

otherwise leaves the molecule and its entire electron complement intact."
Chemisorption is defined as "adsorption which produces a new chemical
species by fragmentation of the molecule or of its electron complement."

Both physical and chemical adsorption can take place simultaneously
on a surface, especially at lower temperatures. A good example of this is
the adsorption of carbon dioxide on a $NiO-SiO_2$ surface. Addition of
carbon dioxide to a $NiO-SiO_2$ sample gives rise to an infrared spectrum
in which a band due to physically adsorbed CO_2 is observed at 2345 cm^{-1}.
This is very close to the gas-phase value (2349 cm^{-1}), and since this band
is easily removed by evacuation at room temperature, it is readily identified as being due to a physically adsorbed species. In addition to this
band, further peaks are observed at 1615 and 1360 cm^{-1}. These bands are
not removed by pumping at room temperature, and they are thus attributed to a chemisorbed species. In actual fact the carbon dioxide has
reacted with the surface, and the observed bands are attributed to the
formation of a surface carbonate.

$$Ni_s—O + CO_2 \rightarrow Ni_s(CO_3)$$

1-3. PHYSICAL ADSORPTION

A. Adsorption Isotherms

The amount of gas that is physically adsorbed on a solid surface is a
function of both the temperature of the system and the partial pressure
of the adsorbate. In Fig. 1-2 the amount of nitrogen adsorbed on a
silica–alumina catalyst is plotted as a function of pressure. As would
be expected for a weak van der Waals type of bond, the amount of nitrogen
adsorbed is directly related to the pressure and inversely related to the
temperature. This type of graphical representation is known as an
adsorption isotherm, and many mathematical interpretations of adsorption
isotherms have been given. One of the best known of these is an empirical
equation of the form

$$x/m = kp^{1/n} \tag{1-2}$$

where x is the mass of gas adsorbed, m is the mass of adsorbate, p is the
pressure, and k and n are constants that are dependent on both the system
and the temperature. This isotherm is usually known as the Freundlich
isotherm although, as Glasstone (9) points out, the equation was used by
earlier workers and was in fact originally rejected by Freundlich. Equation
(1-2) is entirely empirical, but it is widely used because of its simplicity
and good agreement with a variety of adsorption data.

Historically, the close correlation between heats of adsorption and heats of vaporization led early workers to suppose that the process involved condensation of the adsorbing gas on the surface of the adsorbate even at low pressures. Langmuir, however, pointed out that this concept was unlikely due to the rapid falloff of intermolecular forces with distance, and he introduced the idea of monomolecular films. In this approach

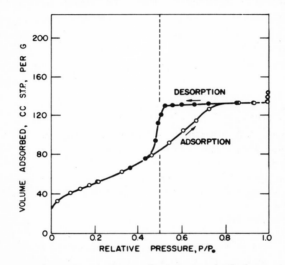

Fig. 1-2. *Adsorption–desorption isotherm of nitrogen adsorbed on a silica–alumina cracking catalyst that has been predried at 970°C.* [*Data taken from Reference (20).*]

the adsorption process is considered to be an equilibrium process in which the rate at which molecules hit a surface and are adsorbed is equal to the rate at which molecules of gas are *desorbed* from the surface.

If the fraction of surface covered with adsorbed gas at any time is θ and if the heat of adsorption is assumed to be independent of surface coverage, the rate of desorption is proportional to the surface coverage:

$$R_{\text{des}} = k'\theta \tag{1-3}$$

Now, if μ is the rate at which gas molecules strike the surface and α is the fraction of these molecules that stick on the surface for an appreciable length of time (i.e., are adsorbed), then the rate of adsorption is proportional to the fraction of surface that is not covered by gas molecules and is given by

$$R_{\text{ads}} = (1 - \theta)\alpha\mu \tag{1-4}$$

At equilibrium

$$R_{ads} = R_{des} \tag{1-5}$$

Therefore,

$$k'\theta = (1 - \theta)\alpha\mu \qquad \text{and} \qquad \theta = \frac{\alpha\mu}{k'}\bigg/ 1 + \frac{\alpha\mu}{k'} \tag{1-6}$$

The rate at which the molecules strike the surface, μ, is proportional to the pressure P, and so

$$\mu = k''P$$

Therefore,

$$\theta = \frac{kP}{1 + kP} \tag{1-7}$$

where $k = \alpha k''/k'$. This is known as the *Langmuir isotherm*.

At very low pressures Eq. (1-7) reduces to $\theta = kP$. This is a restatement of Henry's law, and consequently this part of the adsorption isotherm is often known as the Henry's law region. At high pressures θ approaches 1 and indicates monomolecular coverage.

At intermediate pressures one might expect an expression that is intermediate between $\theta = 1$ and $\theta = kP$ to hold, i.e., an expression of the type

$$\theta = kP^{1/n} \tag{1-8}$$

where n is more than 1. This can be compared with Eq. (1-2) and is seen to be identical with the Freundlich equation.

Five main types of isotherm have been found, and they have been classified by Brunauer (*10*) into the five shapes illustrated in Fig. 1-3. The volume of gas adsorbed is plotted against either the pressure P or the ratio P/P_0, where P_0 is the saturation vapor pressure of the adsorbate.

The type I, III, and IV isotherms are those most commonly encountered, particularly with oxides and catalytic materials. The type I isotherm is the one predicted by the Langmuir equation, and it indicates that mono-layer adsorption is attained only when the saturated vapor pressure is reached. The S shape of the type II and type IV isotherms is taken as an indication of multilayer adsorption.

The type III and V isotherms are not common and are interpreted by using a model in which it is considered that the slow initial rise is due to an adsorption process in which the monolayer forces are small. The change of slope in the upper portion of the type V isotherm and the sharp leveling off of the type IV isotherm at high pressures are due to pore volume limitations.

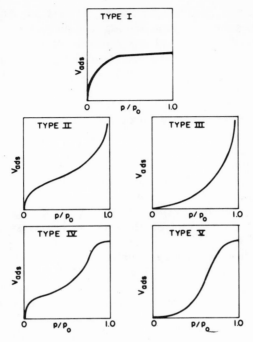

Fig. 1-3. Classification of adsorption isotherms. [*After Brunauer (10).*]

B. BET Theory

A significant advance in the interpretation of the physical adsorption process was made in 1938 by Brunauer, Emmett, and Teller (*11*). Starting with the basic concepts of Langmuir, these authors assumed that the rate of evaporation from the nth adsorbed layer was equal to the rate of condensation of the $(n - 1)$th layer. From this assumption it proved possible to derive the now famous equation

$$\frac{P}{V(P_0 - P)} = \frac{1}{V_m C} + \frac{(C - 1)P}{V_m C P_0} \qquad (1\text{-}9)$$

where V is the total volume adsorbed at pressure P, P_0 is the saturation vapor pressure of the adsorbate, V_m is the volume of gas needed to form a monolayer, and C is a constant that is approximately equal to $\exp{(E_1 - E_L)/RT}$. E_1 is the heat of adsorption of the gas in the monolayer, and E_L is the heat of liquefaction of the gas. This multilayer approach to physical adsorption has had profound influence on experimental approaches to physical adsorption and is widely known as the BET theory.

Equation (1-9) is linear, and a plot of the left-hand side against P/P_0 should give a straight line of slope $(C - 1)/V_m C$, the intercept on the ordinate axis being $1/V_m C$. From a knowledge of these two parameters it is possible to calculate V_m, the volume of gas necessary to give monolayer coverage. Emmett and Brunauer (12) have calculated that the cross-sectional area of an adsorbed nitrogen molecule is 16.2 $Å^2$, and thus a simple substitution of this into the experimental V_m value enables a reliable estimate of the surface area of the adsorbent to be made. This method is generally used in determining the surface areas of solids, and it represents one of the most important practical contributions to the field of surface chemistry.

It has been found from experience that, when nitrogen is used as the adsorbing gas, the intercept on the ordinate is very small and can be drawn through the origin with little loss in accuracy. Accordingly, this makes it possible to determine the surface area by the measurement of one adsorption point at a relative pressure of between 0.1 and 0.3. For accurate work, however, at least three points are recommended. For complete information on practical details the reader is referred to an article by Joyner (13).

Examination of the BET equation makes possible the following conclusions:

1. When $E_1 > E_L$, $C \gg 1$ and thus the adsorption curve is type II.
2. When $E_1 < E_L$, C is small and the adsorption curve is of type III.
3. When monolayer coverage only is obtained, then the BET equation reduces to

$$\frac{P}{V} = \frac{1}{kV_m} + \frac{P}{V_m}$$

an equation that is similar to the Langmuir equation (1-7) and predicts a type I isotherm.

4. The BET theory has been extended to give expressions that are more complicated than Eq. (1-9) and that predict the less common isotherms.

C. Desorption

In the preceding discussion of the type II, IV, and V isotherms the upper concavity was airily explained as being due to a pore volume limitation. The concept of physical adsorption requires that at the saturation vapor pressure the whole pore structure is filled with liquid adsorbate and thus the volume adsorbed at this point is a measure of the total pore volume. For the sake of simplicity the pores in a solid are usually considered to consist of narrow cylindrical tubes that are open at both ends. Adsorption takes place in uniform layers on the walls of a pore until the films join at one point. When this situation occurs, condensation immediately takes place in that particular pore and the process is repeated until all the pores have been filled and adsorption is complete.

If the relative pressure is now reduced, however, it is observed that the adsorption isotherm is not necessarily reproduced and a desorption branch that is "higher" than the adsorption branch is obtained (Fig. 1-2). At intermediate relative pressures more gas remains on the surface during the desorption process than existed on the surface during the adsorption process. This phenomenon is reversible, and the hysteresis effect has an explanation based on the work of Thomson (Lord Kelvin) nearly a century ago. In his work on surface tension Thomson showed that the vapor pressure of a spherical drop of liquid is different from the vapor pressure of a planar liquid film and is given by the equation

$$\ln \frac{P}{P_0} = \frac{2\gamma}{r} \frac{M}{\rho RT} \tag{1-10}$$

where P is the vapor pressure of the liquid over the drop, r is the radius of the drop, P_0 is the normal vapor pressure of the liquid over a flat surface, γ is the surface tension of the drop, and ρ is the density of the drop. M, R, and T have their usual connotation. A consideration of a small, cylindrical pore filled with liquid readily reveals that the capillary effect will cause the liquid in the pore to have a concave surface, and thus the vapor pressure above the meniscus will be given by

$$\ln \frac{P}{P_0} = - \frac{2\gamma}{r} \frac{M}{\rho RT} \tag{1-11}$$

The negative sign is introduced to allow for the change in curvature.

In other words, the vapor pressure above the concave meniscus of the liquid in a pore is less than the vapor pressure of the bulk liquid. During the adsorption process, the pores are not filled until adsorption is complete. An equilibrium between gaseous and adsorbed gas that is independent of the liquid properties is thus established. During the desorption, however, the equilibrium is governed by the surface tension of the liquid and therefore by the Kelvin equation. Since the vapor pressure above the meniscus must always be less than the vapor pressure of the bulk liquid, the desorption branch must always be "higher" than the adsorption branch.

D. Pore Size Determinations

The Kelvin equation has been used to estimate the average diameter of the pores existing in porous solids and to determine the pore size distribution curve. If we assume that the pores in the adsorbate are cylindrical, then Eq. (1-11) can be rewritten

$$r = -2\gamma \frac{M}{PRT} \ln \frac{P_0}{P} \qquad (1\text{-}12)$$

If P_0 and P are known experimentally from the desorption isotherm, the average radius of the pores at any coverage can be determined and compared with the volume of gas that is still adsorbed. In other words, a distribution curve can be obtained. It should be noted that the value for the pore radius that is obtained by this method is the radius of the cylinder from which evaporation takes place and neglects effects of the monolayer. Accordingly, a distance equivalent to at least one molecular layer should be added to the radius obtained by this method in order to determine the actual pore size of the material. Schull and Wheeler (14) have extended the theory outlined above to correct for multilayer adsorption. Reference should be made to their original articles for practical details.

If a very narrow pore size distribution is known to be obtained, then, by assuming cylindrical pores, the average pore radius can be estimated very simply from a knowledge of the total amount of nitrogen that can be condensed in the capillaries (the volume of gas adsorbed at $P = P_0$) and the surface area. Thus, if there are n cylindrical pores of length l

$$\text{Surface area} = 2\pi r l n$$
$$\text{Pore volume} = \pi r^2 n l$$
$$\text{Therefore, } r = 2 \times \frac{\text{pore volume}}{\text{surface area}}$$

Values obtained by this method are usually within 2 Å of the values obtained by the more complicated approaches.

From this discussion it is seen that the open cylindrical pore theory can account for the hysteresis effect in the adsorption–desorption isotherms. However, an alternative explanation due to McBain (15) is worthy of note. This is based on the assumption that the hysteresis is caused by the presence of "bottleneck" pores in the adsorbent. Such pores would have a small mouth and a large body and can be envisioned as being formed by a cluster of spheres. During the condensation process, the pores would fill at a pressure which was dependent on the radii of the pores. Condensation would occur initially at the points that exhibited the narrowest radius and extend to wider portions as the relative pressure increased.

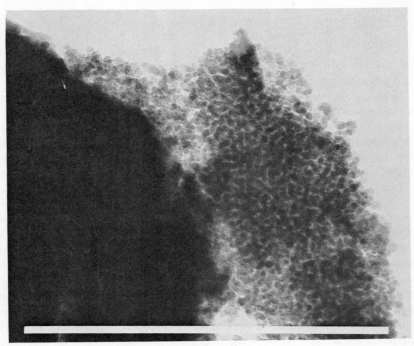

Fig. 1-4. *Transmission electron micrograph of a chip of porous glass, Corning Code 7930.* [*Courtesy of G. B. Carrier and Corning Glass Works.*]

Thus, the pore would not be filled until the saturation pressure was reached. On a lowering of the relative pressure, no evaporation would take place until the pressure had fallen to a value corresponding to the largest opening to the pore, at which point the pore would empty quickly. Thus, for any given pressure, the desorption branch of the isotherm would always lie at higher V_{ads} values than the adsorption branch.

The above explanation is in accord with experimental observation. Although it is much simpler to consider the pores in a high-area solid to be cylindrical, the McBain picture is probably much closer to the truth. Examination of Fig. 1-4, for instance, shows that the structure of microporous glass, as observed by transmission electron microscopy, indeed consists of a collection of small silica balls, about 300 Å in diameter, connected in a random fashion. Adsorption–desorption studies on this material show it to be almost identical in its properties with a silica gel that has a surface area of about 200 m²/g. Assumption of cylindrical pores gives an average pore radius of 19.8 Å, whereas application of the Schull method gives an average radius of 21.4 Å (*16*). The shape of the pore size distribution curve is Gaussian, and 96% of the pores vary less than ±3 Å from the average radius. Such results might be taken as a clear indication that the pores are cylindrical if the electron micrographs did not clearly indicate that they are not!

The gas adsorption methods are thus somewhat suspect in regard to the conclusions that are drawn from them. They have, however, proved their efficiency in that they have enabled workers in a multitude of laboratories to obtain comparable results and correlation of other properties. Surface area measurements are of great importance to the surface spectroscopist, because he must be able to estimate the number of molecules he can expect to adsorb on a surface in order to ensure that he has sufficient material present in his cell to give an identifiable spectrum. Moreover, it is well known that the heat of adsorption is usually dependent upon the degree of surface coverage obtained. This implies either a natural or an induced surface heterogeneity, and it might be expected that the spectrum of an adsorbed molecule would also change with coverage. It has been found that the intensities of the spectral bands due to adsorbed molecules are particularly sensitive to surface coverage, a good example being the adsorption of carbon monoxide on a platinum surface. This is fully discussed in Chapter 6, but quick reference to Fig. 6-5 immediately shows that both the frequency of vibration and the intensity of the vibration of the adsorbed carbon monoxide are sensitive to the degree of surface coverage. In many cases, therefore, this information is necessary before the spectrum of an adsorbed species can be fully interpreted.

1-4. THE NATURE OF THE SURFACE BOND

Whereas the nature of the bond formed between the adsorbent and the adsorbate during the physical adsorption process is adequately defined at this stage as being due to weak intermolecular attractions of the van der Waals type, it will become clear later that infrared investigations of the physical process show that a certain specificity can occur that is of the charge-transfer type. Any chemical bond involves some form of electron transfer, and in a chemisorption process, electron transfer between the adsorbent and adsorbate must occur and lead to alterations in the properties of both materials. Whether the surface bond is ionic or covalent will depend upon the ability of both the adsorbent and adsorbate to transfer the electrons.

The energy required for an atom or molecule to lose an electron is known as the ionization potential I, and the energy released when an electron is added to an atom or molecule is known as the electron affinity of the material.

Thus, for an atom X

$$X \rightarrow X^+ + e \qquad I \text{ electron volts}$$

and

$$X + e \rightarrow X^- \qquad E \text{ electron volts}$$

Half the sum of the ionization potential and the electron affinity has been defined by Mulliken (*17*) as being the electronegativity of X. Bearing

2 × electronegativity

TABLE 1-1

	I	E	$I + E$
N	14.53	−0·1	14.43
O	13.61	1.47	15.08
Na	5.14	0.4	5.54

these definitions in mind, it is of interest to consider the type of bond that is formed when sodium, nitrogen, and oxygen are adsorbed on a clean tungsten surface. The values for the ionization potentials and electron affinities of these materials are as shown in Table 1-1. From this it is clear that, of the three elements, the sodium atom is the most likely to lose an electron and form a positive ion. The low electron affinity makes it unlikely that sodium will form a negative ion, and thus on a metallic surface we might expect formation of a species

$$Na^+ \qquad W^{(-)}$$

in which complete electron transfer is observed and a positive sodium ion is formed on the surface. Similarly, with oxygen, the high ionization potential makes it unlikely that a positive oxygen ion will be formed. The high electron affinity indicates that the negative ion is easily formed, and thus, in this case, electron transfer from the metal to the oxygen would be proposed.

$$O^- \qquad W^+$$

In the case of nitrogen the high ionization potential and low electron affinity argue against the formation of either type of charged species. Consequently, nitrogen might be expected to form a covalent bond with a clean tungsten surface. These three species have indeed been experimentally observed on a tungsten surface in accord with the prediction (*18*).

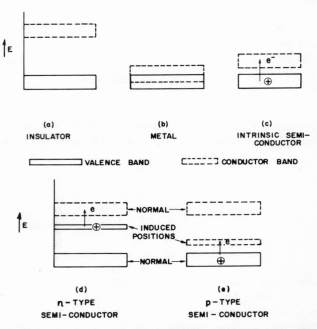

Fig. 1-5. *Diagrammatic representation of energy bands and classification of conductivity types.* [*After Prettre (19).*]

Clearly, the electron transfer from and to the adsorbent must also depend on the solid-state properties of the adsorbent and the transfer of electrons must be accompanied by an increase or decrease in the electrical conductivity.

By their electrical properties, materials can be divided into three groups: insulators, metals, and semiconductors. In band theory all substances have two discrete energy levels that are termed the valence band and the conduction band, and the energy difference between these bands represents the resistance to electronic conduction. Electrons in the valence band can be excited into the conduction band, and it is this transfer of electrons from one energy level to the next that gives rise to the electrical properties of the solid. The transfer of an electron leaves a positive hole or electron vacancy in the valence band. This concept is illustrated diagrammatically in Fig. 1-5, where the energy differences between the valence and conduction bands are represented for a series of conductivity types.

In the case of the insulator [Fig. 1-5(a)] it is seen that the energy gap between the conduction and the valence bands is very large. Such substances have very poor electrical conductivity and are typically represented by materials such as silica and alumina. In the case of metals the conduction and valence bands overlap and good conductivity is obtained. The semiconducting oxides have properties intermediate between those of metals and those of insulators and can be subdivided into two types: the intrinsic semiconductor, in which the energy gap between the two bands is so slight that electron transfer can take place very easily, and the n- and p-type semiconductors that achieve conductivity because of their nonstoichiometry. Crystals can be made with either anion or cation excess or deficiency, and the introduction of these defects gives rise to energy levels that are intermediate between those of the conduction and valence bands. This is shown in Fig. 1-5(d) and 1-5(e). The introduction of defects into a crystal is usually accomplished by preparing the material in the presence of small quantities ($1/10\%$) of an oxide that differs from the parent oxide in the valence of its cation, a process known as *doping*. Thus, introduction of Li_2O into the nickel oxide (NiO) lattice causes the formation of a number of Ni^{3+} ions. These cause the doped NiO to exhibit semiconducting properties.

REFERENCES

1. A. F. Wells, *Structural Inorganic Chemistry*, 3rd ed., Clarendon, Oxford, 1962.
2. *Chem. Week*, August 17th and 24th, 1963.
3. A. M. Buswell, K. Krebs, and W. H. Rodebush, *J. Am. Chem. Soc.*, **59**, 2603 (1937).
4. N. G. Yaroslavskii and A. N. Terenin, *Dokl. Akad. Nauk SSSR*, **66**, 885 (1949); through *CA*, **43**, 7343h (1949).
5. N. G. Yaroslavskii, *Zh. Fiz. Khim.*, **24**, 68 (1950); through *CA*, **44**, 2853f (1950).
6. N. G. Yaroslavskii and A. V. Karyakin, *Dokl. Akad. Nauk SSSR*, **85**, 1103 (1952); through *CA*, **47**, 967g (1953).
7. L. N. Kurbatov and G. G. Newimin, *Dokl. Akad. Nauk SSSR*, **68**, 341 (1949); through *CA*, **44**, 435f (1950).
8. H. P. Leftin and M. C. Hobson, *Advan. Catalysis*, **14**, 115 (1963).
9. S. Glasstone, *Textbook of Physical Chemistry*, Van Nostrand, Princeton, N.J., 1946.

10. S. Brunauer, L. S. Deming, W. E. Deming, and E. Teller, *J. Am. Chem. Soc.*, **62,** 1723 (1940).

11. S. Brunauer, P. H. Emmett, and E. Teller, *J. Am. Chem. Soc.*, **60,** 309 (1938).

12. P. H. Emmett and S. Brunauer, *J. Am. Chem. Soc.*, **59,** 1553 (1937).

13. L. G. Joyner, *Scientific and Industrial Glass Blowing and Laboratory Techniques*, Instruments Publishing Co., Pittsburgh, 1949.

14. C. G. Schull, *J. Am. Chem. Soc.*, **70,** 1405 (1948); A. Wheeler, *Catalysis*, Vol. II, Reinhold, New York, 1954.

15. J. W. McBain, *J. Am. Chem. Soc.*, **57,** 699 (1935).

16. I. D. Chapman and K. W. Hansen, Corning Glass Works, unpublished data, 1964.

17. R. S. Mulliken, *J. Chem. Phys.*, **2,** 782 (1934).

18. R. Suhrmann, *Advan. Catalysis*, **7,** 303 (1955).

19. M. Prettre, *Catalysis and Catalysts*, Dover, New York, 1963.

20. H. E. Ries, Jr., *Catalysis*, **1,** 1 (1954).

2

Infrared Spectroscopy: Theory

2-1. INTRODUCTION

If two quantized energy levels E_1 and E_2 are placed in an electromagnetic field and the difference in energy between the two states is equal to a constant multiplied by the frequency of the incident radiation ν, a transfer of energy between the field and the molecule can occur. Thus,

$$\Delta E = h\nu \qquad (2\text{-}1)$$

where h, known as Planck's constant, is equal to 6.63×10^{-27} erg-sec.

All spectra arise from the absorption or emission of radiation that occurs between definitely quantized energy levels when the above condition is satisfied. When ΔE is positive, the molecule absorbs radiation and an *absorption spectrum* is obtained; when ΔE is negative, radiation is emitted during the energy transfer and an *emission spectrum* is obtained. When the energetics of Eq. (2-1) are satisfied (in conjunction with certain quantum-mechanical selection rules) a spectrum unique to the molecule under investigation is obtained. This spectrum is usually represented as a plot of the light intensity against the frequency, and a peak occurs whenever the conditions of Eq. (2-1) are satisfied.

Frequency ranges that can be encountered in this spectrum vary from those of γ rays, which have wavelengths of about 10^{-10} cm, to radio

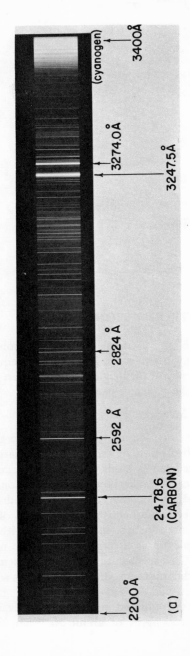

Fig. 2-1. (*a*) *The atomic spectrum of copper. The bands at 3274.0, 3247.5, 2824, and 2592 Å are due to copper. The band at 2478.6 is due to carbon from the arcing electrodes.* (*b*) *The rotational fine structure of the ν_4 band of ammonia.*

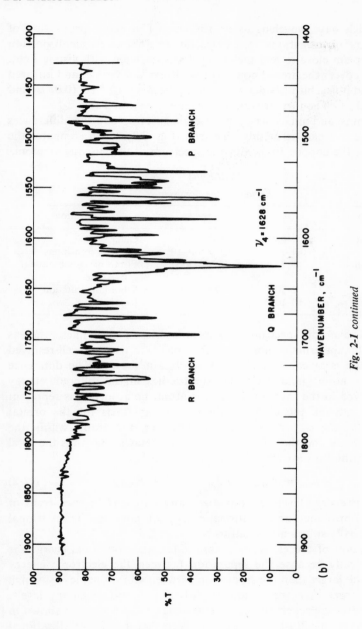

Fig. 2-1 continued

waves, which have wavelengths of 10^{10} cm. The major proportion of spectroscopic investigations are carried out in a relatively small portion of the spectrum close to and including that associated with visible light. This range covers the areas known as the ultraviolet, visible, and infrared regions, and it is arbitrarily defined as being between 10^{-6} cm (0.01 μ) and 10^{-3} cm (10 μ). The further subdivisions are shown in Table 2-1.

Both atoms and molecules give rise to spectra, but the differences between the two can be readily seen from Fig. 2-1, which compares the spectrum of the copper atom with the spectrum of the gaseous ammonia

TABLE 2-1

Regions of the Spectrum

Region	μ	cm^{-1}	Transition
Ultraviolet	10^{-2}–0.4	10^6–2.5×10^4	Outer shell
Visible	0.4–1	2.5×10^4–10^4	Electron transitions
Near infrared	1–2	10,000–5000	Electronic + vibrational overtones
Infrared	2–50	5000–200	Vibration—rotation
Far infrared	50–1000	200–10	Rotation

molecule. The atomic spectrum consists of a series of sharp lines, whereas the molecular spectrum exhibits a series of bands in which a well-resolved line spectrum is revealed at the high resolution shown. The difference between the atomic and molecular spectra lies in the different energy levels involved in the transitions. In the atom the absorptions represent transitions between the different allowed energy levels for the orbital electrons. In the case of a molecule, however, the atoms within the molecule vibrate and the molecule as a whole rotates, and thus the total energy contributions are represented by the equation

$$E_{tot} = E_{elec} + E_{vib} + E_{rot} + E_{trans} \qquad (2\text{-}2)$$

The separate energy levels are quantized and only certain transitions of electronic, vibrational, and rotational energy are possible. Translational energy is usually sufficiently small to be ignored.

The isolation of the electronic, vibrational, and rotational energies is permissible only because the separation between the electronic energy levels is much larger than the separation between vibrational levels, which in turn is larger than the separation between rotational energy levels. This qualitative approach gives rise to the energy-level diagram shown in Fig. 2-2. From this illustration it can be seen that a series of vibrational levels are associated with each electronic level and that a series of rotational levels are associated with each vibrational level.

Transitions between the electronic levels give rise to spectra that are observed in the visible or ultraviolet region of the spectrum and are known as *electronic spectra.* Transitions between vibrational levels in the same electronic state give absorption in the infrared region of the spectrum.

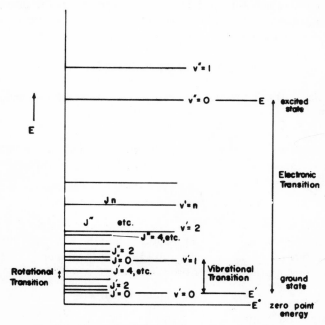

Fig. 2-2. Energy-level diagram for a diatomic molecule.

These vibrational transitions are usually accompanied by rotational transitions, and the resulting spectra are known as *vibration–rotation spectra.* Pure rotation spectra usually occur at low frequencies in the far infrared (below 500 cm^{-1}). The division of the spectrum into three separate regions is somewhat arbitrary, because pure rotational spectra may be observed in the infrared region if transitions to higher states are involved and pure electronic transitions may appear in the near-infrared region if the electronic levels are closely spaced.

Quantum-mechanical considerations show that not all transitions between quantized levels are possible, and certain rules have been invoked to determine whether a transition is allowed or forbidden. These selection rules have been well defined, and application of group theory has led to successful interpretation of the vibrational motions of polyatomic molecules.

At this stage in its development the interpretation of the infrared spectra of surface species depends almost completely on classical concepts and on correlation with the spectra of previously identified molecules. In view of this, no attempt will be made to develop the group theory approach, and the interested reader is referred to a number of excellent texts on the subject (1–3).

2-2. SPECTRAL UNITS

The relationship between frequency v and wavelength λ is given by the equation

$$\lambda v = c \tag{2-3}$$

where c is the velocity of light (3×10^{10} cm/sec). The wavelength may be expressed in many units, the most common of which is the micron, μ.

$$1 \text{ micron } (\mu) = 10^{-4} \text{ cm} = 10^4 \text{ Å}$$
$$1 \text{ millimicron } (m\mu) = 10^{-7} \text{ cm} = 10 \text{ Å}$$

It seems more sensible to report spectral data as a function of energy, and it is now becoming common practice to use the wave number $\bar{v}$, which is the reciprocal of the wavelength. For practical purposes the wave number is given in units of reciprocal centimeters, and thus

$$\bar{v} \text{ (cm}^{-1}) = 1/\lambda \text{ (cm)} = 10^4/\lambda \text{ (μ)} \tag{2-4}$$

The energy and frequency are directly proportional to each other and are related by the following equations:

$$E = hv = hc/\lambda = hc\bar{v} \tag{2-5}$$

$$1 \text{ electron volt (eV)} = 8068 \text{ cm}^{-1} = 23.063 \text{ kcal} \tag{2-6}$$

2-3. VIBRATIONAL SPECTRA

A. The Harmonic Oscillator

Quantum-mechanical considerations have shown that the vibration of a diatomic molecule can be reduced to the motion of a single particle of reduced mass μ_m. Classically, the problem is treated very simply by considering the diatomic molecule to be analogous to the harmonic oscillator shown in Fig. 2-3. In this harmonic oscillator the two masses m_1 and m_2 are joined by a perfect spring of length r_0. When the spring is extended to a distance $r_0 + r$, a restoring force f that is directly proportional to the distance r from the equilibrium position is engendered, and simple harmonic motion results. Thus,

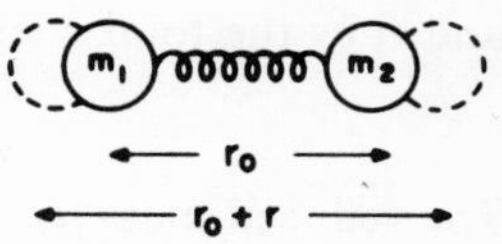

$$f = -kr = \mu_m \frac{d^2 r}{dt^2} \qquad (2\text{-}7)$$

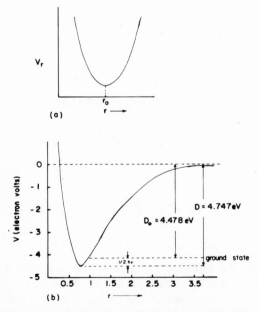

Fig. 2-3. *The diatomic molecule as a simple harmonic oscillator.*

where k is a constant that is representative of the spring and is known as *the standard-type force constant*.

The restoring force f is a function of the potential energy V such that

$$f = -\partial V/\partial r = -kr \qquad (2\text{-}8)$$

$$V_r = \tfrac{1}{2} kr^2 \qquad (2\text{-}9)$$

This equation is parabolic and gives rise to the energy curve shown in Fig. 2-4(a).

Fig. 2-4. (a) *Potential-energy–internuclear distance curve for the simple harmonic oscillator.* (b) *Potential-energy–internuclear distance curve for the hydrogen molecule.*

The kinetic energy associated with the simple harmonic vibration is

$$E_{\text{kin}} = \tfrac{1}{2}\mu_m(dr/dt)^2 \tag{2-10}$$

and thus the total energy of vibration is

$$E_{\text{vib}} = \tfrac{1}{2}\mu_m(dr/dt)^2 + \tfrac{1}{2}kr^2 \tag{2-11}$$

The reduced mass μ_m is determined from the equation

$$\frac{1}{\mu_m} = \frac{1}{m_1} + \frac{1}{m_2} \qquad \mathcal{M}_m = \frac{m_1 m_2}{m_1 + m_2} \tag{2-12}$$

The potential-energy fraction can be inserted into the Schrödinger wave equation with the result that

$$\frac{d^2\psi}{dr^2} + \frac{8\pi^2\mu_m}{h^2}(E - \tfrac{1}{2}kr^2)\psi = 0 \tag{2-13}$$

where E is the total energy. From this, the energy of vibration

$$E_{\text{vib}} = h\nu(v + \tfrac{1}{2}) \tag{2-14}$$

where ν is the frequency of vibration of the oscillator and v is the vibrational quantum number. Thus, for any transition between quantized levels in which $v' \pm v'' = 1$,

$$E' - E'' = \Delta E = h\nu \tag{2-15}$$

which has already been given as Eq. (2-1).

The frequency of the simple harmonic vibration is given by classical mechanics, and it is

$$v = \frac{1}{2\pi}\left(\frac{k}{\mu_m}\right)^{1/2} \tag{2-16}$$

or, combining (2-16) with (2-3),

$$\frac{1}{\lambda} = \frac{1}{2\pi c}\left(\frac{k}{\mu_m}\right)^{1/2} = \bar{\nu} \tag{2-17}$$

B. Molecular Force Constants

In considering the vibration of atoms, the chemical bond is often equated with the "spring" concept of the harmonic oscillator. The "strength" (or force constant) of the spring is considered analogous to the "strength" of the chemical bond, and thus a determination of k gives a measure of the strength of a chemical bond. The force constant actually measures the *curvature* of the potential well rather than the depth. The correlation between bond strength and force constant is therefore valid only if it can be assumed that narrow potential wells are deep. This can be seen by reference to Eq. (2-8), where the restoring force is given as

$$f = -kr = -\delta V/\delta r$$

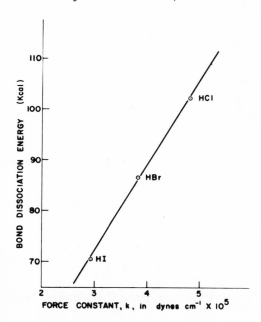

Fig. 2-5. *The relationship between bond dissociation energy and force constant for the hydrogen halides.*

From this it follows that, as $r + r_0$ approaches the equilibrium separation distance r_0,

$$k = (\delta^2 V/\delta r^2)_{r \to 0} \qquad (2\text{-}18)$$

That larger force constants are indeed indicative of stronger chemical bonds is illustrated in Fig. 2-5, where the dissociation energies of the carbon halides are plotted as a function of force constant. The linear relationship substantiates the above assumption.

This simple treatment of the harmonic oscillator gives rise to several interesting results that are of immediate practical application to the interpretation of vibration spectra. The constant $1/2\pi c$ in Eq. (2-17) is easily calculated, and thus a knowledge of any two of the three variables will give a value for the third. For example, the HCl molecule is known to give a stretching vibration that corresponds to an absorption at 2886 cm^{-1} in the infrared. The reduced mass of the HCl molecule is 0.9726 atomic mass units (amu), and, therefore, the force constant is calculated from the equation

$$k = \bar{v}^2(2\pi c)^2\mu_m$$

$$= \frac{(2886 \times 2 \times 3.14 \times 3 \times 10^{10})^2 \times 0.97}{6 \times 10^{23}} \text{ g/sec}^2 \qquad (2\text{-}19)$$

$$= 4.8 \times 10^5 \text{ g/sec}^2$$

TABLE 2-2

Vibrational Frequencies of Diatomic Molecules Corrected for Anharmonicity[a]

Molecule	Frequencies, cm^{-1}	
	Observed	Corrected
H_2	4161.13	4395.24
D_2	2993.55	3118.46
N_2^{14}	2331	2358.6
O_2^{16}	1551	1580.4

[a] From Reference (*4*).

The force constant is more conventionally expressed in dynes (g cm/sec²). Therefore,

$$k = 4.8 \times 10^5 \text{ dynes/cm} = 4.8 \times 10^{-3} \text{ dynes/Å}$$

Changes in the position of the vibrational frequency upon adsorption of the HCl molecule on a surface can thus be directly attributed to changes in the strength of the bond that gives rise to the particular vibration. Shifts to lower wave numbers indicate a weakening of the bond (smaller force constant), and shifts to higher wave numbers indicate strengthening of the bond under consideration.

From Eq. (2-17) it also follows that, for a series of compounds in which the force constant is the same, the frequency of the vibration is dependent upon the mass of the atoms. Isotopic substitution therefore alters the vibrational frequency, as can be seen from the data in Table 2-2. Thus, whereas the vibrational frequency of the hydrogen molecule is 4161 cm^{-1}, that of the deuterium molecule is 2994 cm^{-1}. The force constant must of course remain essentially the same. The purposeful introduction of isotopes into molecules has been widely used as a method for the identification of certain vibrations, and several examples will be found later in the text. In particular, the method has been employed in the identification of the surface hydroxyl groups that exist on silica and other surfaces. When freely vibrating, this OH group gives rise to an absorption in the infrared at 3750 cm^{-1}. In order to completely identify the OH group and to establish that it is on the surface, the hydrogen atoms have been exchanged with deuterium atoms (from D_2O) to give surface OD groups. The exchange proceeds readily, and the band at 3750 cm^{-1} is replaced quantitatively, the new OD group producing a band at 2750 cm^{-1}. If the OH group is treated as a simple diatomic harmonic oscillator, it follows from Eq. (2-17) that

$$\frac{\bar{\nu}_1}{\bar{\nu}_2} = \left(\frac{\mu_2}{\mu_1}\right)^{1/2} \tag{2-20}$$

Since H = 1, D = 2, and O = 16, it is seen from Eq. (2-12) that $\mu_1 = \frac{16}{17}$ and $\mu_2 = \frac{32}{18}$, whence

$$\frac{\bar{\nu}_1}{\bar{\nu}_2} = \left(\frac{16}{9} \times \frac{17}{16}\right)^{1/2} = \left(\frac{17}{9}\right)^{1/2} = 1.37$$

but $\bar{\nu}_1 = 3750$ cm^{-1}, and therefore

$$\bar{\nu}_2 = 3750/1.37 \simeq 2740 \text{ cm}^{-1}$$

This is in good agreement with the band that is found at 2750 cm^{-1} and confirms that surface deuteration has taken place.

C. The Ionic Bond

The simple picture of the harmonic oscillator and the potential diagram as drawn in Fig. 2-4(a) causes consternation as soon as we compare it with the potential-energy–internuclear distance plot for ionic molecules. Thus, if we consider two ions with charges q_1 and q_2 brought together from infinity to a distance r, the attractive force between the ions may be represented by a potential

$$V = -q_1q_2/r \tag{2-21}$$

When the ions are brought so close together that their electron clouds begin to overlap, a repulsive force comes into prominence because of the mutual repulsion of the electrons and the two nuclei. This potential is usually represented by the function

$$V = be^{-r/a} \tag{2-22}$$

where a and b are constants. Therefore, the net potential for the two ions is

$$V = -(q_1 q_2/r) + be^{-r/a} \tag{2-23}$$

This potential-energy function is obviously not a simple parabola and takes a form similar to that shown for the covalent hydrogen molecule in Fig. 2-4(b). The minimum in the potential curve, however, is much larger than for the hydrogen molecule, and the stable internuclear distance r_0 occurs at 2.51 Å for the gaseous Na^+Cl^- molecule.

D. Covalent Bond

The potential-energy curve for the hydrogen molecule is shown in Fig. 2-4(b). A minimum in this curve occurs when the hydrogen atoms are 0.74 Å apart, and this corresponds to the stable internuclear distance r_0. The vibration is not harmonic, and, as the internuclear separation increases, the molecule becomes dissociated into atoms. The chemical heat of dissociation is given by the height from the asymptote at $V = 0$ to the ground state of the molecule and is known to be 4.478 eV. The spectroscopic heat of dissociation D_e is the height from the asymptote to the minimum in the potential curve and is found to be 4.747 eV. The difference between the two arises directly as a result of the quantum-mechanical derivation of Eq. (2-14):

$$E = h\nu_0(v + \tfrac{1}{2})$$

When the vibrational quantum number v is zero, there is still an energy contribution equal to $\tfrac{1}{2}h\nu_0$. This is known as the zero-point energy, and is illustrated in Fig. 2-4(b). It is equal to the difference between the chemical and spectroscopic heats of dissociation and is thus determined to be 0.27 eV.

E. Anharmonic Vibrations

The anharmonicity of the potential-energy–internuclear distance curve that obtains for both ionic and covalent compounds shows that the simple model of the harmonic oscillator cannot be strictly applied in the interpretation of vibrational spectra. Not only does the simple harmonic picture forbid the dissociation of a molecule but, moreover, the quantum mechanics of the simple model allows quantum jumps to take place only between one vibrational level and the next (i.e., $v'' - v' = 1$). The presence of overtone and combination bands in a spectrum are thus forbidden, because these bands involve jumps between several quantum levels. For the anharmonic oscillator, these stringent rules are relaxed and overtone and combination bands can appear in spectra based on this model. In order to allow for anharmonicity, Eq. (2-11) is adjusted so that the potential-energy curve is expressed as a power series in $v + \frac{1}{2}$. Thus,

$$E_{\mathrm{vib}} = h\nu(v + \tfrac{1}{2}) - x_e(v + \tfrac{1}{2})^2 + y_e(v + \tfrac{1}{2})^3 \cdots \qquad (2\text{-}24)$$

Usually only the first two terms in this series are considered, and thus,

$$E_{\mathrm{vib}} = h\nu(v + \tfrac{1}{2}) - x_e(v + \tfrac{1}{2})^2 \qquad (2\text{-}25)$$

The symbol x_e is known as the anharmonicity constant, and its introduction gives a potential curve of the form shown in Fig. 2-4(b). With many diatomic molecules the correction for anharmonicity is slight, as can be seen for the values for simple diatomic gases given in Table 2-2.

Examination of Eq. (2-25) shows that the vibrational energy levels are no longer evenly spaced, but that their separation decreases slowly as v increases (Fig. 2-2). The appearance of overtones and combination bands is now allowed.

2-4. ROTATIONAL SPECTRA

The rotational motion of molecules can be treated in terms of a simple mechanical model in which the molecule is considered to consist of n atoms of mass m_n that are distributed in space at a distance r_n from the center of gravity. The moment of inertia I of the molecule is given by

$$I = \sum m_n r_n^2 \qquad (2\text{-}26)$$

The simplest case is that of a linear molecule such as HCl. Here we have the typical "dumbbell rotator" that is shown in Fig. 2-6. For this diatomic

Fig. 2-6. *The dumbbell rotator. The diatomic molecule is treated as a single particle.* [*Redrawn from W. J. Moore, Physical Chemistry, 1950, courtesy of Prentice-Hall, Inc., Englewood Cliffs, N.J.*]

species

$$I = m_1 r_1^2 + m_2 r_2^2 \qquad (2\text{-}27)$$

$$I = \mu_m r^2 \qquad (2\text{-}28)$$

where μ_m is the reduced mass.

All molecules have three moments of inertia which are defined by the x, y, and z axes. In the case of the linear molecule, the component in the x axis is zero and the moments in the y and z axes are equal. Four different types of molecules can be considered.

A. The Linear Molecule

$$I_x = 0 \qquad I_y = I_z \qquad (2\text{-}29)$$

For such a molecule the potential energy is zero and the Schrödinger equation becomes

$$\nabla^2 \psi + \frac{8\pi^2 \mu}{h^2} E \psi = 0 \qquad (2\text{-}30)$$

This can be solved to give

$$E_{\text{rot}} = \frac{h^2}{8\pi^2 \mu_m r^2} J(J+1) = \frac{h^2}{8\pi^2 I} J(J+1) \qquad (2\text{-}31)$$

J is the rotational quantum number and can have the values 0, 1, 2, 3, etc.

The angular momentum P_{rot} and the kinetic energy of rotation E_{rot} are given by the equations

$$P_{\text{rot}} = \omega I \qquad (2\text{-}32)$$

$$E_{\text{rot}} = \tfrac{1}{2} I \omega^2 \qquad (2\text{-}33)$$

from which

$$E_{\text{rot}} = \frac{P_{\text{rot}}^2}{2I} \qquad (2\text{-}34)$$

Combining (2-31) with (2-34),

$$P_{\text{rot}} = \frac{h}{2\pi} [J(J+1)]^{1/2} \qquad (2\text{-}35)$$

From (2-31) it is seen that

$$\Delta E = E - E' = \frac{h}{8\pi^2 I} h[J(J+1) - J'(J'+1)] \qquad (2\text{-}36)$$

Rotational transitions are generally restricted to those in which $\Delta J = 1$, and therefore Eq. (2-36) becomes

$$\Delta E = \frac{h}{8\pi^2 I} 2Jh \qquad (2\text{-}37)$$

Also, since $\Delta E = h\nu$,

$$\nu = \frac{h}{8\pi^2 I} 2J \qquad (2\text{-}38)$$

$$\nu = 2BJ \qquad (2\text{-}39)$$

The constant

$$B = \frac{h}{8\pi^2 I c} \qquad (2\text{-}40)$$

is known as the rotational constant and has the units of reciprocal centimeters when the frequency is converted into those units. The value of $h/8\pi^2 c$ is 27.986×10^{-40} cm^{-1}.

The rotational frequency of this simple molecule is thus a linear function of the rotational quantum number. If the dipole moment and internuclear distance of the molecule are known, then the energies of the rotational transitions can be calculated. These are usually in good agreement with those obtained from gas-phase spectra.

B. The Spherical-Top Molecule

$$I_x = I_y = I_z$$

The second simple case of rotation that can be considered is that of the so-called spherical-top molecule. This is exemplified by a completely symmetrical molecule such as carbon tetrachloride, CCl_4. Discussion in this case is simple, because rotations in the x, y, and z planes all produce identical moments of inertia. The molecule thus exhibits no rotational spectrum.

C. The Symmetrical-Top Molecule

$$I_x = I_y \neq I_z$$

The ammonia molecule is known as a symmetrical-top molecule and is of interest mainly because it has often been used in spectroscopic investigations of surface activity. The center of gravity of the molecule lies below the nitrogen atom and between the three hydrogen atoms. Thus, the moments of inertia in the x and z directions are equal but different from the moment of inertia in the y direction.

D. The Asymmetrical-Top Molecule

$$I_x \neq I_y \neq I_z$$

By far the most usual rotator encountered is the asymmetrical-top molecule. In this classification the moments of inertia in all three directions are different. Even some of the simplest molecules belong to this class. Thus water, a nonlinear triatomic molecule, is an asymmetric-top molecule.

From this discussion it is clear that the rigid rotator may only be used to characterize perfectly rotating molecules. However, since all molecules vibrate, this immediately creates an imperfection that introduces errors into the pure rotational approach. This nonideality is usually treated in the same manner as the anharmonicity correction applied to the harmonic oscillator. A further term is introduced into the equation for the frequency of rotation of the simple rotator, and Eq. (2-40) is adjusted to become

$$E_{rot} = BhJ(J + 1) - DhJ^2(J + 1)^2 \qquad (2-41)$$

D is thus a measure of the deviation from ideal behavior in the same manner as the anharmonicity constant. Fortunately, D is usually about 10,000 times smaller than B and can be ignored.

2-5. VIBRATION–ROTATION SPECTRA

In the preceding dissussions the vibrational and rotational frequencies have been treated independently of each other. The rotation of a molecule, however, creates a centrifugal force that couples with the vibration, and the resultant spectral absorption is due to the combined vibration–rotation. Thus,

$$E = E_{vib} + E_{rot} \qquad (2-42)$$

and

$$\nu = \frac{\Delta(E_{vib} + E_{rot})}{h} \qquad (2-43)$$

From Eqs. (2-42), (2-14), and (2-31),

$$E = E_{rot} + E_{vib}$$

$$= \frac{h^2 J(J + 1)}{8\pi^2 I} + h\nu_0(v + \tfrac{1}{2}) \qquad (2-44)$$

For simultaneous transitions from J' to J'' and v' to v'' it follows that

$$\Delta E = E' - E''$$

$$= h\nu_0(v' - v'') + \frac{h^2}{8\pi^2 I}[J'(J' + 1) - J''(J'' + 1)] \qquad (2-45)$$

For a pure rotational spectrum, the selection rule is that $J' - J'' = \pm 1$.

For a fundamental vibration $v' - v'' = 1$. When $J' - J'' = +1$,

$$E = h\nu_0 + \frac{h^2}{4\pi^2 I} J' \tag{2-46}$$

and when $J' - J'' = -1$,

$$E = h\nu_0 - \frac{h^2}{4\pi^2 I} (J' + 1) \tag{2-47}$$

In this case it is possible for J' to be zero.

Equations (2-46) and (2-47) can be combined to give a relationship of the form

$$E = h\nu_0 + \frac{h^2}{4\pi^2 I} m \tag{2-48}$$

where m is a *molecular* rotation quantum number that can have values ± 1, ± 2, ± 3, etc. The frequency of such a combination vibration–rotation is given by the equations

$$\nu = \frac{\Delta E}{h} = \nu_0 + \frac{2h}{8\pi^2 I} m \tag{2-49}$$

$$\nu = \nu_0 + 2Bm \tag{2-50}$$

where B, the rotational constant, has already been defined. The practical implications of Eq. (2-50) are that when the frequency conditions are fulfilled, the value of ν_0 defines the position of the center of the fundamental vibration–rotation band and the second term determines the rotational fine structure.

When m is positive, a series of lines are produced on the high-frequency side of ν_0; when m is negative, a series of lines are produced on the low-frequency side of ν_0. These are known as the R and P branches, respectively. In some molecules it is possible for the molecule to have an angular momentum about the axis joining the nuclei. Under these circumstances the vibrational change can occur without the company of a rotation, and in this case m is equal to zero. Very small changes in the rotational energy give rise to fine structure in the vicinity of ν_0, and this is known as the Q branch of the absorption. The presence of the Q branch is common in polyatomic molecules, but for diatomic molecules it is not observed unless the molecule has an unpaired electron (e.g., nitric oxide, NO). Part of the spectrum of gaseous ammonia is shown in Fig. 1-1(b). There the P, Q, and R branches are well resolved, and the positions of the maxima show close agreement with theory.

2-6. THE VIBRATIONS OF POLYATOMIC MOLECULES

A. Number of Vibrations

The diatomic models discussed thus far are simple in that only one mode of vibration exists. It is obvious that, as soon as a third atom is added to the molecule, additional vibrations are possible. This is shown

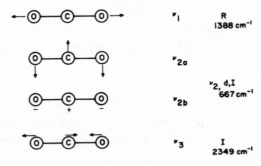

Fig. 2-7. *Vibrations of linear triatomic molecules,* CO_2.

in Figs. 2-7 and 2-8 for linear and nonlinear triatomic molecules, where three vibrational modes can be presumed. Even in these polyatomic molecules, however, the vibrations can be accounted for by a consideration of simple analogous mechanical models.

The position of any atom in space can be represented by three coordinates. Thus, if we consider a polyatomic molecule containing n atoms, a maximum of $3n$ coordinates are required to describe the motions of the atoms completely. Three of these coordinates are used to describe the motion of the center of gravity of the molecule, thus leaving $3n - 3$ coordinates to describe the vibrations. In the case of a diatomic molecule two coordinates will be used to describe the rotational motion, and therefore the number of vibrations occurring in the diatomic molecule will be $3n - 5$ (i.e., 1). This is in agreement with observed data. Similarly, in a linear triatomic molecule the rotational motion is

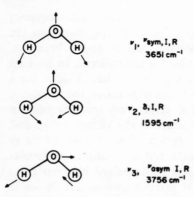

Fig. 2-8. *Vibrations of bent triatomic molecules,* H_2O.

described by two coordinates and thus $3n - 5$ (i.e., 4) vibrational modes are possible. For polyatomic molecules in general, three coordinates are needed to define the rotational motion and $3n - 6$ vibrations are possible. Of these, $n - 1$ can be defined as *stretching* or *valence* vibrations and $2n - 5$ are *bending* or *deformation* vibrations.

B. Nomenclature

The literature of infrared spectroscopy has evolved a series of terms and symbols that, hopefully, conjure up an image of the particular atomic motion under discussion. Thus, in the case of diatomic O—H species the vibratory motion is one in which the O and H atoms move in opposite directions.

$$\leftarrow\text{O—H}\rightarrow$$

This is known as the O—H stretching vibration. If this species became triatomic, then a different type of vibration, in which the O and H atoms moved at an angle to each other, could occur:

$$\text{X—O—H}$$

This is known as the O—H bending vibration. These various vibrational modes are illustrated in Table 2-3. Arrows are used to illustrate motions in the plane of the paper and plus and minus signs respectively refer to movements toward and away from the reader.

C. Degenerate Vibrations

From the vibrational analysis presented in the preceding section it would be expected that a molecule like carbon dioxide, being linear and triatomic, would exhibit $3n - 5$ vibrational modes. The four possible vibrations are illustrated in Fig. 2-8. Two stretching vibrations and two bending vibrations would be expected and these should be observed at the following frequencies:

$$\bar{\nu}_1 \quad 1388 \text{ cm}^{-1} \quad R$$
$$\bar{\nu}_3 \quad 2349 \text{ cm}^{-1} \quad I$$
$$\bar{\nu}_{2a} \quad 667 \text{ cm}^{-1} \quad I$$
$$\bar{\nu}_{2b} \quad 667 \text{ cm}^{-1} \quad I$$

An examination of the infrared spectrum of CO_2 reveals the presence of only two absorptions: at 2349 and 667 cm^{-1}. The $\bar{\nu}_{2a}$ and $\bar{\nu}_{2b}$ vibrations have the same frequency and can be distinguished only in that they are

TABLE 2-3

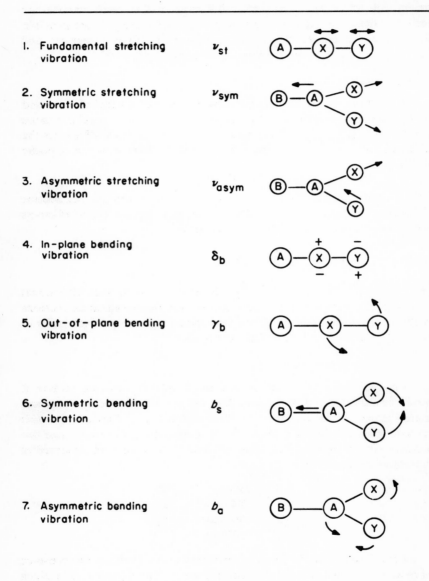

1. Fundamental stretching vibration ν_{st}

2. Symmetric stretching vibration ν_{sym}

3. Asymmetric stretching vibration ν_{asym}

4. In-plane bending vibration δ_b

5. Out-of-plane bending vibration γ_b

6. Symmetric bending vibration b_s

7. Asymmetric bending vibration b_a

TABLE 2-3 (*continued*)

8. In-plane rocking vibration	ρ_r	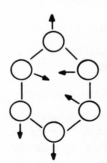
9. Out-of-plane wagging vibration	χ_w	
10. Twisting vibration	τ_t	
11. Ring deformation in plane	d	
12. Ring deformation out of plane	d	

perpendicular to each other. Such vibrations are said to be *doubly degenerate*. Triply degenerate vibrations can also occur in some molecules.

D. Selection Rules

Reference to the vibrations illustrated in Fig. 2-7 shows the $\bar{\nu}_1$ vibration for the linear CO_2 molecule would not give rise to a change in the dipole moment of the molecule. This vibration does not, therefore, appear in the infrared spectrum and is said to be *inactive*. This result illustrates the primary selection rule in the interpretation of infrared spectra.

1. Vibrations are active in the infrared spectrum (I) only if the vibration gives rise to a change in the dipole moment of the molecule.

2. Vibrations are active in the Raman spectra (R) if the vibration causes a change in the polarizability of the molecule.

E. Normal Vibrations of Some Common Structures

The assignment of the vibrations of the examples given in this section are those of Herzberg (2) unless otherwise indicated.

1. Two-Atom Molecules

These have already been discussed in some detail. Only one vibration is observed.

2. Three-Atom Molecules

a. Linear Triatomic Molecules, X_3 or YXY. The vibrational modes of these molecules are shown in Fig. 2-7 and have been discussed above in terms of the CO_2 molecule.

b. Linear Triatomic Molecules, XYZ. The vibrational modes of linear XYZ species are the same as for the X_3 molecule. The introduction of the Z atom introduces a change of symmetry in the molecule, and all the vibrations are both infrared- and Raman-active. Typical molecules of this type are HCN, CSSe, N_2O, and the halogen cyanides.

c. Bent Triatomic Molecules. The normal vibrations of bent triatomic molecules are illustrated in Fig. 2-8. The molecule may be of the symmetrical X_3, XY_2 type or the asymmetrical XYZ or XXY type. $\bar{\nu}_1$ and $\bar{\nu}_3$ are the symmetric and asymmetric stretching frequencies, and $\bar{\nu}_2$ is a bending frequency. Typical molecules in this classification are the important H_2O and H_2S molecules, O_3, NO_2, SO_2, SCl_2, and the halogen oxides, X_2O.

3. Four-Atom Molecules

a. Pyramidal XY_3 *Molecules.* This group of molecules includes the NH_3 molecule, which has received much attention in its adsorbed state. In the gaseous state the XY_3 molecules undergo the vibrations shown in Fig. 2-9. Six vibrations are possible for this type of structure. Four vibrations are normally observed; two of them, $\bar{\nu}_1$ and $\bar{\nu}_3$, are classified as symmetric and asymmetric stretching vibrations. The other two, $\bar{\nu}_2$ and $\bar{\nu}_4$, are bending vibrations. Both $\bar{\nu}_3$ and $\bar{\nu}_4$ are doubly degenerate.

The pyramidal XY_3 molecules are able to resonate between two structures:

$$\overset{..}{N} \diagdown \mid \diagdown \quad \text{and} \quad \diagup \mid \diagdown$$

H H H   H H H

and, since these structures are equally probable, the vibrational levels are split into positive and negative components. Transitions between these new levels cause splitting of the $\bar{\nu}_1$ and $\bar{\nu}_2$ vibrations, and this effect is known as *inversion doubling.*

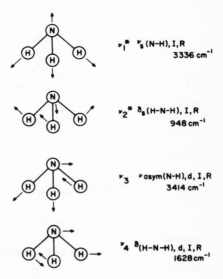

Fig. 2-9. *Vibrations of pyramidal four-atom molecules,* NH_3. *The asterisk denotes vibrations subject to inversion doubling. The quoted frequencies represent an average value.*

b. Pyramidal ZXY_2 *Molecules.* As a result of the asymmetry that is introduced into these molecules by the replacement of a Y atom in the XY_3 structure, the degeneracy observed with XY_3 molecules is removed and all $3n - 6$ vibrations are found. A typical molecule of this group is $SOCl_2$.

c. Planar XY_3 *Molecules.* The boron halides are the best known four-atom molecules that exist in a planar configuration. The modes of vibration of BF_3 are shown in Fig. 2-10. Degeneracy of the $\bar{\nu}_3$, $\bar{\nu}_4$, $\bar{\nu}_5$, and $\bar{\nu}_6$ vibrations reduces the number of observable vibrations to four. Only three of these vibrations are actually observed in the infrared, the $\bar{\nu}_1$ vibration being only Raman-active.

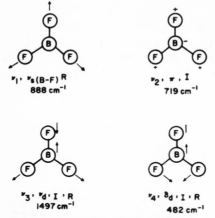

Fig. 2-10. *Vibrations of planar four-atom molecules, $B^{10}F_3$.*

ν_1, ν_s(B-F) R
888 cm^{-1}

ν_2, π, I
719 cm^{-1}

ν_3, ν_d I R
1497 cm^{-1}

ν_4, δ_d I R
482 cm^{-1}

d. Planar ZXY$_2$ *Molecules.* Introduction of asymmetry into the planar XY$_3$ molecule gives rise to all six theoretical vibrations. A few well-known molecules have this molecular configuration; among the best known are the carbonyl halides such as phosgene,

$$\underset{Cl \qquad Cl}{\overset{\overset{\textstyle O}{\parallel}}{C}}$$

e. X$_2$Y$_2$ *Molecules: Nonlinear.* These molecules are typified by the hydrogen peroxide molecule shown in Fig. 2-11. They have six normal modes of vibration. The number of vibrations visible in the infrared spectrum is dependent upon the planarity of the molecule. In the planar X$_2$Y$_2$ configuration the $\bar{\nu}_6$ vibration is normally only Raman-active. Infrared activity is immediately introduced, however, by distorting the molecule.

f. X$_2$Y$_2$ *Molecules: Linear.* If the X$_2$Y$_2$ molecule is linear, then seven vibrations are possible. These are shown in Fig. 2-12. The $\bar{\nu}_4$ and $\bar{\nu}_5$

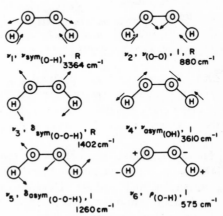

ν_1, ν_{sym}(O-H), R
3364 cm^{-1}

ν_2, ν(O-O), I, R
880 cm^{-1}

ν_3, δ_{sym}(O-O-H), R
1402 cm^{-1}

ν_4, ν_{asym}(OH), I
3610 cm^{-1}

ν_5, δ_{asym}(O-O-H), I
1260 cm^{-1}

ν_6, ρ(O-H), I
575 cm^{-1}

Fig. 2-11. *Vibrations of nonlinear, planar, four-atom molecules,*
H$_2$O$_2$. [*Following Nakamoto* (4).]

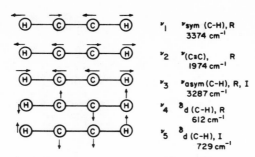

ν_1 ν_{sym} (C–H), R
          3374 cm^{-1}

ν_2 ν(C≡C),   R
          1974 cm^{-1}

ν_3 ν_{asym} (C–H), R, I
          3287 cm^{-1}

ν_4 δ_d (C–H), R
          612 cm^{-1}

ν_5 δ_d (C–H), I
          729 cm^{-1}

Fig. 2-12. *Vibrations of linear four-atom molecules,* C_2H_2.

vibrations are doubly degenerate and, therefore, only five vibrations are observed. Of these, only two are infrared-active.

The linear X_2Y_2 molecule is typified by the catalytically important acetylene (C_2H_2) molecule, which has been examined in its adsorbed state. It has also been suggested as a possible product formed during the dissociative adsorption of ethylene.

4. Five-Atom Molecules

a. XY_4 Tetrahedral Molecules. The five-atom molecules contain the well-known tetrahedral and square planar configurations. The five atoms should give rise to nine vibrational modes. Typical molecules with this structure are the group IV hydrides and halides. In the symmetrical XY_4 configuration only four modes are observed, owing to degeneracy (Fig. 2-13). The $\bar{\nu}_3$ and $\bar{\nu}_4$ vibrations are triply degenerate, and the $\bar{\nu}_2$ vibration is doubly degenerate. The NH_4^+ ion also has this symmetrical configuration, and formation of this species on "acidic" surfaces after ammonia adsorption has been used as proof of the presence of protons.

b. Z_2XY_2 Tetrahedral Molecules. The introduction of two dissimilar atoms into the XY_4 molecule causes all nine vibrations to become active. Eight of these vibrations are infrared-active. A typical molecule of this type would be D_2CH_2.

c. ZXY_3 Tetrahedral Molecules. If only one foreign atom is introduced into the XY_4 tetrahedral molecule, six vibrations are observed in the infrared spectrum. The most common molecules with this structure are DCH_3 and the group V oxyhalides ($POCl_3$, $VOCl_3$, etc.).

d. Planar XY_4 Molecules. Ions with this symmetry, e.g., $PtCl_4^{2-}$, are well known in inorganic chemistry but need little attention as far as adsorbed species are concerned. Only seven of the nine possible vibrations

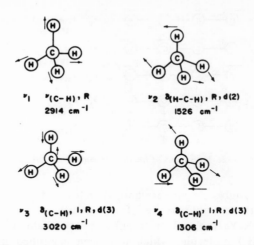

Fig. 2-13. *Vibrations of symmetrical tetrahedral molecules,* CH₄.

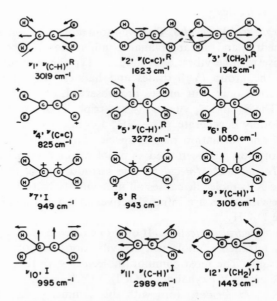

Fig. 2-14. *Vibrations of* X₂Y₄ *molecules,* C₂H₄.

are permissible, owing to degeneracy of the $\bar{\nu}_3$ and $\bar{\nu}_7$ modes, and of these only $\bar{\nu}_3$, $\bar{\nu}_6$ and $\bar{\nu}_7$ are active in the infrared.

5. Six-Atom Molecules

a. XY_5 Trigonal Bipyramidal Molecules. Six-atom molecules of the XY_5 type are exemplified by the pentavalent group V halides such as PCl_5. These molecules are almost always trigonal bipyramidal in structure, and since their application to surface studies has been negligible, no discussion is planned.

b. X_2Y_4 Molecules. X_2Y_4-type molecules include the ethylenic hydrocarbons that are of great importance in surface chemistry and catalysis. Many spectroscopic investigations have been made of adsorbed ethylene. The 12 possible vibrations of the ethylene molecule are shown in Fig. 2-14. Only five of these vibrations are active in the infrared.

6. Seven-Atom Molecules

Octahedral species such as SF_6 are often very stable, and their spectra in the adsorbed state have not been examined. No further discussion is considered necessary at this stage.

7. Eight-Atom Molecules

These molecules are important because they include the ethane molecule. This compound is frequently involved in catalyzed surface reactions, though its spectrum in an adsorbed state does not appear to have been recorded. The vibrational modes of the ethane molecule are given in Fig. 2-15.

Dimeric, trivalent molecules such as the aluminum halides and diborane also belong to this class of molecule. They are, however, of little interest to surface chemists and need no further discussion.

2-7. GROUP FREQUENCIES

As the number of atoms in a molecule increases, it can be seen from Figs. 2-14 and 2-15 that physical interpretation of all the vibrational movements becomes a complicated procedure. For a simple aromatic molecule such as benzene, C_6H_6, some 30 vibrations are possible, although degeneracy reduces the number of observable vibrations to 20. Fortunately, in most cases it is not necessary to identify all the vibrations that can occur in order to identify a molecule. This is due primarily to the development of the concept of *group frequencies*, which has proved to be

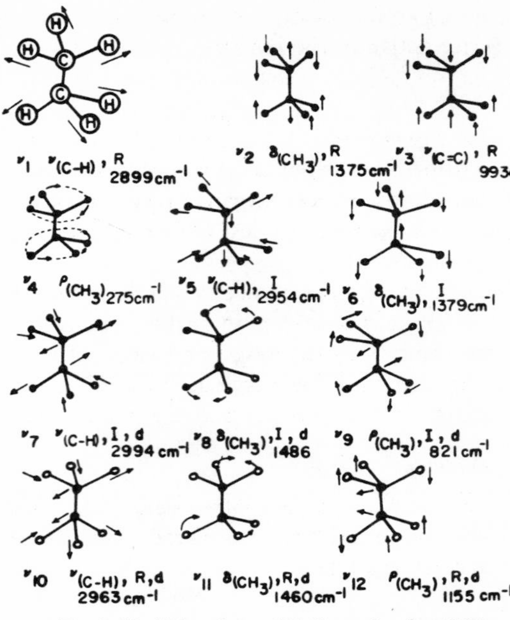

Fig. 2-15. Vibrations of X_2Y_6 *molecules,* C_2H_6.

one of the most important qualitative contributions to infrared spectroscopy. An examination of the vibrational frequencies of the methane, ethane, ethylene, and acetylene molecules, as given in Figs. 2-13, 2-15, 2-14, and 2-12, respectively, shows that all these molecules have a $\bar{\nu}_1$ vibration that is designated a C—H stretching vibration. This vibration occurs at 2914, 2899, 3019, and 3374 cm^{-1} for the four respective hydrocarbons. The fact that the C—H stretch occurs at a similar frequency for these vastly different compounds means that the molecule is behaving almost as if it were a simple X—C—H molecule in which the hydrogen atom and carbon atom are vibrating in a manner that is essentially independent of the rest of the molecule. In other words, despite the varying nature of the bonding that occurs in the group designated by X, and despite the wide differences in the total weight of the atoms in group X, the vibration frequency is relatively unaffected. Many other pairs of atoms or groups of atoms give rise to vibrations whose frequencies are essentially independent of the constitution of the rest of the molecule, and these frequencies have become known as *group* or *characteristic frequencies*. In the past decade, many tabulations of characteristic frequencies have been prepared to provide the analytical chemist with a simple tool for the ready identification of molecules or types of molecule. This qualitative technique has contributed considerably to the wide development and use of infrared spectroscopy as a routine tool in many laboratories.

The nature of the group X in the preceding example does have an important effect on the actual position of the C—H bond and permits further subdivision of the group frequencies. The group analysis can then be carried one stage further. Reference to Table 2-4 shows that, when the

TABLE 2-4
Vibrational Frequencies of Some Common Bonds[a]

Group	Bond-stretching vibration, cm^{-1}	Group	Bond-stretching vibration, cm^{-1}	Group	Bond-bending vibration, cm^{-1}
$\equiv$C-H	3300	-C$\equiv$C-	2050	$\equiv$C-H	700
$=$C-H	3020	C=C	1650	=C(H)(H)	1100
-C-H	2960	-C-C-	900	-C-H(H)(H)	1000
-O-H	3680	-C-F	1100	C(H)(H)	1450
-S-H	2570	-C-Cl	650	C(H)(H)(H)	1450
-N-H	3350	-C-Br	560	C-C$\equiv$C	300
C=O	1700	-C-I	500		
-C$\equiv$N	2100				

[a] From Herzberg's *Infrared and Raman Spectra of Polyatomic Molecules.* Copyright 1945, D. Van Nostrand Company, Inc., Princeton, N.J. (2).

C atom of the C—H group is singly bonded to three other groups, the $\geqslant$C—H bond stretching vibration occurs at 2960 cm^{-1}, and only slight variations from this position are observed. Introduction of a double or triple bond causes the C—H vibration to move to higher frequencies, and absorptions occur at 3020 and 3300 cm^{-1}, respectively, for the

$\underset{|}{=}$C—H and $\equiv$C—H groupings. The position of the C—H stretching frequency is thus indicative of the presence of unsaturated bonds attached to the carbon atom.

In many cases further identification of an unknown species can be made. Thus, in the case of the $\geqslant$C—H bond, which occurs at about 2960 cm^{-1}, it is found that the C—H vibration of a —CH$_3$ group is always distinct from the C—H vibration of a >CH$_2$ group. Both species give rise to asymmetric and symmetric C—H stretching vibrations, the former at 2962 and 2872 cm^{-1}, the latter at 2926 and 2853 cm^{-1}. Since the deviations are rarely more than 10 cm^{-1}, the bands due to the asymmetric vibrations can easily be distinguished. This procedure is exceedingly useful, particularly in the examination of polymeric species. The intensity ratio of these two vibrations may be used to estimate the rate of growth and the length of the polymer chain. This technique has been used by Lucchesi and Yates (5) in their studies on the polymerization of ethylene on alumina and by Little et al. in their study of butene polymerization on porous glass. (6)

The characteristic group frequencies are not limited to stretching vibrations, and excellent confirmatory evidence is supplied in many cases by a study of the various bending modes. Thus, for instance, the $\equiv$C—H group gives rise to an absorption at about 1450 cm^{-1}. A combined observation of both the characteristic stretching frequency and a characteristic bending frequency is usually excellent evidence for the presence of the suspected molecular grouping. Table 2-4, originally compiled by Herzberg, represents one of the earliest listings of group frequencies. More complete tabulations of characteristic frequencies are now available, much of this development being due to the efforts of Colthup. The original and best known tabulation by Colthup is reproduced in Appendix A and further, more involved tabulations can be obtained from his book (7).

The theoretical origins of characteristic group frequencies have been discussed by Mecke (8), by Cross and Van Vleck (9), and by Herzberg (2). It has been found that characteristic frequencies occur:

1. When end atoms are being considered and when the masses of the end atoms are small compared to the rest of the molecule.

2. When internal atoms are being considered and either (a) the force constants between two atoms of like mass are considerably different or (b) the masses of the two atoms are considerably different.

The interpretation of the infrared spectra of adsorbed species has relied heavily on the concept of group frequencies, and a word of caution seems in order. It must be remembered that the whole concept of characteristic frequencies is completely phenomenological. As in all such interpretations, the possibility of gross deviations always exists and due care should be exercised when employing this approach.

2-8. USEFUL EMPIRICAL RULES

Since the frequency of any vibration is a function of bond force constant [Eq. (2-17], which in turn is usually considered to be a measure of the bond strength, it might be expected that a simple relationship could be obtained between vibrational stretching frequencies and the electronegativity of the atoms involved in the bond. Many interesting formulations have been postulated, the two best known being due to Badger and Gordy. Badger (10) developed an empirical relationship between the bond force constant k and the interatomic distance r that states:

$$k = \frac{a}{(r-b)^3} \qquad \text{or} \qquad r = \left(\frac{c}{k}\right)^{1/3} + d \qquad (2\text{-}51)$$

where a, b, c, and d are constants that are dependent upon the positions of the atoms in the periodic table. This equation is frequently referred to as Badger's rule.

Gordy's relationship (11) between electronegativity x, bond order n, force constant, and interatomic distance is of the form

$$k = an\left(\frac{x_A x_B}{r^2}\right)^{3/4} + b \qquad (2\text{-}52)$$

where a and b are again constants.

These relationships provide a very rapid method for determining the approximate vibrational frequency of any characteristic stretching frequency or, alternatively, of estimating the internuclear distance from the vibrational frequency.

2-9. VIBRATIONAL CHANGES ON ADSORPTION

From the preceding discussions it is apparent that the spectrum of any molecule is uniquely dependent upon the vibrations of the atoms within the molecule and the rotation of the molecule as a whole. When a molecule is adsorbed on a surface, it is clear that the rotational movement of the molecule will be severely restricted, and if a chemical adsorption is involved, the vibrational modes will be severely affected. In order to speculate on the spectroscopic changes that will be observed during the adsorption process, let us consider the fate of a carbon monoxide molecule after adsorption on a metal surface. The CO molecule is diatomic, and thus its spectrum consists of only one band due to the single vibratory mode. On contacting the metal surface, three processes can occur:

1. The molecule will be physically adsorbed.
2. The molecule will be chemisorbed.
3. The molecule will react with the surface and be "dissociatively" chemisorbed.

In the first case the molecule will lose much, if not all, of its rotational movement, but the molecular vibrations will be little affected by this process. Accordingly, the infrared spectrum of the adsorbed CO should be similar to that of the gas and a band should be observed at about 2140 cm^{-1}.

If, however, the carbon is chemisorbed, the symmetry of the CO species is changed to that of an X—Y—Z (X—C—O) molecule, where X, the surface atom, must be considered to have a large mass. The three-atom molecule must now produce three vibrational modes, and thus the infrared spectrum of chemisorbed CO must show at least three bands, one of which is characteristic of the C—O vibration. In actual fact, two of these bands have been observed, the third being experimentally inaccessible.

Under normal conditions the carbon monoxide is not dissociatively chemisorbed. If oxygen is present on the surface, however, an entirely different species is produced. The characteristic C—O vibration is not observed, but instead, two new bands appear at about 1360 and 1560 cm^{-1}. The position of these bands is very similar to that found in carbonate complexes, and it can be attributed to the formation of this type of species on the surface. The C—O has clearly been oxidized to a

$$-C\begin{matrix}\nearrow O \\ \searrow O\end{matrix}$$

type of molecule, the single C—O vibration being replaced by symmetric and asymmetric C—O stretching vibrations associated with the X—Y—Z_2 type of structure. These bands are in the range of the characteristic frequencies of the carboxylate ion, and they are thus identified. The characteristic frequency of the expected grouping is not observed, but the characteristic frequencies of the new species provide initial identification.

REFERENCES

1. F. A. Cotton, *Chemical Applications of Group Theory*, Wiley (Interscience), New York, 1963.
2. G. Herzberg, *Infrared and Raman Spectra of Polyatomic Molecules*, Van Nostrand, Princeton, N.J., 1945.
3. E. B. Wilson, J. C. Decuis, and P. C. Cross, *Molecular Vibrations*, McGraw-Hill, New York, 1955.
4. K. Nakamoto, *Infrared Spectra of Inorganic and Coordination Compounds*, Wiley, New York, 1963.
5. P. J. Lucchesi, J. L. Carter, and D. J. C. Yates, *J. Phys. Chem.*, **66,** 1451 (1962).
6. L. H. Little, H. E. Klauser, and C. H. Amberg, *Can. J. Chem.*, **39,** 42 (1961).
7. N. B. Colthup, L. H. Daly, and S. E. Wiberley, *Introduction to Infrared and Raman Spectroscopy*, Academic, New York, 1964.
8. R. Mecke, *Z. Physik. Chem.* (*Frankfurt*), **B16,** 409, 421 (1932); **17,** 1 (1932).
9. P. C. Cross and J. H. Van Vleck, *J. Chem. Phys.*, **1,** 350 (1933).
10. R. M. Badger, *J. Chem. Phys.*, **2,** 128 (1934); **3,** 710 (1935).
11. W. Gordy, *J. Chem. Phys.*, **14,** 305 (1946).

3

The Application of Transmission Spectroscopy
to Surface Studies: Experimental Considerations

3-1. ABSORPTION, TRANSMISSION, AND REFLECTION

A. Beer's Law

When light strikes a body, it can undergo one of three transitions: it can be reflected and scattered, it can be absorbed, or it can be transmitted. Mathematically this can be written

$$(r + S) + a + t = 1 \qquad (3\text{-}1)$$

The magnitudes of these effects are all dependent upon the wavelength of the incident radiation and the properties of the substance under investigation. The majority of the studies of the spectra of adsorbed molecules have utilized transmission spectroscopy rather than reflectance spectroscopy and, since the two are experimentally incompatible, reflection effects must be minimized as far as possible. The major problems in the practical examination of the spectra of adsorbed molecules lie in the reduction of light scattering and increasing light transmission. The absorption of radiation is a characteristic of the electronic and vibrational properties of the substance under investigation, and nothing can be done directly to reduce this factor except to alter the amount of material in the path of the incident light.

If radiation of intensity I_0 impinges upon a layer of substance of thickness d, the intensity of the emerging radiation is given by the equation

$$I = I_0 e^{-\epsilon d} \tag{3-2}$$

or

$$\ln (I/I_0) = -\epsilon d \tag{3-3}$$

This relationship, known as the Lambert-Bouguer law, provides the basis for all quantitative investigations in spectroscopy. In actual practice the use of natural logarithms is not advantageous and the relationship

$$\ln (I_0/I) = 2.303 \log (I_0/I) \tag{3-4}$$

is utilized. The quantity ϵ is known as the *extinction coefficient* and the product ϵd is known as the *optical density*. The optical density is dimensionless, the extinction coefficient having the dimension of reciprocal centimeters. The extinction coefficient is characteristic of the material being investigated and is independent of the sample size. It is a function of wavelength, and thus a plot of optical density against wavelength gives the *spectrum* of the substance under consideration. In actual practice, the spectrum is usually recorded in terms of the transmittance T, which is defined as

$$T = I/I_0 = e^{-\epsilon d} \tag{3-5}$$

The *absorbance* A is given by

$$A = \ln (1/T) = \ln (I_0/I) = \epsilon d \tag{3-6}$$

Equation (3-2) shows that the absorption of light by any body will be a function of the number of molecules in the path of the radiation. The extinction coefficient, as defined above, gives a complete description of the absorbing power of the substance, and, provided the number of molecules in the path of the incident radiation remains constant, the optical density will also completely describe the absorption characteristics of the material at any given wavelength. This, however, will be true only for solids and pure liquids. For solutions and gases, Eq. (3-2) is not directly applicable to analytical measurements. The number of molecules in the path of the incident radiation depends directly on the concentration of the substance and, since the absorbance is a linear function of the concentration,

$$A = \epsilon c d \tag{3-7}$$

Equation (3-7) is the familiar Beer law, which is usually combined with

Eq. (3-2) to give the relationship known as the Beer-Lambert law.

$$I = I_0 e^{-\epsilon c d} \tag{3-8}$$

If the concentration c is given in moles per liter and the path length d is given in centimeters, the proportionality factor ϵ is called the molar extinction coefficient and has the dimensions liter per centimeter per mole.

B. Application to Surface Chemistry

In the early applications of infrared spectroscopy to the study of ad-sorbed molecules some doubt was expressed as to whether sufficient gas could be adsorbed on a solid in the path of an infrared spectrometer to give sensible data about the adsorbed molecule. However, a simple application of the Beer-Lambert law shows that this is indeed possible, and it enables an intelligent guess to be made regarding the amount of transmission one might expect to observe.

If we place a disc of porous material in the path of a beam of incident light and adsorb a gas on the surface of the material, there will be a reduction in the amount of transmitted light due to absorption by both the adsorbent and the adsorbate. The amount of light absorbed by the former is of great practical importance but is neglected for the present discussion. The amount of light absorbed by the adsorbate will depend on the amount and extinction coefficient of the material in the path of the beam. The amount of adsorbed gas present will be a function of the surface area of the adsorbent and the degree of surface coverage by the adsorbate.

Let us first consider a typical adsorbent such as a piece of porous glass or silica gel with an internal surface area of 100 m²/g. For the purpose of this calculation we can consider it to be in the form of a disc $\frac{1}{10}$ mm thick and 1 cm² in area. The bulk density of this material is about 2 g/cc, and thus the "thickness" of the 1-cm² sample can also be expressed as being 20 mg/cm². This terminology is of use in describing pressed discs whose thickness cannot be determined accurately. Each gram of the porous adsorbent will have approximately 100×10^{20} Å² of surface available for adsorption, and if we are considering small molecules such as N_2 or CO, the effective area of one adsorbed molecule is about 17 Å². Thus about 6×10^{20} molecules could adsorb on 1 g of this material and give mono-layer coverage. Now 6×10^{23} molecules occupy 22.4 liters at STP, and thus 1 g of the porous adsorbent will adsorb approximately 22.4 ml of gas in giving a monolayer coverage or about 2.24 ml if 0.1 monolayer coverage is obtained.

The maximum extinction coefficient of a $>C{=}O$ vibration is about 3.3×10^5 cm^2/mole, or

$$\frac{3.3 \times 10^5}{6 \times 10^{23}} \simeq 0.5 \times 10^{-18} \, \text{cm}^2/CO \text{ group}\dagger \qquad (3\text{-}9)$$

If $\theta = 0.1$, there will be an adsorption of 2.24 ml of gas per gram of adsorbent, or about 6.0×10^{19} molecules. In this case, therefore, with a sample thickness of $\frac{1}{10}$mm (or 20 mg/cm^2) we would have $6.0 \times 10^{19} \times 10^{-2}$ CO molecules/cm^2 of the infrared beam, a figure that corresponds to the cd term of Eq. (3-8).

Thus, if I_0 is the radiation falling on the sample and I is the amount of radiation measured after passage through the sample, then, since $I/I_0 = e^{-\epsilon cl}$,

$$\epsilon cl = 0.5 \times 10^{-18} \times 6.0 \times 10^{17} = 0.3$$

from which

$$I/I_0 \simeq 0.8.$$

This can be clearly resolved on a good spectrometer.

It is well known that carbonyl groups are very strongly absorbing and easily recognized. In the case of hydrocarbons, however, the situation is less straightforward, and reference to Table 3-1 shows that the integral absorption of the $>CH_2$ group is less than half that of the $>C{=}O$ group. For the $-CH_2$ group it is found that absorptivities are usually about 4000 cm^2/g (1). The molecular weight of the $-CH_2$ group is 14, and therefore the extinction coefficient can be written

$$\epsilon = \frac{4 \times 10^3 \times 14}{6 \times 10^{23}} \, \text{cm}^2/CH_2 \text{ group}$$

$$\simeq 0.01 \times 10^{-17} \, \text{cm}^2/CH_2 \text{ group}$$

Thus, in the case of ethylene adsorption, when $\theta = 0.1$, we would have, as before, 6.0×10^{17} CH$_2$ groups/cm^2 of the infrared beam, and therefore

$$\epsilon cl = 6.0 \times 0.01 = 0.06$$

from which

$$I/I_0 = 0.95$$

In general, a spectrometer will record up to a value of 0.99 and thus, in this case, although the ethylene should be detected, the sensitivity of the

† Heyne and Tompkins (3) have recently reported a value of 2×10^{-18} cm^2/CO molecule for carbon monoxide adsorbed on platinum.

TABLE 3-1[a]

Absolute Absorption Intensities for Several Group Vibrations[a]

Group	Position of bands, cm^{-1}	Integral absorption, cm^2/mole-sec $\times 10^7$
C=O	ca. 1720	
Esters		13
Alkylketones		8
Ketosteroids		9–20
C—O	ca. 1200	
Esters		15
Alkylketones		2.5
Acetoxysteroids		21
N—H	ca. 3400	
Dialkylamines		0.05
Alkylanilines		1.7
Diarylamines		2.2
Pyrroles, carbazoles		5.4
Indoles		6.6
C≡N	ca. 2250	
Alkylcyanides		0.25
CH_3	ca. 2900	
Hydrocarbons		4.4
—$COCH_3$		0.74
—$COOCH_3$		2.54
CH_3	ca. 1460	
Hydrocarbons		0.54
—$COCH_3$		1.3
—$COOCH_3$		2.0
CH_2	ca. 2900	
Hydrocarbons		3.8
—$COCH_2$—		0.5
CH_2	ca. 1460	
Hydrocarbons		0.23
—$COCH_2$		1.17
—$COOCH_2$—		0.65

[a] Taken from Reference (7), courtesy of John Wiley & Sons, Inc.

instrument would be much reduced and weaker bands might pass unnoticed.

In the previous discussion, the I_0 and I values that are used are those which are determined solely by the adsorbate, and the I_0 value is thus the transmission value of the adsorbate prior to the adsorption of the carbon monoxide or the ethylene. In ordinary analytical work these values are usually determined by drawing a tangent to the transmission curve (Fig. 3-1) to remove the background absorption. The I values thus obtained

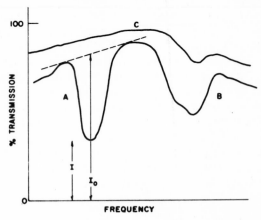

Fig. 3-1. *The tangent method for determining extinction coefficients. The curve AB represents the recorded spectrum of an adsorbed species. It is superimposed on the sample background, C. The tangent method may be used for peak A, but for peak B the spectra must be redrawn and the absorption due to the sample must be subtracted.*

are used in the quantitative application of Eq. (3-8). In surface-chemical applications the tangent method often cannot be applied, because the adsorbent rarely gives rise to a linear background. In this case the true shape of the peak due to the adsorbed molecule can be obtained only by an actual measurement of I and I_0 and subsequent replotting of the spectrum by using optical densities. Since the band shape of the adsorbed species may well be asymmetrical owing to the heterogeneous nature of the surface, mechanical subtraction is of no use in quantitative applications. Figure 3-1 also demonstrates that high I_0 values (and therefore high sensitivity) can be obtained only when the sample background is a minimum. The nature of the adsorbent thus restricts the use of spectroscopic techniques in surface chemistry. Two factors, however, are of great assistance in the study of the spectra of adsorbed molecules. The first is that the substrates that have been of primary interest thus far are the materials that have a high internal surface area. This factor helps to increase the ratio of adsorbate to adsorbent in the path of the incident light.

Second, surface spectroscopists have been greatly assisted by the fortuitous circumstance that the extinction coefficient of a molecular vibration is often considerably increased when the parent molecules are in an adsorbed state. This feature will be discussed more definitely in the detailed analysis of results obtained by various workers. However, it is general rule of thumb that this effect occurs, the increase in intensity being inversely related to surface coverage. One of the earliest references to this effect was made in a 1939 paper by Sutherland and Tutte (2). These authors examined a series of thin polymolecular hydrocarbon films and noted that the absorption coefficient appeared to be increased by a factor of almost 100. Without such an immense effect these workers claim they would not have been able to obtain successful spectra on the hydrocarbon films, which were only about 200 molecules in thickness. In the case of the previous calculation of the transmission properties of adsorbed carbon monoxide, the spectroscopist is considerably aided by the fact that the integrated intensity of the adsorbed carbon monoxide is about 200 times larger than that of gaseous carbon monoxide (27). In this case, surface coverages down to 0.01 monolayer should be observable.

C. Refractive Index, Particle Size

Two other factors are important in determining the infrared spectra of solids: the differences in the refractive indexes of the material under investigation and of the dispersion medium and the dimensions of the individual particles under study. The second effect is of the utmost importance in the study of infrared spectra of adsorbed molecules, because excessive scattering by the adsorbent causes a large reduction in the I_0 value that can be obtained. Also, the effect of large particle size is to reduce both the apparent intensity of the absorption and the resolution of the spectrum. This is shown clearly by the results of Duyckaerts (4), Fig. 3-2, where the infrared spectra of calcium carbonate has been determined as the particle size is decreased from 55 to 5 μ.

The effect of particle size on light scattering was originally treated theoretically by Lord Rayleigh, who showed that the amount of scattering was an inverse function of the fourth power of the wavelength of the incident light:

$$S \propto d^3/\lambda^4 \qquad (3\text{-}10)$$

where d is the particle diameter.

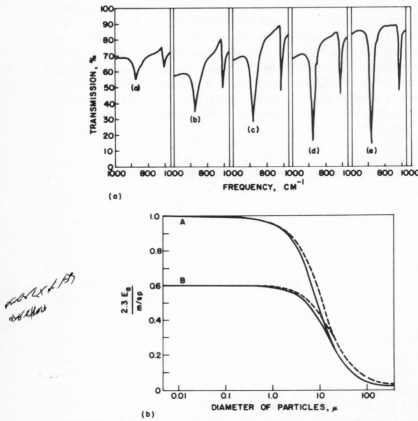

Fig. 3-2. (a) *Effect of particle size on infrared spectrum of calcite in KBr discs:* (a) 55 μ; (b) 40 μ; (c) 23 μ; (d) 14.7 μ; (e) 5 μ. (b) *Theoretical variation of extinction with particle size. Curve A:* $K = 0.8$, $k = 1.0 \, \mu^{-1}$. *Curve B:* $K = 0.8$, $k = 0.6 \, \mu^{-1}$. *Solid line represents cubes, dashed line represents spheres.* [*Redrawn from Reference (4) by courtesy of the Society for Analytical Chemistry.*]

Thus, as we move to lower frequencies, the amount of scattering should be reduced. This effect has been noted many times in the study of adsorbed species. Perhaps the best known examples lie in the study of surface hydroxyl groups where the samples have been purposely deuterated so that the surface OD group ($\simeq 2700 \, cm^{-1}$) can be studied in preference to the surface OH groups ($\simeq 3600 \, cm^{-1}$), the transmission being superior at the lower frequency.

Duyckaerts (4) has considered the amount of scattering produced by a collection of particles of density ρ and diameter d that are dispersed randomly in a disc of cross-sectional area S, mass m, and length l. The disc was considered to consist of a number of layers n arranged in such a manner that each layer contained the same number of particles and that the incident light interacted only once with each particle. If K represents the geometrical fraction of the surface normal to the incident light in each layer and if θ is the transmission of one particle, then

$$I/I_0 = (1 - K) + K\theta \tag{3-11}$$

For n equal layers,

$$I/I_0 = [(1 - K) + K\theta]^n \tag{3-12}$$

and

$$A = \log (I_0/I) = -n \log [(1 - K) + K\theta] \tag{3-13}$$

For cubic particles,

$$\theta = e^{-kd} \quad \text{(Beer's Law)} \tag{3-14}$$

where k is the true extinction coefficient of the material, n may be inferred from the values of ρ, d, S, m, and K, and introduction of this parameter into and expansion of Eq. (3-13) gives the limiting value of the extinction. Duyckaerts thence obtains the expression

$$\lim_{kd \to 0} A = \frac{m}{S\rho} \frac{k}{2.3}$$

A plot of $2.3AS\rho/m$ against d for two values of k (0.6 and 1.0 μ^{-1}) is given in Fig. 3-2, and it is seen that maximum transmission is obtained when the particle size is less than about one micron, i.e., less than the wavelength of the incident light. It has been generally found that good results are obtained if particle sizes are reduced to less than one micron. This particle size is often difficult to achieve with some catalytic particles, but the results obtained after this treatment are usually sufficient to convince the experimenter of the value of the effort involved.

Clewell (5) has pointed out that, as particle sizes are increased, there must come a point where the particles become so large that they approach the bulk crystalline material in their absorption properties. The transmittance must therefore go through a minimum. It is presumably because of this effect that materials such as porous glass and the silica–alumina gels described by Peri (6) are so unique in their light-transmitting qualities compared with pressed silica discs containing material of apparently similar fundamental particle size.

In discussing the effect of particle size on light scattering, it was assumed that the material was embedded in a medium of equal refractive index. This is not usually possible in practice, but it is a general rule of thumb that wherever possible the material under examination should be immersed in a liquid or solid whose refractive index is as close as possible to that of the particle under investigation. This reduces scattering and considerably enhances the attainable resolution. The effect is particularly striking when a pressed disc of silica gel is immersed in a fluorolube oil. The transmittance, which initially may be only 20%, is immediately increased to about 80% owing to the effectiveness of the oil in reducing light scattering. Unfortunately, however, the use of such oil is generally frowned upon in surface studies because of the possibility of producing surface contamination.

3-2. INFRARED SPECTROMETERS

A. General Outline

Since the limiting factor in the determination of the infrared spectra of adsorbed species lies in the sample preparation, it is not the purpose of this chapter to discuss infrared spectrometers that are available commercially. It is sufficient to note that the good spectrometers that are now available are perfectly adequate for the determination of the spectra of surface species. As the science of surface spectroscopy is now progressing, it is evident that future discussions will revolve around relatively small changes in the frequency and intensity of various vibrational bands, and therefore the greater the resolution of the spectrometer the better. Single-beam instruments have been used in the study of surface species, but the use of a double-beam instrument offers many advantages to surface chemists. The greatest of these is the ability to attenuate the reference beam by insertion of identical samples. The problems of nonlinear backgrounds are thus overcome, and the tangent method (Fig. 3-1) becomes acceptable in the determination of intensity data.

Infrared spectrometers consist essentially of three major components: a source, a detector, and an intermediate optical system (Fig. 3-3). The two most common sources of infrared radiation are the Nernst glower and the globar. The former is a hollow rod of zirconium, yttrium, and thorium oxides that produces an intense radiation up to about 10 μ (1000 cm^{-1}). Its normal life is several hundred hours. Globars are made from silicon carbide and operate at temperatures of about 1400°C. They are more stable than the Nernst glower, and the radiation emitted approximates that of a black body. Globar life, however, is relatively short, and power consumption is relatively high.

The wavelength of any black-body radiation is given by the Planck equation

$$W_\lambda = (C_1/\lambda^5)[\exp{(C_2/\lambda T} - 1)]^{-1} \qquad (3\text{-}15)$$

where W_λ is the amount of radiation emitted by the black body per unit surface area, T is the absolute temperature of the black body, λ is the wavelength of the emitted radiation in centimeters, and C_1 and C_2 are constants with the numerical values of 3.7402×10^{-12} watts/cm² and

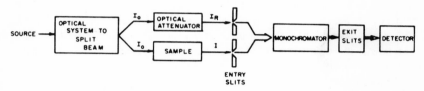

Fig. 3-3. Schematic outline of a double-beam spectrometer.

1.43848 cm/deg, respectively. The displacement of the maximum intensity of the emitted radiation with temperature is given by the Wein displacement law

$$\lambda_{max}T = K \qquad (3\text{-}16)$$

where K, a constant, is equal to 2897 μdeg when the wavelength is given in microns.

The optical portions of commercial infrared spectrometers are complicated and contain several types of patented mirrors, which are used to prevent spherical aberration, astigmatism, and reflection losses at the lens surfaces. The most important functional part of the optical system is the monochromator, which is used to resolve the radiation.

The infrared radiation from the source is usually passed through the sample before entering the monochromator. The radiation then passes through two parallel slits that vary in width between about 10 and 100 μ and that are accurately machined and mounted so that the slit width is reproducible. After passage through these entry slits, the radiation enters the monochromator, where it is resolved into its wavelength components by either a prism or a grating. After passing through the optical portion of the spectrometer, the infrared radiation passes through a second set of slits whose width, in practice, is the same as that of the first set and thence to a detector where the incident radiation is quantitatively analyzed. Thermocouples represent the most common type of detector, but photo-electric mechanisms are sometimes employed.

B. Resolution

The efficiency of a spectrometer is given by its ability to distinguish between closely spaced bands in the spectrum. It is this ability of the instrument that determines whether two neighbouring bands in the spectrum will appear as separate entities or as a single band. For a band of infinite thinness, the resolution of both prisms and gratings are given by classical optical theory and are dependent on the line spacing, in the case of the grating, and on the angle and the refractive index of the prism. The value obtained is known as the *theoretical resolving power*. In practice, however, the band of incident light covers a range of wavelengths that depends on the width of the entry slit. The effect of this parameter is to reduce the theoretical resolving power of the instrument, and a practical *resolution* is obtained. Methods of determining spectrometer resolution are based on measurement of the fine rotational structure of gases such as ammonia whose spectra have been determined accurately on instruments of the highest caliber. Details of these techniques and further pertinent information are given by Brugel (7).

C. Slit Width

The actual width of the slits is known as the *finite* (or *mechanical*) *slit width*, whereas the small region of energy isolated by the exit slit is known as the *spectral slit width*. The distribution of energy as a function of wavelength emitted from the exit slit is known as the *slit function*, and it can usually be considered to be triangular with its apex at the wavelength being monitored. The *resolution* of the instrument is dependent on the spectral slit width and is proportional to the mechanical slit width. Better resolution is obtained when narrower slits are used. However, the energy received by the detector is proportional to the square of the mechanical slit width, and thus reducing this width to improve resolution also decreases the efficiency of the instrument.

In any quantitative investigation the slit width or resolution should be less than the width of the band under investigation, since large slit widths broaden the observed band, sometimes beyond recognition. In high-resolution spectroscopy it should always be remembered that the *scanning speed* is also an important parameter. As the slits are narrowed, the detector is harder worked and the pen response is slower. Fast scanning under these conditions can introduce considerable error in the recorded spectrum.

An investigation of the effect of different slit widths on extinction coefficients has been made by Robinson (8), who found that Beer's law was obeyed when the ratio of the slit width to band width was of the order of 0.4. However, as this ratio became larger, deviations from Beer's law were observed. The deviations were greatest both at the largest slit widths and as the extinction coefficients approached a maximum. Even when the slit width was equal to one-half the band width, the true and observed maximum extinction coefficients differed by as much as 20%.

D. Band Shape

Although classical theory indicates that energy absorption due to any vibrational–rotational transition should take place between discrete energy levels, it is found in practice that all absorption bands have a finite width. This is due partly to the uncertainty principle and the inability to define the energy levels exactly but in practice it is due mostly to the instrumental inadequacies already discussed. If the latter are ignored, a plot of optical density against wave number for any absorption band can usually be represented by a Lorentz-type curve of the form

$$\ln \frac{I_0}{I} = \frac{a}{(v - v_0)^2 + b^2} \tag{3-17}$$

The maximum optical density is thus

$$\ln \left(\frac{I_0}{I} \right)_{v_0} = \frac{a}{b^2} \tag{3-18}$$

and the *band half-width*, defined as being the width of the absorption band at half the maximum extinction, is given by

$$\Delta v_{1/2} = 2b \tag{3-19}$$

where a and b are constants (9).

Introduction of a slit function into Eq. (3-17) leads to results that show considerable deviations from theoretical values. As noted previously, the effect is to increase the band half-width and decrease the maximum extinction coefficient. Under standardized conditions the half-width of a band can be as helpful as the extinction coefficient in identifying a molecule.

E. Integrated Absorption

It is clear from the above discussion that the maximum extinction coefficient is not a good parameter to use in discussing intensity data. The problem of reproducibility and elimination of spectrometer inefficiencies can be solved by integrating the extinction coefficient over the observed wavelength range of the band, i.e.,

$$A = \int_{-\infty}^{+\infty} E_v \, dv = \frac{1}{cd} \int_{-\infty}^{+\infty} \ln \frac{I_0}{I} \, dv \qquad (3\text{-}20)$$

A is then known as the *integrated absorption coefficient* and is the area under the optical density curve after the background absorption has been removed. Its units are given in centimeters per mole. In practice, Eq. (3-20) is not integrated between $-\infty$ and $+\infty$ but rather between two arbitrary values v_1 and v_2 on either side of v_0. If the curve is symmetrical,

$$v_0 = \tfrac{1}{2}(v_1 + v_2) \qquad (3\text{-}21)$$

This approximation leads to certain small errors, known as wing errors, that are usually ignored.

The concept of integrated absorption has worked very well and has been found to be a reliable unit for use in quantitative analysis. Whereas the extinction coefficient may vary widely under different experimental conditions, the integrated absorption remains remarkably uniform.

Although most of the spectroscopic work carried out to date has involved only the frequency of the vibrational bands, the use of intensity data is now becoming more widespread. The intensity of a band is a very useful parameter in that it gives fundamental information regarding the nature of the bonds between two atoms. Theoretically, it is related directly to the change in the dipole moment of the bond between the two atoms during the vibratory process (*10*).

The dipole moment p of a diatomic species of charge e separated by a distance r is given by

$$p = er \qquad (3\text{-}22)$$

and the absolute intensity of the absorption is given by

$$I_{\text{abs}} = a \left(\frac{\partial p}{\partial r} \right)^2$$

where a is a constant.

Some data on the integrated absorption intensities of a series of compounds that could not be distinguished on the basis of their group frequencies are presented in Table 3-1. The wide variation in absolute intensity thus adds a valuable parameter for the identification of molecules, and the construction of characteristic-intensity tables similar to the characteristic-frequency tables can be expected in the future. However, since the intensity of an adsorbed species changes with surface coverage, it is doubtful whether such data could be used in the identification of an adsorbed species.

3-3. THE PREPARATION OF SAMPLES

A. Disc Techniques

In the early applications of infrared spectroscopy to the study of chemisorption, the powdered adsorbents were placed in the path of the infrared radiation simply by sprinkling the material on an infrared-transmitting window and ensuring that the infrared radiation passed through the sample in a vertical direction. This arrangement was not very satisfactory, because it required certain modifications to be made to the spectrometer, and light scattering was a serious problem, even though the particle size was of the right order of magnitude.

In the application of infrared spectroscopy to the routine quantitative analysis of solid materials the potassium bromide disc technique has achieved considerable utility. In this method, a weighed quantity of the material under investigation is finely ground with a quantitative excess of potassium bromide, either by itself or in the presence of an inert volatile solvent such as benzene (11). The mixture of the unknown and the potassium bromide is then compressed into an optically acceptable pellet by applying pressures of about 20,000 lb/in.². The resultant spectra are well resolved, and quantitative results can be obtained by using this method. However, it is now known that this technique must be used with caution, because the material under investigation can undergo both polymorphic and crystalline distortions during the process of pellet formation. The most common and the most disturbing of the interactions that can occur in the pressed pellet technique, however, is an ion-exchange reaction that can take place between the alkali halide support medium and cations that may exist in the species under investigation. Thus, when potassium bromide and benzoic acid are ground together for an extended period of time, the resultant spectrum shows the formation of potassium benzoate (4). This type of ion-exchange reaction,

$$\phi COOH + KBr \rightarrow \phi COOK + HBr$$

can also take place between the potassium ions and cations that have been formed on catalyst surfaces. Fortunately, this was noticed very early in the study of chemical adsorption by infrared techniques, and the potassium bromide disc method as a whole has fallen into disrepute in its application to surface chemistry. A typical example of this effect on catalyst surfaces has been given by Pliskin and Eischens (*12*). These workers showed that the NH_4^+ ion, formed when ammonia was adsorbed on a silica-alumina surface, underwent ready ion exchange with the KBr. Thus, when the ammoniated catalyst was embedded in the KBr disc, the resultant spectrum, although still recognizable as an NH_4^+ species, was not the same as had been observed in the absence of KBr. Rather, it resembled the spectrum of ammonium bromide. Clearly, the close contact between the catalyst surface and the potassium bromide had enabled the exchange reaction

$$(Si-Al)_s NH_4^+ + KBr = (Si-Al)_s K^+ + NH_4 Br$$

to take place. The reaction was probably facilitated by the presence of some water on the surface of the silica–alumina, a condition that is hard to avoid in using the potassium bromide discs.

It has now been shown that the catalytically active oxides can be pressed into thin, waferlike discs without the aid of potassium bromide, and this is the preparative method now employed in most spectroscopic investigations of surface activity. Dies suitable for preparing these discs may be purchased commercially (*13*). Pressures of the order of 20,000 lb/in.² are required to get discs that exhibit adequate transmission of infrared radiation, and the particle size should be reduced to the order of 1 μ before pressing. The thickness of the discs must be kept down to about $\frac{1}{10}$ mm (about a 20-mg sample) and, since the thickness cannot be readily measured, it is often expressed in terms of milligrams per square centimeter. The usual disc diameter is about 2.5 cm.

Commercial dies are equipped with facilities for pressing under vacuum, but this process does not always lead to the best samples. The author has achieved better results by not evacuating during the pressing process and by not thoroughly drying the sample before pressing. Sticking of the sample to the faces of the die is often a problem, and circumventing it can be a major part of the research program. Blyholder and Richardson (*14*) have found that preheating the die before pressing can help. Alternatively, the material can be pressed between thin sheets of Teflon or Saran film. It should be mentioned here that these organic surfaces often impart a contamination to the disc that must be removed before use.

A method that has proved very successful in the author's laboratory is the use of tissue paper in the pressing operation. The finely divided powder is pressed between two pieces of tissue paper. The sample is impressed into the paper and, on release of the pressure, both the paper and sample are easily removed from the die. The paper is then oxidized off in the usual manner at 500°C before spectral investigation. A certain small amount of ash must be produced in this process, but the method provides samples that have good transmittance and will survive a remarkable amount of maltreatment. The tissue backing also allows the sample to be cut into alternative shapes and mounted before it is finally oxidized and cleaned.

In the pressed disc technique, it is clear that pressing together the surfaces of the discrete particles can induce alterations in the nature of the surfaces. Moreover, since localized high temperatures often exist during the pressing process, surface annealing might be expected to occur. This effect was first investigated by McDonald (15) on Cab-O-Sil® silica. He found that, when the silica particles were compressed at pressures of about 100,000 lb/in.², there was evidence that the freely vibrating surface silanol groups were diminished in intensity owing to hydrogen-bonded interaction. An increase in the intensity of the hydrogen-bonded groups at lower frequency was also noted. On heating to 400°C in air, the band due to the bonded hydroxyl groups was completely removed and the intensity of the band due to the free silanol groups was increased by about 10%. Presumably, siloxane (Si—O—Si) cross-links were being formed between the individual particles during the heating process.

This effect has been further discussed by Hambleton and others (16), who have shown that the OH–OD exchange reaction on the surface is considerably altered by the pressing process. In particular, it appears that regions inaccessible to H_2O and D_2O may be formed during the process. This effect increases as the compression is increased, and thus it is clear that pressed disc samples should be prepared at the lowest pressure consistent with good disc formation.

The use of porous glass as a support material has already been mentioned. This material gives rise to very good transmission characteristics, but it suffers from a heterogeneity of surface properties. A series of silica, alumina, and silica–alumina aerogels have been obtained in "glassy" form by Peri (6) by use of a tenchique that involves controlled drying of a hydrogel. The main trick in this procedure is to prevent cracking of the gel during the drying process. Interfacial sticking between the gel and the container must be avoided at all costs, and patience appears to be an integral part of the procedure. The resultant plates are almost transparent and are equivalent to porous glass in their transmitting properties. Full experimental details are given by Peri (6).

Infrared investigations of metallic surfaces have been plagued by problems of sample heterogeneity. In industrial practice most of the "interesting" metallic surfaces have been associated with materials in which the metal is supported on an "inert" oxide such as silica or alumina. In the case of these materials, the pressed disc technique may be employed for sample preparation if care is taken to ensure that the supported metal has a small particle size. Increasing the metal loading beyond about 5–10% can cause tremendous loss of transmission, because sintering frequently takes place either before or during the adsorption process. The metal is normally introduced onto the inert oxide surface by impregnating with an aqueous solution containing a decomposable salt of the metal under consideration. Nitrates have been frequently employed. After drying, the salt is decomposed to the oxide, which must then be reduced to the metal. Since the effect of remaining oxygen on the spectrum of an adsorbed species can be considerable (17), the reducing technique can have a major influence on the results obtained. Where possible, a flow system should be employed, and reduction should be carried out until uniform results have been obtained.

B. Evaporated Metals

In order to circumvent the problems associated with supported metals, several different techniques have been developed to prepare suitable specimens of metallic surfaces. The most obvious technique is to employ the reflection of infrared radiation from an evaporated metal film. Studies in this area have been made by Pickering and Eckstrom (18), and they are discussed in a separate section. Evaporation of the metal in situ has been employed by Garland and his co-workers (19), by Blyholder (20), and by Nash and DeSieno (21). In Garland's method the cell used contains tungsten filaments placed between infrared transmitting windows. These filaments are charged with the appropriate metal for evaporation, and, after evacuation to a pressure of 10^{-6} torr and slow heating to desorb entrapped gases, porous metal films are flash-evaporated onto the cell walls and windows in the presence of small amounts of carbon monoxide or argon. In the former case, the metal surface contains chemisorbed CO, which may then be investigated.

A variation of this technique has been employed by Nash and DeSieno (21). The use of a higher pressure of inert gas (760 mm) allows electrical explosion of the metal wires and production of a metal aerosol that settles out on the windows. This metal film may then be investigated in situ. The surface activity of the materials prepared in this fashion is somewhat different from that of the supported metals.

The first efforts to produce evaporated metal particles were due to Blyholder (20). In this technique the metal is evaporated onto a thin film of oil that is suspended on the cell windows. A "mull" of metal suspended in oil is thus obtained, and the adsorbent gases may then be admitted to the system. Transmission through metals prepared this way is very good because of the reduction of reflection losses by the presence of the oil. Although the method may be criticized by purists because of the possibility of contamination by the oil and the fact that the interface investigated is solution–solid rather than gas–solid, the results obtained by Blyholder have been unique and have added considerably to our knowledge of the adsorbed state.

The main advantage of all three techniques lies in their ability to produce a sample that is spectroscopically transparent down to about 400 cm^{-1}. The region between 1400 and 400 cm^{-1} is normally blacked out by the supporting oxide and is unavailable for examination. Many important bending vibrations are observed in this region, and the presence or absence of some of these bands has enabled more definite assignments to be made in many cases.

C. Mull Techniques

A very rapid method, useful for looking at the properties of surfaces and surface complexes that are relatively unaffected by air, is the mull technique. In this method the sample to be investigated is simply ground with a slight excess of hydrocarbon or fluorocarbon oil, and the resultant paste is smeared between two infrared-transmitting windows and mounted on the spectrometer. Once the samples are embedded in the oil, atmospheric contaminants have negligible effect on the surface. The oil itself modifies the surface properties somewhat and, for example, causes a slight perturbation of the surface hydroxyl vibrations (about 20 cm^{-1}). Excellent transmission can be obtained because of the small particle sizes used and the reduction in light scattering afforded by the oily matrix.

The amount of sample in the path of the beam can be controlled simply by squeezing the windows closer together, regrinding with an excess of oil, or both. An additional advantage of this technique is that an identical reference sample can be prepared by the squeezing process, and very flat backgrounds can be obtained by using a double-beam spectrometer.

Examples of the use of this technique in the study of surface complexes have been given (22). Water, oxygen, and carbon dioxide contamination are ever-present problems, but the method is rapid and can be made quantitative (23). Its usefulness in the investigation of samples that are normally exposed to atmospheric conditions could be considerable.

3-4. INFRARED CELLS

A variety of vacuum cells for supporting pressed discs of samples in an infrared beam prior to admission of gaseous molecules of interest have been described in the literature. These cells consist of essentially two types: those that enable the sample to be heated at the same time that the infrared spectrum is recorded and those in which the sample is moved to a different portion of the apparatus for heat treatment. In the latter case the infrared spectra are always recorded at room temperature. Diagrams illustrating these two types of apparatus are shown in Figs. 3-4(a) to 3-4(d).

Cells of the type shown in Fig. 3-4(a) are very simple to construct; they consist essentially of an all-glass system onto which two Irtran® windows have been sealed with Pliobond® adhesive. The sample disc is placed in a magnetic-metal holder and is moved in and out of the infrared beam by means of an external magnet. A more elegant variation of this type of cell (b) has been used by Peri (17). O'Neill and Yates (24) have constructed a cell in which the windows were sealed directly to the glass system. If magnesium oxide is used as the window material, it may be sealed to a high-expansion glass that is used as the cell material. Such a cell is able to withstand a temperature of 400°C.

In quantitative applications of infrared spectroscopy to surface phenomena it is desirable that the sample be held in place in the infrared beam and not moved during any heating processes. This avoids the possibility of changes in sample thickness and damage to the sample, and it also enables the kinetics of reactions to be recorded spectroscopically. The construction of this type of cell is relatively difficult, because an in situ furnace for the sample, a cooling system for the windows, and thermocouple and vacuum connections must be constructed within a space of about five inches. Several cells that fulfill these requirements have been designed. Two of them are shown in Figs. 3-4(c) and 3-4(d). The first is due to Courtois and Teichner (25); the second, which is of all-metal construction is due to Harrison and Lawrence (26) and has been employed successfully by the author. Cells capable of going to low temperatures

($-100°$C) have been described by Eischens and Jacknow (27), and an all-metal system capable of operating from $-196°$ to 500°C without changing samples has been described by Smith and Quets (28). Leftin (29) describes a cell suitable for both ultraviolet and infrared measurement. Lynds (30) describes a unique method of sample heating. Instead of being heated in an external furnace, the samples under investigation were supported on a small-pore nickel screen that was then heated electrically.

In order to make the spectroscopic method quantitative, it is necessary to make gravimetric measurements on separate samples under conditions identical with those employed with the sample in the infrared beam or to use less accurate volumetric techniques directly with the small sample in the infrared cell. Seanor and Amberg (31), however, have designed a null-reading microbalance that is capable of measuring to 0.02 mg or better and that is integrally attached to the sample in the infrared beam. A similar apparatus has also been described by Peri (32). In discussing the capabilities of their equipment, Seanor and Amberg are at pains to point out a source of error in the quantitative determination of intensities, namely, the possibility that there is a contribution to the weight adsorbed from species that are not spectroscopically observed. This point has been ignored by most workers for obvious reasons.

3-5. MISCELLANEOUS EFFECTS

A. External Focusing

For highly scattering solid samples, it is advantageous if the infrared radiation can be focused on the sample (24). Such focusing can be achieved by the use of an external optical attachment. This type of device offers a further advantage in that the space restrictions on furnace design are not as stringent as in the arrangement employed in the conventional spectrometer, and it therefore offers distinct possibilities in future experimental work.

B. Heating Effect of the Beam

It should be remembered that the infrared radiation that is absorbed by the sample itself creates a heating effect that can be of great importance, particularly in studies of weakly adsorbed molecules. Thus McDonald (15) has measured the intensities of the bands due to water adsorbed on silica for a sample that was placed first in the monochromatic beam of radiation between the exit slits and the detector, and then, in the conventional manner, in the undispersed beam between the source and the

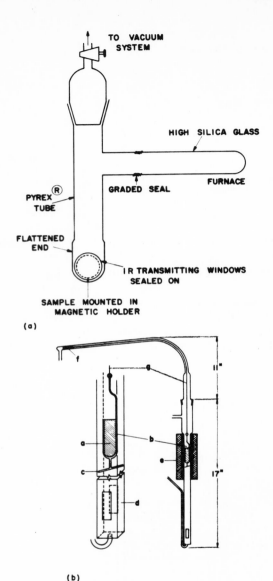

Fig. 3-4. *Cells used for studies of adsorbed molecules. (a) Simple form of infrared cell. (b) An improved version of (a). [Designed by Peri (17) and reproduced with permission of The Faraday Society.] a, Aerogel sample; b, sample holder; c, silica cane oriented at a 45° angle with plane of the sample; d, cell body of 1-in.-square silica tubing; CaF₂ windows waxed to cell; e, external furnace; f, borosilicate-glass–enclosed magnet; g, silica fiber. (c) In situ cell designed by Courtois and Teichner (25). [Reproduced with permission of the Journal of Catalysis (Academic Press).] (d) All metal, in situ, infrared cell designed by Harrison and Lawrence (26). [Reproduced by courtesy of the Institute of Physics and The Physical Society.] 1, Main body; 2, water cooling chamber; 3, cell and caps; 4, O-ring seals; 5, sample holder; 6, heater windings; 7, silica sleeve; 8, asbestos-mica washers.*

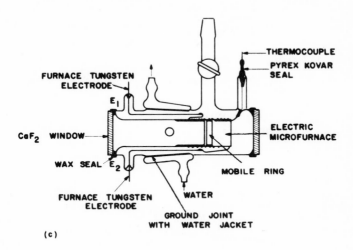

(c)

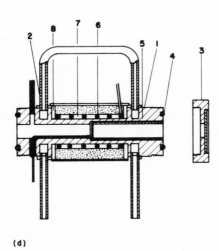

(d)

Fig. 3-4 (*continued*)

TABLE 3-2

Optical Materials Useful in Infrared Studies

Material	Useful range, cm^{-1}	Refractive index (at 0.54μ)	Comments
NaCl (rock salt)	>500	1.54	Widely used, cheap, and easily worked; must be kept dry, however
KBr	>310	1.53	Soft and easily scratched. Similar to NaCl, but has greater range. Used as powder for pressed disc technique.
CsBr	>240	1.69	Easily worked, but harder than the other halides. Expensive. Not hygroscopic.
Quartz (SiO_2)	>2500	~ 1.5	Insoluble and easy to work in fused form. Useful for high-temperature work and in the overtone region.
Sapphire (Al_2O_3)	>1600	1.77	Has high mechanical strength but is expensive.
MgO (Irtran 5[a])	>1200	1.74	Hard and costly. Can be sealed to a high-expansion glass (*24*).
LiF	>1200	1.38	Very useful in the near infrared because of good dispersion. Scratches easily.
CaF$_2$ (fluorite)	>900	1.41	Inert to most chemicals, but tends to be costly. Good from $-200°$ to $1000°C$. Has low solubility in all except NH_4^+ salts.
AgCl	>400	2.07	Soft material. Has low melting point, is corrosive and photosensitive.
MgF$_2$ (Irtran 1[a])	1333	1.38	Strong. Will withstand temperature of $900°C$. Chemically durable.
ZnS (Irtran 2[a])	714	2.37	Chemically durable, good up to $800°C$, strong, very useful.
ZnSe (Irtran 4[a])	500	2.89	Useful up to $300°C$. Soluble in acids.

[a] Eastman Kodak Co., Rochester, N.Y.

entry slits. The intensity of the bands due to the adsorbed water was reduced by a factor of 4 in the latter case, an effect that is ascribed to the heating effect of the beam.

C. Far Infrared

In Chapter 2 it was seen that the pure rotational bands of many molecules occur in the far-infrared region, an area not available to most workers in the field. Yates (*33*) has recently investigated the spectrum of several physically adsorbed molecules in this region (300–30 cm^{-1}), but he has been unable to observe any bands due to the adsorbed molecules. Whether this has been due to an absence of vibrations in this spectral region or due to a lack of intensity has not been established.

3-6. MATERIALS FOR INFRARED STUDIES

In examining the spectrum of any material it is important that the windows of the cell in which the material is being held or supported absorb as little of the incident radiation as possible and exhibit a background that is as flat as possible. Many materials have been employed for window purposes, and the most common are tabulated in Table 3-2 with some comments on their applicability. The choice of material depends upon the experimental condition to be employed, and particularly upon the spectral region under investigation and the temperature to which the material will be subjected.

REFERENCES

1. S. A. Francis, *Anal. Chem.*, **25**, 1466 (1953).
2. G. B. B. M. Sutherland and W. Tutte, *Nature*, **144**, 707 (1939).
3. H. Heyne and F. C. Tompkins, *Proc. Roy. Soc.* (*London*), **292**, 460 (1966).
4. G. Duyckaerts, *Analyst*, **84**, 201 (1959).
5. D. H. Clewell, *J. Opt. Sci. Am.*, **31**, 521 (1941).
6. J. B. Peri, *J. Phys. Chem.*, **69**, 211 (1965); **70**, 2037 (1966).
7. W. Brugel, *An Introduction to Infrared Spectroscopy*, Methuen, London, 1962.
8. D. Z. Robinson, *Anal. Chem.*, **23**, 273 (1951).
9. H. A. Lorentz, *Proc. Acad. Sci.* (*Amsterdam*), **8**, 591 (1906).
10. G. Herzberg, *Infrared and Raman Spectra*, Van Nostrand, Princeton, N.J., 1945.
11. J. J. Kirkland, *Anal. Chem.*, **27**, 1537 (1955).
12. W. A. Pliskin and R. P. Eischens, *J. Phys. Chem.*, **59**, 1156 (1955).
13. Beckman Instrument Co. (Limit Accessories).
14. G. Blyholder and E. A. Richardson, *J. Phys. Chem.*, **66**, 2598 (1962).
15. R. S. McDonald, *J. Phys. Chem.*, **62**, 1168 (1958).

16. F. H. Hambleton, J. A. Hockey, and J. A. G. Taylor, *Nature*, **208**, 138 (1965).
17. J. B. Peri, *Discussions Faraday Soc.*, **41**, 121 (1966).
18. H. L. Pickering and H. C. Eckstrom, *J. Phys. Chem.*, **63**, 512 (1959).
19. C. W. Garland, R. C. Lord, and P. F. Troiano, *J. Phys. Chem.*, **69**, 1188 (1965).
20. G. Blyholder, *J. Chem. Phys.*, **36**, 2036 (1962).
21. C. P. Nash and R. P. DeSieno, *J. Phys. Chem.*, **69**, 2139 (1965).
22. M. L. Hair and I. D. Chapman, *J. Phys. Chem.*, **69**, 3949 (1965); in *Proceedings Third International Congress on Catalysis, Amsterdam, 1964*, North-Holland, Amsterdam, 1965, p. 1091.
23. K. B. Bradley and W. J. Potts, Jr., *Appl. Spectry.* **12**, 77 (1958).
24. C. E. O'Neill and D. J. C. Yates, *J. Phys. Chem.*, **65**, 901 (1961).
25. M. Courtois and S. J. Teichner, *J. Catalysis*, **1**, 121 (1962).
26. F. R. Harrison and J. J. Lawrence, *J. Sci. Instr.*, **41**, 693 (1964).
27. R. P. Eischens and J. Jacknow, in *Proceedings Third International Congress on Catalysis, Amsterdam, 1964*, Paper 136, North-Holland, Amsterdam, 1965.
28. A. W. Smith and J. M. Quets, *J. Catalysis*, **4**, 163 (1965).
29. H. P. Leftin, *Rev. Sci. Instr.*, **32**, 1418 (1961).
30. L. Lynds, *Spectrochim. Acta*, **2**, 1369 (1964).
31. D. A. Seanor and C. H. Amberg, *Rev. Sci. Instr.*, **34**, 917 (1963).
32. J. B. Peri, *Actes du Deuxième Congrès International de Catalyse, Paris, 1960*, Vol. 2, Editions Technip, Paris, 1961, p. 1333.
33. D. J. C. Yates, *J. Chem. Phys.*, **40**, 1157 (1964).

4

Silica Surfaces

The surfaces that have been most studied by the infrared techniques are undoubtedly those of the high surface area silica materials. The application of infrared spectroscopy to the study of adsorption processes on these materials has given surface chemists an understanding of the nature of the surfaces of "pure" silica and of the atomic steps that occur during the adsorption of a variety of materials upon silica surfaces. The reasons for the popularity of silica as an adsorbent are not hard to find. Not only does the high-area gel have great commercial importance as an absorbent and catalytic support, but its surface is relatively uncomplicated, and it is a material that is easily prepared and studied by the infrared technique. The transmission of the dried silica gels is good down to about 1450 cm^{-1}, and since the dry gel particles are readily pressed into thin transparent discs, their practicality is obvious. Porous glasses containing 96% SiO$_2$ have also been used as supports for the study of adsorbed molecules and for the investigation of surface reactions. This material may be obtained in a rigid form in thicknesses down to 1/10 mm and was widely used by early experimenters. In addition to its rigidity, the nature of its preparation ensures that all the microstructural silica units are joined together. This results in improved transmission characteristics owing to a reduction in the amount of scattering of the incident light. Recent work on porous glass, however, has indicated that the surface of this 96% silica material is not as

79

simple as it might appear to be in that a considerable amount of boron apparently exists on the surface. Consequently, in the ensuing discussion, work on silica will be divorced from work on porous glass, and, when possible, any deviations that can be attributed to the impurities present in the glass surface will be commented upon.

4-1. THE SILICA SURFACE:
HYDRATION–DEHYDRATION STUDIES

A. Dehydration of Silica

Nearly all crystalline forms of silica have a structure in which the silicon atoms are tetrahedrally surrounded by four oxygen atoms. This unvarying tetrahedral character of the silicon atom, when combined with oxygen, makes it likely that amorphous silica gels and glasses will possess the same types of structure. The noncrystalline materials will be characterized by a random packing of the (SiO_4) tetrahedra and give rise to a nonperiodic structure that is not susceptible to routine X-ray examination.

The amorphous silicas of commercial importance have a high surface area ($100–500$ m²/g) and find industrial use as adsorbents, catalyst supports, and fillers for paints, toothpaste, etc. Two prime methods are used for their manufacture: (1) precipitation from aqueous sodium silicate solutions and (2) high-temperature oxidation or hydrolysis of silicon tetrachloride. The infrared spectra of these two extreme forms of high-area silica reveal many similarities and certain sharp differences (1). Both materials exhibit strong absorption bands at 1200, 1100, and 800 cm⁻¹ that are attributable to fundamental silicon–oxygen vibrations and that are observed in all forms of silicon dioxide.

Examination of the high-frequency region ($2800–4000$ cm⁻¹) of these spectra, however, reveals certain distinct differences (Fig. 4-1). Thus, whereas the spectrum of Cab-O-Sil®, a silica prepared at high temperature, exhibits a strong absorption at 3747 cm⁻¹, this band is not discernible in the spectrum of the precipitated silica (MSBS).† The band at 3747 cm⁻¹ is sharp and slightly asymmetric on the low-frequency side, and it merges into a very broad band that has a maximum absorption at about 3500 cm⁻¹. The spectrum of the precipitated silica, however, shows a very broad asymmetric absorption between 3700 and 3000 cm⁻¹ that reduces transmittance to zero over most of this range. When these samples are degassed for 2 hr at 27°C, considerable changes in the spectra are obtained. The

† MSBS = Mallinckrodt Special Bulky Silicic Acid.

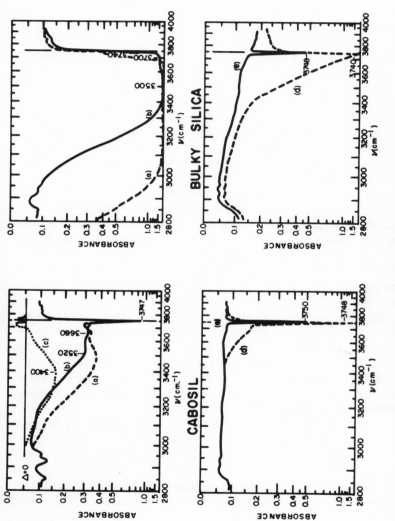

Fig. 4-1. The infrared spectra of Cab-O-Sil® and bulky silica: (a) before degassing; (b) after degassing for 3 hr at 30°C in vacuo; (c) difference between (a) and (b); (d) degassed 30 min at 500°C in vacuo; (e) degassed 8.5 hr at 940°C in vacuo. [Spectra reproduced from Reference (1) by courtesy of the Journal of the American Chemical Society.]

transmission in the region of 3500 cm^{-1} is considerably increased in the case of the precipitated silica, and new peaks are observed in each spectrum. With the Cab–O–Sil®, two new peaks can be distinguished at 3520 and 3660 cm^{-1} in addition to the sharp band at 3747 cm^{-1}.

In the case of the precipitated silica, a peak is noted at 3700 cm^{-1}, a broad band at 3500 cm^{-1} becomes obvious, and a shoulder at 3740 cm^{-1} is just discernible on this broader band. A more drastic heat treatment (500°C, $\frac{1}{2}$ hr in vacuo) causes the peak at 3500 cm^{-1} to disappear in both cases. However, whereas the peak at 3747 cm^{-1} is very sharp in the case of the Cab–O–Sil®, the same peak on the precipitated silica exhibits considerable broadening on the low-frequency side, the band half-width being about 150 cm^{-1}. Further vacuum heating for 8 hr at 940°C causes further changes in the spectra; and after this treatment, both silicas exhibit identical spectra in which one, very sharp, symmetric absorption is observed at 3748 cm^{-1}.

The spectra reproduced in Fig. 4-1 were originally obtained by McDonald (1) in 1958 and represent some of the earliest infrared studies on surfaces. Prior to this, Yaroslavskii and other Russian workers (2–4) had examined the porous glass surface by infrared techniques and had suggested an interpretation of the changes occurring during the dehydration treatment. These papers are now classics, and the interpretations given at that time are now accepted with almost complete unanimity by workers in the field. The single sharp band that is observed at 3750 cm^{-1} after the drastic dehydration at 940° is attributed to the fundamental stretching vibration of a hydroxyl group attached to a silicon atom on the surface of the silica. The frequency of the band is typical of freely vibrating OH groups, and its symmetrical appearance indicates that there are no interactions between it and other molecules or surface groups. These groups are variously referred to as "free hydroxyl groups" or "isolated silanol groups."

The presence of these terminal hydroxyl groups comes somewhat as a surprise to most chemists accustomed to think of solid-state reactions. The silicon atoms to which they are attached are presumably tetrahedrally coordinated to three other oxygen atoms and hence to the bulk silica, the inference being that, at low temperatures, the surface silicon atoms prefer to complete their coordination requirements by attachment to the monovalent hydroxyl group rather than by formation of strained siloxane-type groups,

$$\underset{-\text{Si}-\quad\ -\text{Si}-}{\overset{\text{O}}{\diagup\ \diagdown}}$$

or charged species such as —O⁻. The term *vicinal hydroxyl groups* is sometimes applied to OH groups that are adjacent on the surface:

and, where two hydroxyl groups are attached to the same silicon atom, the term *geminal groups* has been used, i.e.,

The strong, broad adsorption band that appears to peak at about 3500 cm⁻¹ is attributed to molecular water that is physically adsorbed upon the surface. Reference to Fig. 4-1(c) shows that the material that is removed by pumping at room temperature actually gives rise to a peak at 3400 cm⁻¹. Since liquid water exhibits two vibrations (ν_3 and ν_1) at 3445 and 3219 cm⁻¹, there is good reason for assigning the broad peak at about 3400 cm⁻¹ to molecular water. Confirmatory evidence is provided by a study of the spectrum of adsorbed water in the bending region of the spectrum (5). Addition of water to a completely dehydrated sample of silica gel causes the appearance of bands at 3400 and 1635 cm⁻¹. Both bands increase concomitantly in intensity with the addition of water, and, since the position of the band at 1635 cm⁻¹ compares favorably with the H—O—H bending vibration found in liquid water at 1627 cm⁻¹, the assignment is well established.

Confirmatory evidence that the bands observed in the 3200–3800-cm⁻¹ region of the spectrum are due to surface species has been provided by Benesi and Jones (5). These workers treated a dehydrated silica surface with D_2O and observed the spectral changes. Exposure of the sample to D_2O vapor followed by evacuation, and repetition of this process six or eight times within the space of half an hour, caused complete removal of the OH groups. A sharp band observed at 3730 cm⁻¹ and assigned to a free OH stretching vibration was moved to 2760 cm⁻¹ during the deuteration, and the broad band at 3580 cm⁻¹ attributed to surface water was moved to 2620 cm⁻¹. Clearly, isotopic relacement of H by D had occurred, the isotopic shift ratio of 1.35 being almost the same as that calculated for a diatomic OH species. The rapid replacement of H by D suggests that the atoms involved in the exchange are probably all surface atoms, and thus the original conclusions of McDonald are confirmed. On deuteration, the bending mode of the adsorbed water at 1635 cm^{-1} was shifted initially to 1430 cm^{-1}. At this frequency, the vibration involved is the bending mode of an adsorbed H—O—D molecule.

If the surface hydroxyl groups are considered as a linear X—O—H molecule, they would be expected to give rise to a bending vibration that would cause an absorption to occur at about 1000 cm^{-1}. Benesi and Jones (5) did observe a band of medium intensity at 870 cm^{-1}, and since this was shifted to a lower frequency region (spectroscopically inaccessible) upon deuteration, it was attributed to the bending mode of the surface group.

Davydov et al. (6) also have examined the deuteration of the silica surface by using infrared spectroscopy. These authors report that some of the OH groups that contributed to a broad absorption at 3650 cm^{-1} cannot be converted into OD groups and are therefore thought to be "internal" and inaccessible. This suggestion finds confirmation, in that the intensity of this band was directly proportional to the size of the individual silica particles. Young (7) also reports the presence of some internal OH groups. By determining the amount of water liberated during the dehydration process, the Russian workers were able to calculate the number of hydroxyl groups that existed on the surface after various heat treatments in vacuo, and they showed that at equilibrium the number present per unit area of surface was essentially independent of the silica gel employed and was almost inversely proportional to the temperature of heat treatment. Thus, at 150°C there are approximately 5 OH groups/100 Å² of surface, whereas at 800°C there is only 1 OH/100 Å² of surface.

B. Rehydration of Silica

The rehydration of silica surfaces was monitored spectroscopically by Young (7) in his thorough investigation of the hydration–dehydration characteristics of the silica–water system, and kinetics of this process are reported by Fripiat and co-workers (8). Young observed that the amount of water physically adsorbed on the silica was directly related to the number of hydroxyl groups existing on the surface, and he concluded that the adsorption of water occurred on those groups. Data obtained by Benesi and Jones (5) on a deuterated silica gel sample that had been evacuated at 400°C showed that, on exposure to D_2O vapor, the band ascribed to the isolated OD groups increased very little in height but was considerably broadened during the adsorption process. Moreover, its integrated intensity was more than doubled. This provides an indication that the D_2O is reacting with the silica surface, forming adjacent Si-OD groups, and is then adsorbing upon these groups in preference to the free OD groups. Many examples of this preferential adsorption upon either the single or the adjacent surface hydroxyl groups have since been observed and can be found later in the text.

Although these and other data indicate that water adsorption on a silica surface occurs preferably on adjacent hydroxyl groups, McDonald (1) has commented that readsorption of water on a highly dehydrated sample caused a diminution in intensity of the band due to the free hydroxyl group and indicates interaction with that group. Similarly, Hockey and Pethica (9) have shown that for samples of silica gel that have been heated in excess of 400°C the rehydration process at less than monolayer coverage ($P/P_0 = 0.6$) causes only an increase in the height of the band due to single OH groups. In this case, the band due to the perturbed groups appears only at multilayer coverages.

Heating a fully hydroxylated silica gel to 400°C evidently causes a fundamental change to occur in the nature of the silica surface. Gravimetric data on the number of condensed hydroxyl sites that can be rehydrated, as compared with the total number of hydroxyl sites existing on the silica surface, have been obtained by Young, and a graphical summary of these results is given in Fig. 4-2. From the graph it can be seen that:

1. Truly physically adsorbed water is completely removed by pumping at room temperature.

2. Surface silanol groups start to condense and eliminate water at about 170°C.

3. The dehydration is completely reversible up to about 400°C.

4. Above 400°C the dehydration is not reversible and the amount of chemisorption that can occur is an inverse function of the temperature of heat treatment.

5. Above 850°C no chemisorption of water can occur and the surface is hydrophobic.

6. Sintering starts to occur at 900°C. In this connection, it is of passing interest to note that Young found that the loss in surface area of the silica was linearly related to the time of heat treatment. This indicates that the sintering mechanism is predominantly one of viscous flow rather than surface diffusion. The effect of impurities is to lower the sintering temperature, presumably by increasing this viscous flow.

From the combined infrared and gravimetric data, therefore, we have a good description of the silica–water interface and an atomic explanation of why completely dehydrated silica surfaces are hydrophobic.

As prepared at room temperature in a gelatinous form, the silica surface has a structure in which every surface silicon atom terminates in a hydroxyl group.† At this stage there are about eight hydroxyl groups per 100 Å² of surface. Removal of adsorbed water is achieved by prolonged

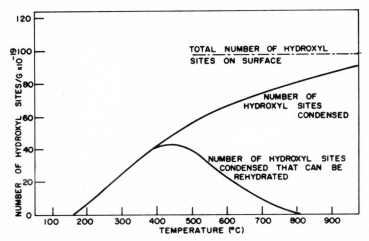

Fig. 4-2. *Changes in the number of surface silanol sites with temperature of heat treatment. [Redrawn from Reference (7) by courtesy of the Journal of Colloid Science (Academic Press).]*

evacuation at temperatures up to about 150°C, leaving a surface that is still maximally hydroxylated. Heating between 170° and 400°C causes a reversible dehydroxylation [Fig. 4-3(a)] with the elimination of water and the formation of both monomeric and dimeric surface silanol groups. It can be seen that, at 400°C, less than half of the surface hydroxyl groups have been eliminated. Most of the remaining groups are therefore adjacent to one another and are suitably positioned to give rise to preferential water adsorption [Fig. 4-3(e)]. This, coupled with the reversibility of the dehydroxylation, gives the dried silica gel its superb dehydrating properties.

† This is a widely held point of view. However, the recent observations of Peri (*10*) on the "aging" of silica gels and the change in reactivity toward $SiCl_4$ should be noted (Section 4-4J). Hockey (*11*) has also speculated that freshly formed silica gel surfaces contain geminal groups.

Heating above 400°C causes a drastic, irreversible elimination of adjacent hydroxyl groups until, at 800°C, only single hydroxyl groups remain. When the silica has been completely dehydrated, the reverse of reaction (a) is very slow. When this silica surface is exposed to water vapor, the molecules cluster around the single hydroxyl groups even at pressures

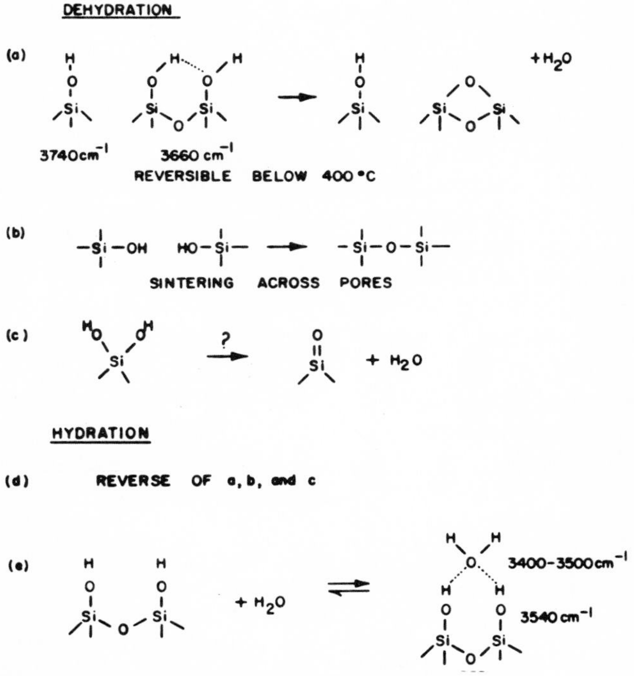

Fig. 4-3. The hydration and dehydration of a silica surface.

approaching saturation. Most of the surface, therefore, is bare. Under these conditions the silica is unable to adsorb sufficient water to give statistical monolayer coverage, and capillary condensation occurs before this point is reached. In other words, the surface is hydrophobic.

During the sintering process, hydroxyl groups probably condense across pore necks [Fig. 4-3(b)]. The possible dehydration step shown in Fig. 4-3(c) has been suggested by Kiselev (12) as occurring during the low-temperature dehydration. This step is considered unlikely, however, because the Si=O groups would be expected to be highly active, a situation that has not yet been observed.

C. Overtone Region

The adsorption of water on the silica surface has been studied in the overtone region (4000–8000 cm^{-1}) by Anderson and Wickersheim (*13*). These authors showed that the spectrum of silica that had been dehydrated at 750°C showed sharp absorptions at 3740 and 7326 cm^{-1}, together with a broader band at 4550 cm^{-1}. The band at 3740 cm^{-1} is readily identified with the fundamental OH stretching vibration, and the band at 7326 cm^{-1} is the first overtone of this vibration ($\simeq$2 × 3740 cm^{-1}). The broad band at 4550 cm^{-1} is assigned as a combination band due to the OH stretching and bending vibrations (3740 cm^{-1} + ν_2). This assignment predicts a bending frequency of about 810 cm^{-1} or larger. Benesi and Jones (*5*) have observed a band attributable to this vibration at 870 cm^{-1}, and thus the assignment of the 4550-cm^{-1} band as a combination band seems reasonable. (It should be noted, however, that Peri (*10*) has recently suggested that this band is due to a combination of the Si—O—H stretching vibration and an out-of-plane OH deformation vibration. This deformation band is observed in alcohols at about 770 cm^{-1}.) This hydroxyl group was termed an OH$_1$ group.

Upon hydration the 7326-cm^{-1} band becomes less intense, and on complete hydration it is missing altogether. This provides further evidence for McDonald's assertion that single hydroxyl groups will interact with adsorbed water. The intense absorptions due to the water molecules themselves preclude observation of changes in the position of both the fundamental stretching vibration and its overtone. However, the formation of a new hydroxyl group is indicated by the appearance of a new combination band at 4420 cm^{-1}. This group is termed OH$_2$. The bending frequency of this group will be relatively constant as compared with the frequency of the stretching vibration, and consequently, if a bending frequency of 870 cm^{-1} corresponding to that found by Benesi and Jones is assumed, the position of the fundamental can be estimated by subtracting the bending frequency from the frequency of the combination band. Thus,

$$\nu_{OH_2} \text{ (stretch)} + \nu_{OH_2} \text{ (bend)} = \nu_{OH_2} + 870 = 4420 \text{ cm}^{-1}$$

$$\nu_{OH_2} = 3550 \text{ cm}^{-1}$$

The OH$_2$ fundamental stretching vibration is observed 200 cm^{-1} from that of the free hydroxyl groups. It probably corresponds to the band noted by McDonald at 3520 cm^{-1}, and it is attributed to single hydroxyl groups (OH$_1$) that are perturbed by strong hydrogen bonding to water molecules.

At low levels of hydration, sharp bands appear at 3660 and 3540 cm^{-1}, 7090, and 6850 cm^{-1}, and 5290 and 5180 cm^{-1}. The intensity changes upon adsorption indicate that all these bands are connected with the same group, and their close similarity to the spectrum of small quantities of water dissolved in CCl_4 indicates that they are due to molecular water. The bands are very sharp and indicate that the water is adsorbed in a monomeric form at this stage. Further hydration leads to a blurring of the bands in the overtone region and the formation of an intense band at about 3400 cm^{-1} that is typical of bulk water.

D. Rotational Motion of Surface Hydroxyl Groups

The terminal hydroxyl groups on the silica surfaces might be expected to have some rotational movement, and it has been pointed out by McDonald that a freely rotating OH group, fixed in space by attachment to a surface, should have the same rotational spectrum as a simple plane rotator. In other words, if the surface $\geqslant$Si—OH group is linear, only a Q branch appears in the observed spectrum; whereas if the group is non-linear, P and R branches should be observed on either side of the 3740-cm^{-1} band, the separation of the two wings being dependent on the Si—O—H bond angle. Until recently, no trace of P and R branches had been observed, though it was impossible to know whether this was due to the linearity of the surface hydroxyl groups or to a lack of instrumental resolving power. In a recent study of the silica surface, Peri (*10*) has obtained evidence for the existence of weak P and R branches for both surface OH and surface OD groups (Fig. 4-4). The separations of the band maxima were 200 and 140 cm^{-1}, respectively. A knowledge of these values enables calculation of the Si—O—H bond angle. Following the treatments of Peri and of Herzberg (*14*), the separation of the P and R branches $\Delta\nu$ is given by the equation

$$\Delta\nu = 8kTB/hc = 2.358\ TB\ \text{cm}^{-1}$$

where B, the rotational constant, is equal to $h/8\pi^2cI_B$. If the Si—O—H bond angle is θ and if ϕ is the angle between the axis of rotation and the O—H axis, then

$$I_B = \mu_m r^2 \cos^2(\phi - 90°)$$

where μ_m is the reduced mass.

The equilibrium OH distance r is taken to be that of the water molecule (0.958 Å), and thus the angle ϕ can be calculated. The true Si—O—H bond angle θ is slightly less than ϕ and is calculated to be 113°.

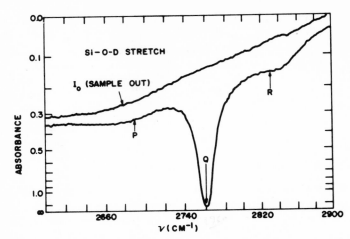

Fig. 4-4. *The P, Q, and R branches of the surface silanol vibration.* [*Reproduced from Reference (34) by courtesy of the Journal of Physical Chemistry.*]

4-2. ADSORBENT–ADSORBATE INTERACTIONS

A. Adsorbent Perturbation

In his original studies on the silica surface, McDonald investigated the perturbation of surface hydroxyl groups that occurred when nonpolar molecules were adsorbed at low temperatures. The spectral changes caused by argon, krypton, xenon, nitrogen, oxygen, methane, and perfluoromethane adsorbed at $-190°$ and $-170°C$ were investigated, as were the effects of water, methanol, benzene, and cyclohexane adsorbed at $30°C$ (*1*). In all these cases the hydroxyl stretching frequency at 3749 cm^{-1} was lowered when appreciable quantities of gas were adsorbed upon the surface. The fact that the hydroxyl-stretching frequency was shifted to lower wave numbers is evidence of interaction with the adsorbent and provides positive proof that the 3747 cm^{-1} band is due to a surface species. The shifts in frequency that were reported by McDonald are reproduced in Table 4-1, and some spectra illustrating the silanol perturbations due to oxygen and nitrogen adsorptions are shown in Figs. 4-5(a) and 4-5(b). It can be seen that the shift in the hydroxyl stretching frequency is a function of the partial pressure of the adsorbed gas (i.e., surface coverage) and the temperature at which the gas is adsorbed. Dry air at $30°$ and atmospheric pressure do not produce any displacement of the hydroxyl stretching frequency, nor does helium adsorbed at $-190°C$ and at 200 mm pressure.

TABLE 4-1

Perturbation of Free Hydroxyl Frequency of Aerosil
Silica by Various Adsorbates[a]

Adsorbate	OH frequency, cm^{-1}	Frequency, shift, cm^{-1}	Polarizability, cm$^3 \times 10^{25}$
None	3749		
Argon	3741	8	16.5
Krypton	3733	16	25.4
Xenon	3730	19	41.3
Nitrogen	3725	24	17.6
Oxygen	3737	12	16.0
Methane	3717	32	26.0

[a] Reproduced from Reference (*31*) with permission.

McDonald found that equilibrium between adsorbent and adsorbate was achieved within a few minutes, and from the data in Table 4-1 it is clear that all the molecules listed undergo interaction with the surface hydroxyl group during the physical adsorption process. Initially, the OH stretching band at 3749 cm^{-1} is very sharp and indicates that the surface groups are sufficiently far apart that mutual hydrogen bonding interaction does not occur. As molecules of gas adsorb on the surface, the hydroxyl stretching frequency is lowered by intermolecular hydrogen bonding and the intensity of the OH band is increased (Table 4-2). Some surface hydroxyl groups do not interact at low relative pressure, and these groups retain their original stretching frequency at 3749 cm^{-1}. Presumably they also retain their original intensity, but this has not been experimentally confirmed. Complete disappearance of the band at 3749 cm^{-1} is taken as evidence that all the surface hydroxyl groups are interacting with the adsorbed species.

The spectral shifts and intensities reported by McDonald for the adsorption of nitrogen, oxygen, and argon as a function of gas pressure are of great interest in that they give an explanation of the actual atomic interactions that take place during the physical adsorption process and exemplify the different specific interactions that can occur. Thus, when nitrogen is adsorbed on the silica sample, the band at 3749 cm^{-1} decreases rapidly and is shifted directly to 3725 cm^{-1}. The position of the 3725-cm^{-1} peak remains essentially constant from very low pressure up to about 5 mm Hg. After this, as the pressure is slowly increased to 50 mm, the peak

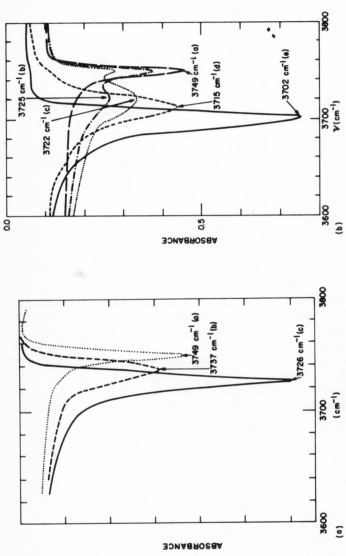

Fig. 4-5. (a) Perturbation of surface silica hydroxyl groups due to oxygen adsorption at −190°C: a, unperturbed Si_s—O—H group; b, oxygen adsorbed at 56 mm; c, liquid oxygen adsorbed on surface. Note the regular change from a to c as the oxygen pressure is increased. (b) Perturbation of silica surface hydroxyl groups due to nitrogen adsorption at −190°C: a, unperturbed hydroxyl group; b, H_2 adsorbed at 1.42 mm; c, 4.85 mm; d, 47.3 mm; e, liquid nitrogen. Note the immediate perturbation to 3725 cm^{-1} followed by the gradual perturbation to 3702 cm^{-1}. [Figure redrawn from Reference (31) by courtesy of the Journal of the American Chemical Society.]

TABLE 4-2

Frequency Shifts and Integrated Intensities of Hydroxyl Bands of Aerosil 2419 with Adsorbed Argon, Nitrogen, and Oxygen[a]

Adsorbate	Frequency shift, cm^{-1}	Half-width, cm^{-1}	Integrated intensity
None	0	12	1.0[b]
Argon (low relative pressure)	8	24	1.5
(vapor condensed in cell)	40	30	2.5
Oxygen (low relative pressure)	12	26	1.5
(vapor condensed in cell)	23	16	3.0
Nitrogen (low relative pressure)	24	34	2.0
(vapor condensed in cell)	43	23	3.5

[a] Reproduced from Reference (*31*) with permission.
[b] Arbitrary units.

maximum slowly shifts to 3715 cm^{-1}. The rate of increase in intensity of the 3715-cm^{-1} band, however, is much less than that of the 3725-cm^{-1} band.

In contradistinction to the nitrogen adsorption, when oxygen or argon is added to the silica, only one band is observed up to high pressures. The position of the peak maximum, however, is shifted progressively to lower frequencies. The peak intensity at first decreases and then passes through a minimum before finally increasing as more gas is adsorbed. McDonald points out that in the case of N_2 adsorption a relative pressure of 0.1 is necessary to achieve BET monolayer coverage at 77°K. Since the OH band on the silica surface has almost disappeared after the addition of 5 mm N_2 at −180°C, it is clear that there is no correlation between complete disappearance of the 3749-cm^{-1} peak and the formation of a monolayer. The nitrogen molecules must adsorb preferentially on the surface OH groups. Moreover, since the first peak at 3725 cm^{-1} does not vary in frequency with surface coverage, all the SiOH–N_2 species must have the same symmetry. A 1:1 correspondence seems most probable, but quantitative data on this are not yet available. Addition of more nitrogen causes a gradual shift to lower frequencies. The symmetry of the adsorbed species must be altering, possibly by the interaction of more than one nitrogen molecule with each hydroxyl group. With argon and oxygen only one band due to the OH stretching vibration is observed, and the frequency shifts slowly to lower values as the gas pressure is increased. In this case it seems obvious that a specific interaction with the surface hydroxyl group is not involved.

In the case of the rare gases, McDonald noted that there appeared to be some correlation between the frequency shifts produced by low concentrations of argon, krypton, and xenon and their various polarizabilities, but he was unable to discover an exact relationship. It is clear that there cannot be any simple relationship between frequency shifts and polarizabilities, since oxygen and nitrogen, which have essentially the same polarizabilities, produce frequency shifts of 12 and 24 cm^{-1}, respectively.

The physical adsorption of nitrogen and oxygen on silica surfaces has been discussed by Frohnsdorff and Kington (15), and the differences in the frequency shifts have been attributed to the differences in the quadrupole moments of the oxygen and nitrogen. Frohnsdorff and Kington calculated the magnitude of the frequency shift that could be expected when a quadrupole was adsorbed in various configurations upon a surface hydroxyl group. A simple calculation showed that, in order to cause the hydroxyl peak to shift to lower frequencies, the quadrupole had to be adsorbed either stationary with its axis lying along the direction of the OH group or rotating uniformly about an axis perpendicular to the OH group. The shift in position of the OH stretching frequency was calculated as a function of the charge on the proton and the Si–N_2 distance. For a proton with an effective charge of 0.15×10^{-10} esu (which is similar to protonic charge in the water molecule), a shift of 16 cm^{-1} in the OH stretching frequency would be expected. McDonald's experimental observation indicated a shift of 12 cm^{-1} at low pressure.

A more general approach to the bonding that occurs between the adsorbent and adsorbate during the physical adsorption process has been given by Basila (16). The bonding between the surface hydroxyl groups and the adsorbate is a hydrogen-bonding interaction, and it is thus a special type of charge-transfer reaction (17). Basila argued that, if this were so, the strength of the interaction of the surface hydroxyl group should be a function of the ionization potential of the donor molecules and the observed frequency shifts must, therefore, be related to these ionization potentials. Basila observed the shifts of the free hydroxyl group (3743 cm^{-1}) when a series of substituted benzenes were adsorbed on a silica sample at various surface coverages. Extrapolation of these data to monolayer coverage gave shifts that, when plotted against the ionization potential of the adsorbate, gave a smooth curve (Fig. 4-6). A curve of similar shape but different slope was observed when a series of halogenated methanes were adsorbed on the silica surface. Data obtained for the variations in frequency of the hydroxyl group of t-butyl alcohol, dissolved in the same series of substituted benzenes, gave rise to a similar curve, thus indicating the validity of Basila's approach.

Clearly, if the adsorption of simple molecules on silica surfaces involves specific interaction with the surface silanol group, the total adsorption energy must be a function of the number of hydroxyl groups existing on the surface. Moreover, it would be expected that the specific interactions

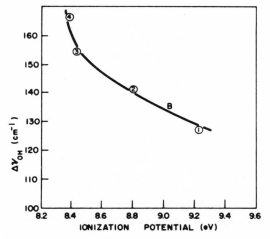

Fig. 4-6. *Correlation between the frequency shifts of surface silica* OH *stretching vibrations and the ionization potentials of some methylbenzene adsorbates.* $\theta = 1$. *(1) Benzene; (2) toluene; (3) p-xylene; (4) mesitylene. [From Reference (16) by courtesy of the Journal of Chemical Physics.]*

would be greatest for polar, quadrupole, and π-electron molecules. This effect has been examined in particular by Kiselev and his colleagues (*18–21*) in a series of papers in which infrared studies were correlated with data on the heat of adsorption of various molecules as a function of surface coverage. Thus, it was found that, whereas for nonpolar molecules such as carbon tetrachloride or hexane the heat of adsorption was essentially independent of the degree of hydroxylation of the surface, the heat of adsorption of a more polar molecule such as benzene was dependent upon the surface hydroxyl concentration. Since the polar groups also caused much greater shifts in the position of the surface hydroxyl group than the nonpolar molecules, it was argued that frequency shift should be a simple function of the heat of adsorption of the adsorbate *on the hydroxyl groups* of the silica. In order to determine this quantity, the Russian workers measured the heats of adsorption of a series of molecules on hydroxylated and dehydroxylated surfaces, the specific heat of adsorption on the hydroxyl group, ΔQ_a, being the difference between these two quantities.

Initial results were obtained for *n*-hexane, benzene, and diethyl ether, but results were later obtained for six other molecules (*22*). These are shown in Fig. 4-7, where the shift in the position of the hydroxyl stretching

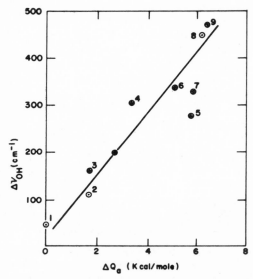

Fig. 4-7. *Plot of $\Delta\nu_{OH}$ against ΔQ_A for several vapors adsorbed on hydroxylated silica surface. 1, n-C$_6$H$_{14}$; 2, C$_6$H$_6$; 3, CH$_3$NO$_2$; 4, CH$_3$CN; 5, CH$_3$COOC$_2$H$_5$; 6, CH$_2$CH$_2$COCH$_2$CH$_2$; 7, (CH$_3$)$_2$CO; 8, (C$_2$H$_5$)$_2$O; 9, CH$_2$CH$_2$OCH$_2$CH$_2$. Filled circle = H$_2$O by Anderson (23). [Reproduced from Reference (22), by courtesy of North-Holland Publishing Company, Amsterdam.]*

frequency at one-half surface coverage is plotted as a function of ΔQ_a. The choice of half surface coverage was completely arbitrary, but it was made standard throughout the series of experiments in order to negate any possible effects due to differences in surface coverage. The relationship between $\Delta\nu$ and ΔQ_a is approximately linear; moreover, as the heat of adsorption is approximately inversely proportional to the ionization potential of the adsorbate, this relationship serves as further evidence that the reaction between the hydroxyl groups and the adsorbate is essentially one of charge transfer as proposed by Basila. Anderson (*23*) has since pointed out that the shift of 200 cm^{-1} noted for water adsorption on silica also lies on the straight line relating $\Delta\nu_{OH}$ and ΔQ_a; it is represented in Fig. 4-7 by the solid point.

This work shows the specific nature of some of the apparently more simple physical adsorption processes and provides an explanation for some apparent anomalies. Thus, it was known that the heat of adsorption of benzene on silica gel decreased as a function of surface coverage, whereas the heat of adsorption of hexane was almost independent of coverage. Moreover, on a completely dehydrated silica, the heat of adsorption of benzene is smaller than that of hexane. Clearly, the heat of specific adsorption of benzene on the surface hydroxyl groups is higher than the heat of nonspecific adsorption, and thus the initial heat of adsorption of the benzene will be much higher than that of the saturated hydrocarbon. As the surface coverage is increased, nonspecific adsorption will start to take place, and the heat of adsorption in the later stages of the process will approach that of the saturated molecule. The values of the heats of adsorption of benzene on silica gel have been used by Kiselev and Lygin (21) to calculate entropies of adsorption. These have been compared with values calculated by assuming five possible rotational movements of the adsorbed benzene. The results are not definitive, but they indicate that the adsorbed molecule undergoes either two-dimensional translation and rotation in the plane of the ring or a motion in which it can also rotate around one of the axes lying in the plane of the ring.

Shifts in the position of surface silanol groups following the adsorption for many gases have now been reported, and they are nearly all summarized in Tables 4-1, 4-2, 4-4, and 4-6 and the references therein. Of particular interest in the wealth of data that have now been gathered for the spectroscopic shifts observed upon adsorption are Basila's results for the adsorption of diethylamine on silica (24). The spectra published by Basila illustrate very clearly the differences in adsorption characteristics that can exist between single and adjacent hydroxyl groups. In Basila's work the sample of silica used had not been completely dehydroxylated and gave the spectrum shown in Fig. 4-8. The peak due to the hydroxyl stretching frequencies is considerably asymmetric, and this can be mechanically separated into two separate overlapping absorptions attributed to single and adjacent hydroxyl groups. The addition of diethylamine to the silica causes the 3743-cm^{-1} peak to shift to about 2753 cm^{-1}, where it appears as a very broad band. The band due to the adjacent hydroxyl groups is clearly observed at 3670 cm^{-1} and is only slightly reduced in intensity. The diethylamine has reacted preferentially with the single hydroxyl group. This behavior seems to be typical of lone-pair donor adsorbents and is to

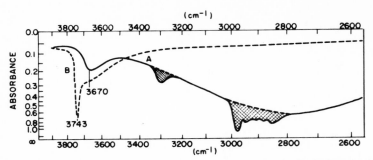

Fig. 4-8. *B. Spectrum of silica dried at 450°C. A. Diethylamine adsorbed on B. The cross-hatched areas are due to diethylamine. Interaction has occurred primarily with the freely vibrating hydroxyl groups. [Redrawn from Reference (24) by courtesy of the Journal of Chemical Physics.]*

be contrasted with the case of the water molecules, which seem to adsorb preferentially on adjacent hydroxyl groups.

B. Adsorbate Perturbation

1. Benzene on Silica

Discussion so far has been concerned with the observation of adsorbent perturbations that occur during the physical adsorption process. It is clear, however, that if a specific interaction occurs between a surface hydroxyl group and, say, the π-electron system of an aromatic molecule, then this effect must lead to changes in the infrared spectrum of the adsorbed molecule. The infrared spectrum of benzene adsorbed on a silica surface as a function of surface coverage has been observed by Galkin et al. (18). Their observations are given in Table 4-3. The spectrum of the adsorbed benzene is little different from that of the liquid, the deviations being less than 10 cm^{-1} and thus typical of physically adsorbed species.

Certain features about this apparently mundane observation are of interest. First of all, it can be noted that at monolayer coverage one of

TABLE 4-3

A Comparison of the Vibrational Frequencies of Benzene Adsorbed on Silica Gel with Those of Liquid and Gaseous Benzene[a]

Liquid	3089	3070	3035	2215	1964	1815	1532	1486	1396	675
Vapor	3099	3073	3045	—	1965	1807	—	1485	—	671
Monolayer	3092	3072	3039	2215	1970	1845	—	1483	—	684

[a] From Reference (18).

the bands that is absent from the gas-phase spectrum yet present in the liquid state is also present in the adsorbed state (2215 cm^{-1}). Thus, it appears that the adsorbed state is somewhere in between a gas and a liquid. The other bands that are absent from the gaseous spectrum appear only when coverage greater than a monolayer is obtained. A second point of interest is that the band at 1483 cm^{-1} that is due to a ring stretching vibration is much more intense in the adsorbed state than in the liquid state.

If the specific interaction of the surface proton is with the aromatic nucleus, then it would be expected that the vibrations that are most perturbed would be those associated with the aromaticity of the compound. The vibrations due to substituent groups would be very little affected. Examination of Table 4-3 shows that the vibration that is most perturbed is the out-of-plane C—H deformation vibration that is observed at 685 instead of 675 cm^{-1}. The C—C stretching vibration is displaced only by 2 cm^{-1} but, as has been mentioned, its intensity is considerably increased.

In view of the data already presented on OH shifts as a function of surface coverage, it would be expected that the actual amount of perturbation of the C—H deformation would depend upon the surface coverage and the hydroxyl content of the sample. The slight perturbations observed for the physically adsorbed benzene as a function of surface coverage or hydroxyl content are insufficient to be adequately observed. However, one might expect considerable change in the dipole moment of the adsorbed species. The intensities of the absorption would thus increase markedly and provide a means for following changes in the electronic distribution of the adsorbed molecule as a function of surface coverage. Since the frequency of the C—H fundamental stretching vibration (3092 cm^{-1}) changes only slightly on adsorption, and in view of the supposition that this band would be one of the least affected by the adsorption process, Galkin et al. assumed that the intensity of this band was linearly related to the amount of benzene present on the surface. They then used this value as a constant reference in order to obtain the relative changes in the intensities of the bands at 1486 and 684 cm^{-1}. Their results are shown in Fig. 4-9, where the relative absorption coefficients are plotted as a function of benzene vapor pressure for a series of samples that have undergone different degrees of dehydroxylation. The greatest perturbations are observed at low coverage and with samples that had most hydroxyl groups on the surface. The intensity ratios initially are about twice those observed for liquid benzene and indicate major changes in the electron distribution in the neighborhood of the atoms giving rise to these vibrations.

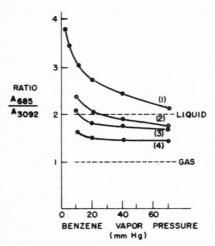

Fig. 4-9. *Effect of surface hydroxyl groups on adsorbed benzene. Silica dehydroxylated at (1) 200°C; (2) 400°C; (3) 600°C; (4) 800°C. [Redrawn from Reference (18).]*

Similar perturbations have been noted for benzene adsorbed on molecular sieves and alkali halides (*25*).

The specific interaction between surface hydroxyl groups and adsorbed benzene has been further considered by Kiselev et al. (*20*) in a simplified molecular-orbital approach. Within the limits of their assumptions, good agreement was obtained between calculated and theoretical values for heats of adsorption.

2. Adsorption of Substituted Benzenes on Silica

It has been amply demonstrated that both aromatic and lone-pair electron compounds will interact specifically with surface hydroxyl groups during the adsorption process. It is of interest, therefore, to consider the changes that take place during the adsorption of compounds such as aniline, $C_6H_5NH_2$, and phenol, C_6H_5OH, on a hydroxylated silica surface. Spectral data on this interaction have been presented by Kiselev and Lygin (*26*).

The effect of the aromatic ring on both the NH_2 and OH groups is to create an inductive effect that makes aniline less basic than the parent ammonia molecule and phenol more acidic than either water or aliphatic alcohols. The inductive effect also causes considerable changes in the electronic spectra of these molecules. Reference to Table 4-4 shows that the effect of aniline physisorption is to cause a perturbation of the surface hydroxyl groups that is intermediate (550 cm⁻¹) between that observed for benzene (110 cm⁻¹) and that for ammonia (900 cm⁻¹). The symmetric and asymmetric N—H stretching vibrations of the aniline molecule are observed in carbon tetrachloride solution at 3394 and 3480 cm⁻¹ and are shifted to 3330 and 3395 cm⁻¹ on adsorption. These vibrations are very close to those observed for the physically adsorbed ammonia molecule (3320 and 3400 cm⁻¹). Moreover, the electronic spectrum of the adsorbed aniline is similar to that of adsorbed benzene. Clearly, the effect of adsorption via the lone pair of electrons on the nitrogen atom is to negate the inductive effect of the aromatic ring; in the adsorbed state the aniline molecule approaches the structure of its parent compounds. A similar change is observed in the electronic spectrum of adsorbed phenol.

Adsorption of nitrobenzene, $C_6H_5NO_2$, on the other hand, proceeds in an entirely different manner. The symmetric and asymmetric N—O stretching vibrations are shifted by only one or two wave numbers from their normal positions, whereas the electronic spectrum is moved considerably (-2650 cm^{-1}) and in the direction opposite to that observed in the case of aniline ($+1450$ cm^{-1}) and phenol (400 cm^{-1}). The mechanism

TABLE 4-4

*Perturbation of Surface Hydroxyl Groups
Caused by Adsorption of Substituted Benzenes
and Comparison with Changes in the Electronic
Spectrum of the Adsorbates*

Adsorbate	$\Delta \nu_{vib}$, cm^{-1}	$\Delta \nu_{elect}$, cm^{-1}
Benzene	110	70
Toluene	130	120
Phenol	350	400
Aniline	550	1450
Nitrobenzene	140	-2650
Ammonia	900	—

of interaction in this case is completely different. The absence of a lone pair and the lack of change in frequency of the N—O vibration argues for interaction of surface hydroxyl groups with the aromatic nucleus in the usual way.

3. Stereoisomerism and Adsorption

The free rotation of molecules is restricted upon adsorption. In view of this it might be expected that, in the case of the molecules that can exist in isomeric forms, one of the isomers would be either more strongly adsorbed or more restricted in its rotations on adsorption on a surface. The relative proportions of the isomeric species existing on a surface might therefore be considerably different from those existing in solution. This effect has been observed by Yoshino (27) in the cases of dichloroethane and acetyl acetone. The former compound has a rotational isomerism, whereas the latter undergoes keto–enol transformation:

TABLE 4-5

Changes in Isomeric Ratio on Adsorption[a]

	Relative ratio for	
Solvent	Dichlorethane, cis/trans	Acetyl acetone, keto/enol
Chloroform solution	1	1
Pure liquid	1.4	2.4
Liquid saturated with water		2.4
Adsorbed	1.9	8.6

[a] From Reference (27).

Isomeric ratios in various solvents were determined by infrared spectroscopy and compared with the value found when the materials were adsorbed on silica gel. Results are shown in Table 4-5. It can be seen that the original supposition is thus maintained and that the isomeric ratio for both the dichloroetahane and acetyl acetone is considerably altered on adsorption.

C. Miscellaneous Studies

1. NH_3 on SiO_2

The spectrum of ammonia absorbed on silica gel has been reported by Cant and Little (28), Chapman and Hair (29), and Peri (10). Ammonia adsorption takes place at room temperature owing to interaction of the nitrogen lone-pair electrons with the surface hydroxyl groups. Primary interaction is with the single hydroxyl groups, but the bands due to both single (3740 cm^{-1}) and adjacent (3666 cm^{-1}) hydroxyl groups are diminished in intensity. The disappearance of the hydroxyl bands is paralleled by the appearance of two bands at 3400 and 3320 cm^{-1}. The physically absorbed ammonia is a ZXY_3 type of structure, and the bands at 3400 and 3320 cm^{-1} are attributed to the asymmetric and symmetric N—H stretching vibrations, respectively. The positions of these bands are very close to those observed for ammonia dissolved in carbon tetrachloride solution (3417 and 3317 cm^{-1}). This confirms the assignment to a physically adsorbed NH_3 species. The OH vibration is shifted by about 900 cm^{-1} and is observed as a very broad absorption at about 2800 cm^{-1}.

Peri (10) has reported that a small amount of ammonia is chemisorbed on a very dry silica surface. The chemisorption led to an increase in the intensity of the free-hydroxyl stretching frequency and to two bands at 3526 and 3446 cm^{-1}. These bands are attributed to asymmetric and symmetric stretching frequencies of an —NH$_2$ species. The former observation indicates formation of an OH species. The reaction can be explained on the basis of dissociative chemisorption of the ammonia and reaction with strained surface-siloxane linkages according to the following scheme:

The maximum number of these strained sites is 1.4 per 100 Å^2.

2. CO on SiO$_2$

The infrared spectrum of CO adsorbed on SiO$_2$ at $-195°$C has been reported by Smith and Quets (30). Upon adsorption of the CO (100 torr), the sharp OH band at 3750 cm^{-1} is perturbed to give a broad band at 3620 cm^{-1}. At the same time physically adsorbed CO is observed as an intense doublet at 2130 and 2150 cm^{-1}. Removal of the CO at $-180°$C caused elimination of the 2130-cm^{-1} band, the 2150-cm^{-1} band becoming very sharp and symmetrical. Partial replacement of the OH groups at 3750 cm^{-1} occurs, and the perturbed hydroxyls give rise to a peak at about 3650 cm^{-1}. This smaller shift at lower coverages is taken to indicate a somewhat weaker interaction.

3. Alcohols on SiO$_2$

Methanol is physically adsorbed on the silica surface at room temperature and dissociatively chemisorbed at higher temperatures. At room temperature, perturbation of the hydroxyl groups is noted and a frequency shift of 330 cm^{-1} is obtained (31). Because of the intermolecular hydrogen bonding of the alcohol itself, the hydroxyl group vibrations are difficult to interpret. By using trimethylcarbinol, $(CH_3)_3COH$, however, Davydov et al. (32) were able to obtain clear spectra that showed that this alcohol hydrogen-bonded with the surface hydroxyl groups, producing a large broad band at 3315 cm^{-1}. The spectra indicate that only the free surface hydroxyl groups were affected by this adsorption, and a good inverse correlation was observed between the intensities of the 3315- and 3749-cm^{-1} bands during both the adsorption and desorption processes.

4. Carbon Dioxide on Silica

Both Eischens and Pliskin (33) and Peri (34) report the adsorption of carbon dioxide on silica. At low pressures the adsorption is negligible, but above 2 torr a band near 2345 cm^{-1} is produced. This species is physically adsorbed and is removed rapidly on evacuation.

5. Pyridine on Silica (35)

The spectrum of pyridine adsorbed on silica shows two bands of major importance at 1447 and 1599 cm^{-1}. These correspond to values obtained in chloroform solution. They are attributed to C—C ring vibrations and are used to distinguish between physically and chemically bonded pyridine. They are completely removed by pumping at 150°C.

6. Nickel Carbonyl on Silica

The infrared spectrum of nickel carbonyl adsorbed on silica at room temperature has been obtained by Parkyns (36). The spectrum of the adsorbed species is characteristic of physically adsorbed and unperturbed nickel carbonyl. Some broadening of the 2055-cm^{-1} band (CO stretching vibration) occurs, and the OH stretching frequency is shifted by 20 cm^{-1}. Addition of oxygen to the adsorbed nickel carbonyl causes slow desorption of the nickel carbonyl. The final spectrum shows a band at 2205 cm^{-1}, which can be attributed to carbon monoxide adsorbed on nickel oxide formed during the desorption process.

7. Nitrosyl Chloride on Silica

In an investigation of the decomposition of nitrosyl chloride (NOCl) on glass and quartz surfaces, Ashmore and Hertl (37) found that the rate of their reaction was dependent upon the surface-to-volume ratio of their reaction vessel. Moreover, the actual kinetics were dependent upon the washing procedure to which the glass had been subjected: Quartz surfaces that had been heated to brilliant white heat were completely inactive but could be reactivated by soaking in water. Suspecting that this reactivity was due to the presence of hydroxyl groups on the glass surface, Ashmore and Hertl investigated the adsorption of nitric oxide, chlorine, and nitrosyl chloride on a pressed silica disc at 350°C. Nitric oxide and chlorine caused little change in the spectra; but when nitrosyl chloride was added to the silica, the NO stretching frequency at 1800 cm^{-1} was perturbed toward the high-frequency end of the spectrum, whereas the OH stretching frequency of the surface silanol groups was perturbed from

3757 cm^{-1} and observed at about 3600 cm^{-1}. After the material stood for two days, apparently some slight reaction took place and HCl and N_2O were observed in the gas phase. The perturbations of the OH and NO stretching frequencies indicate either that there was direct interaction of the nitrogen atom from the nitrosyl chloride with the hydrogen atom of the surface hydroxyl group or, that the NOCl is adsorbed on sites adjacent to SiOH groups and a hydrogen-bonding interaction between the two then occurs. Since the NOCl was adsorbed at 350°C, the latter interpretation is more acceptable.

The shift of the N—O stretching vibration to *higher* wave numbers is of interest in that this type of shift is quite unusual. It is, however, well substantiated that this band will shift to higher wave numbers when NOCl is dissolved in polar solvents (*38*).

4-3. ADSORPTION STUDIES WITH POROUS GLASS

Porous glass has been shown to be a unique adsorbent, and much original work on physical adsorption and surface activity has employed this material. A major attraction as far as spectroscopic studies are concerned is that the amount of light scattering caused by these glasses is much less than that observed with either powders or pressed discs. Moreover, the glasses can be ground and polished or directly fabricated into sheets as thin as $\frac{1}{10}$ mm. The porous glass employed by most workers in the Western Hemisphere has been supplied by Corning Glass Works (Code 7930 porous glass). This material is obtained as an intermediate in the process used for the manufacture of 96% silica glass. The process is described by Hood and Nordberg (*39*) in their original patent and in the article by Nordberg (*40*). Essentially, a glass in the sodium borosilicate system is melted and fabricated by standard glass manufacturing techniques at comparatively low temperatures. After fabrication, it is subjected to a heat treatment that causes the glass to separate into a boron-rich phase and a silica-rich phase. The boron-rich phase is soluble in weak acids and alkalies and may be leached out. The resultant porous body retains its original shape, even on consolidation, and the final product is thus a glass article that contains 96% silica and yet has not been subjected to the high temperatures that are necessary to melt and form silica products. The material that is left after the leaching and before the consolidation process is known as porous glass, and, neglecting water, it has the same chemical constitution as the finished article (SiO_2 96%, B_2O_3 3%, Na_2O, Al_2O_3, etc. 1%). The surface area of the porous glass is usually about 200 m^2/g with an average pore diameter of 40 Å. Since the material is essentially silica, it seemed reasonable to conclude that its surface properties would be analogous to those of a slightly impure silica gel, and original spectroscopic studies tended to support this concept. However, although the surfaces of silica gel and porous glass have many similar features, recent work has shown that the surface of this glass contains sites of the Lewis acid type. Quantitative work by Hair and Chapman (*41*) indicates that the B/Si ratio in the surface layer is probably about 1:3 rather than the 1:18 that might be expected from analysis of the bulk material.

A. Porous Glass–Water System

The close similarities and important differences between the silica gel surface and the porous glass surface can be exemplified by a discussion of the papers of Sidorov (*42*), Cant and Little (*28, 43*), and Chapman and Hair (*29*). The spectra of porous glass in the 4000–3000-cm^{-1} region after various dehydration–hydration treatments is reproduced in Fig. 4-10. These spectra are directly comparable with those shown in Fig. 4-1 for similar dehydroxylation studies on silica gel. Many similarities can be noted. In particular, a definite, sharp band at 3749 cm^{-1} can be observed, together with a distinct band at 3655 cm^{-1}. These are attributed to freely vibrating surface silanol groups, and to hydrogen-bonded adjacent silanol groups, respectively. These assignments are identical with those made

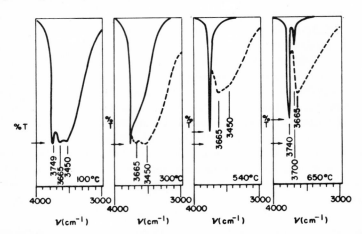

Fig. 4-10. *Spectra showing the dehydration of porous glass at the temperatures indicated. Dotted lines show changes in the spectra observed after reexposure to water vapor at room temperature.*

for silica gel. The peak at 3450 cm^{-1} is again attributable to molecular water and is confirmed by the presence of a bending vibration at 1640 cm^{-1} (44). This water is almost completely removed by heating to 150°C.

On heating at successively higher temperatures up to 650°C, it is seen that the adjacent hydroxyl groups are removed until only a single sharp band (at 3749 cm^{-1}) remains. This is again due to isolated hydroxyl groups. It is worthy of note that Sidorov's spectra also show the presence of a small sharp band at 3700 cm^{-1}. This band is sometimes observed in samples of porous glass (Corning Code 7930) that contain somewhat larger quantities than usual of boron. Many Russian workers have reported the presence of this band, but only recently has its presence been detected in the Corning material. Low and Ramasubramanian (45) report its presence on all the samples of porous glass they investigated, provided that they were subjected to a sufficiently rigorous drying procedure. Since this band can be deuterated and shifted to 2728 cm^{-1}, it is almost certainly due to a surface hydroxyl group, probably attached to a boron atom. Boric acid impregnated in silica gel also exhibits a band at 3700 cm^{-1}, and thus it seems likely that the correlation between the amount of boron present and the appearance of the band is more than fortuitous. Moreover, it is well known that heating porous glass above 500°C, especially in the presence of water vapor, can cause boric acid whiskers to migrate out of the glass. Whether or not this band can be observed on all samples of porous glass remains to be seen. Work in the author's laboratory indicates that its presence and intensity are sensitively dependent upon the exact conditions prevailing at the time of heat treating, pressing, and leaching of the sample.

The effect of water vapor addition to variously dehydrated porous glass samples is also shown in Fig. 4-10. Exposure of a completely dehydrated glass sample to water vapor causes reappearance of the band at 3665 cm^{-1}. This implies that the first step in the rehydration process is the reformation of adjacent surface hydroxyl groups. The simultaneous appearance of the band at 3450 cm^{-1} shows the presence of physically absorbed molecular water. These results (with the exception of the 3700-cm^{-1} band) essentially duplicate those obtained by McDonald for silica gel and indicate that the materials can, as far as their hydration–dehydration behavior is concerned, be considered very alike. Elmer et al. (46) report similar data in their studies of the hydration and dehydroxylation of porous glass. The spectra reported by these authors are of interest in that they show that the band due to the free surface hydroxyl groups (3740 cm^{-1}) tends to increase during the readsorption of water, a further indication that molecular water prefers to adsorb on adjacent hydroxyl groups rather than on the mono-meric groups.

B. Surface Heterogeneity

1. NH₃ on Porous Glass

The adsorption of ammonia on porous glass has been discussed by Chapman and Hair (29) and by Cant and Little (43). On adsorption of ammonia on the porous glass surface at room temperature, immediate interaction with the surface hydroxyl groups is observed. The interaction is apparently identical with that reported for ammonia on silica gel. The infrared spectrum of the adsorbed ammonia exhibits bands at 3320 and 3400 cm^{-1} that are attributed to symmetric and asymmetric N—H vibrations. Interaction with the surface hydroxyl group is indicated by its complete disappearance when sufficient ammonia is adsorbed. Two additional bands, however, are discernible at 3365 and 3280 cm^{-1}.

On evacuation at room temperature the physically adsorbed ammonia is removed. The bands at 3320 and 3400 cm^{-1} disappear, and the hydroxyl stretching frequency returns to its original intensity. The two bands at 3365 and 3280 cm^{-1} are not affected and are removed only by heating to temperatures in excess of 200°C. Spectra recorded when ammonia is added at 150° show the presence of only the two bands. At this tempera-ture physical absorption would not be expected, and the second ammonia species has been identified as being due to NH₃ molecules coordinately bonded to Lewis-acid-type sites on the glass surface.

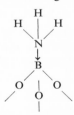

Comparison with the spectrum obtained for ammonia adsorption on silica gel confirms the assignment of the bands at 3400 and 3320 cm^{-1} to ammonia physically adsorbed on surface silanol groups. The frequencies found for ammonia chemisorbed on the surface of porous glass (3365 and 3280 cm^{-1}) compare quite favorably with those reported for the analogous vibrations of the NH₃ species in the NH₃–BF₃ complex (3340 and 3230 cm^{-1}) and can be taken as confirmatory evidence for this assignment (43). Data obtained by Cant and Little on the intensities of both the 3730- and

3665-cm^{-1} hydroxyl bands show that, on addition of ammonia, the band due to the free hydroxyl groups decreased much more rapidly than that due to the adjacent groups. It is thus concluded that the ammonia interacts preferentially with the free hydroxyl groups.

Prior to the publication of the above work, Folman and Yates (47) had studied the adsorption of ammonia upon porous glass and noted that during the desorption process approximately 4 cc of ammonia per gram of glass had been left upon the surface and could not be removed by evacuation at 150°. This effect was utilized by Hair and Chapman (41) in an attempt to estimate the amount of boron extant on the surface of a commercial sample of porous glass. Infrared work by these authors indicated that prolonged evacuation at 50°C removed all spectroscopic evidence of physically adsorbed ammonia; and thus, by quantitative adsorption of ammonia at this temperature, it proved possible to determine the number of boron atoms in the surface, assuming a 1:1 correspondence between boron atoms and adsorbed ammonia. From a knowledge of the surface area, an estimate of the B/Si ratio of 1:3 was made.

Intensity data on the four N—H vibrations as a function of surface coverage have been given by Cant and Little, and data on the apparent extinction coefficients of the adsorbed ammonia have been published by Folman and Yates. The extinction coefficient of the adsorbed ammonia decreases as the surface coverage is increased. This effect has been noted frequently; it can be attributed to either surface heterogeneity or to inductive effects between the adsorbed molecules. At higher temperatures Elmer and Nordberg (48) have shown that ammonia reacts with the surface hydroxyl group of porous glass to produce a single N—H band at 2.96 μ (3373 cm^{-1}). Since this corresponds to the frequency of vibration found for organic secondary amides, it is attributed to a species in which the nitrogen atom is attached to one hydrogen atom and two silicon atoms.

This species is retained on consolidation of the glass and leads to an increase in the annealing point of the glass. The ammonia also removes some of the boron from the glass, and there is evidence that nitrogen is incorporated into the glass structure, possibly by replacement of oxide ion.

110

2. Aging Studies

The difference between porous glass and silica gel is clearly demonstrated by the work of Yaroslavskii and Karyakin (4) in their investigation of the adsorption of nitrogen and oxygen on porous glass at low temperatures. This early work utilized the overtone region of the infrared spectrum, and some of the results are shown in Fig. 4-11. In this region

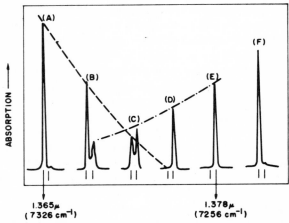

Fig. 4-11. *Effect of adsorbed nitrogen on the* OH *band of porous glass.* (A) *Original;* (B) *1 min at* −180°C; (C) *10 min later;* (D) *20 min later;* (E) *2 hr later;* (F) *after heating to 20°C.* [*Spectra reproduced from Reference* (84) *by courtesy of Academic Press, Inc., New York.*]

of the spectrum a dried sample of porous glass exhibits a single absorption at 7326 cm^{-1} that is the overtone of the fundamental hydroxyl stretching frequency observed at 3740 cm^{-1} in the fundamental region. The Russian workers found that on adsorption of nitrogen at −180°C the band at 7326 cm^{-1} was gradually reduced in intensity until, at the end of about 20 min, it was no longer visible. Concurrently, a band appeared at 7257 cm^{-1}, and this grew in size as the 7326-cm^{-1} band diminished (Fig. 4-11). At the end of 20 min, although the band at 7326 cm^{-1} had completely disappeared, the 7257-cm^{-1} band was only about half as intense as the original band. Heating to 20°C returned the band to its original position and intensity. The band at 7257 cm^{-1} corresponds to the overtone of a fundamental absorption that would occur around 3700 cm^{-1}. A band at this frequency has been observed by several Russian workers and has been discussed previously. A tentative assignment to a B—OH species is given. When oxygen is used as the adsorbate, a similar effect is noted and the band at 7257 cm^{-1} is again produced. In this case, however, the original band is not restored to its original frequency at 20°C, and a temperature of 200°C was found necessary to reverse the observation.

These results can be compared with those obtained for oxygen and nitrogen adsorbed on silica gel. In the case of the porous glass both the oxygen and nitrogen behave in a similar fashion. Both interact with the surface silanol group; identical frequency shifts are observed; there is little broadening of the OH band; and the intensity of the surface hydroxyl group is considerably reduced. With silica gel, however, these gases cause different frequency shifts and considerable increase in the intensities of the OH absorptions. Thus, although it is tempting to assume that the surface hydroxyl groups on porous glass are identical with those on silica gel, these results show that they are not necessarily identical. That the explanation for the adsorbent–adsorbate interaction is different in the case of porous glass is emphasized by the further results of Yaroslavskii and Karyakin (4). When a sample of porous glass was aged for 2 years in an evacuated system, the band at 7326 cm^{-1} was reduced in intensity and was partially replaced by a band at 7250 cm^{-1}. In this case, however, the second band was not removed even by heating to 550°C.

An explanation for these results is still lacking. The Russian workers attribute their results to a possible slow sintering of the surface, but Eischens and Pliskin (84) speculate that the adsorbed molecules relieve surface strains and suggest that there may be a connection between these results and the length changes of porous glass that take place on adsorption. Unfortunately, no comparable data are available for the adsorption of nitrogen and oxygen at low temperatures on Corning's Code 7930 porous glass (which possibly contains less surface boron) in either the overtone or fundamental regions or for similar adsorption on silica gel in the overtone regions.

C. Length Changes upon Adsorption

One of the most effective demonstrations of the utility of infrared spectroscopy in explaining adsorption phenomena was employed by Folman and Yates (47) in their classical experiments on the length changes of porous glass that were observed to occur during the adsorption process. In their original experiments Folman and Yates found that the adsorption of gases upon a porous glass body caused an initial contraction of the glass rod under investigation; this was followed by an expansion. Previous thermodynamic arguments had allowed only for the expansion of materials during the adsorption process. Some of the results obtained by Folman and Yates during the adsorption of chloroform are shown in Fig. 4-12. The changes in length of a rod of porous glass are plotted as a function of coverage at various temperatures. The general pattern that emerges is that the glass first of all expands momentarily and then contracts until a surface coverage of about 0.25 is achieved. After this point is reached, the

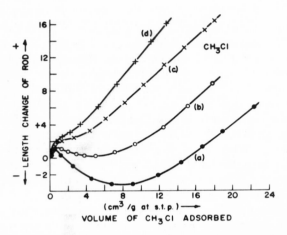

Fig. 4-12. *Length changes of a porous glass rod during adsorption of methyl chloride. Untreated glass (a) at −78°C, (b) at 0°C. Dehydroxylated glass (c) at −78°C, (d) at 0°C. [Redrawn from Reference (47) courtesy of The Royal Society.]*

length increases in an almost linear manner as coverage is increased to the monolayer stage.

An explanation of this effect was not readily apparent, and Folman and Yates speculated that the expansion–contraction effects were the result of a specific interaction between the adsorbate and the surface, in particular with the hydroxyl groups on the surface. The expansion-contraction pattern was the same for all the gases studied with the exception of argon and krypton. The amount of contraction observed is reduced at higher temperatures, and, in order to support their hypothesis, Folman and Yates examined the infrared spectra of the various porous glass–adsorbate systems at various surface coverages in conjunction with the expansion–contraction measurements. The spectra obtained showed clearly that specific interaction did take place between the surface hydroxyl groups and the adsorbate; and, as can be seen from Table 4-6, a good correlation was observed between the average OH frequency shift and the amount of contraction observed. In the case of both acetone and ammonia it can be seen that both the OH frequency shift and the amount of contraction were decreased as the temperature of the system was raised. This

TABLE 4-6

A Comparison between the Shifts in OH Frequencies (Δv) and the Contractions Produced under Similar Conditions[a]

Gas	Temp., °C	Average Δv value, cm^{-1}	Contraction A–B (fringes)
CH$_3$Cl	24	110	0.6
SO$_2$	24	115	0.6
(CH$_3$)$_2$CO	25	330	15.0
	75	305	10.5
	135	270	—
NH$_3$	25	820	25.0
	75	750	21.0
	100	710	17.5
	150	640	10.2

[a] Reproduced from Reference (47) with permission.

strong temperature dependence is in agreement with the original hypothesis that the adsorbate attachment occurs via hydrogen bonding to the surface hydroxyl groups. As the temperature is raised, this hydrogen bonding becomes weaker, and thus a smaller contraction is observed.

Unambiguous proof that the contraction occurred because of interaction with surface hydroxyl groups was also provided spectroscopically. Some of the surface OH groups were reacted with methyl alcohol at 360°C to give surface methoxy groups.

$$—Si—OH + CH_3OH \rightarrow —Si—O—CH_3 + H_2O$$

This methylation of the porous glass surface completely eliminated the contraction effect, thus proving that the contraction is due to interaction between the adsorbed molecules and the surface hydroxyl groups.

Folman and Yates consider the contraction to arise from the system (1). The formation of a hydrogen bond between the adsorbent and adsorbate involves a charge-transfer process in which charge is transferred from the proton acceptor to the proton donor. As a result of this process, the

```
      H                                          H     H
       \                                          \   /
        O → H      H                               O
       /          \                            ··     ··
  CH₃            O(A)    O(B)               H        H
                   |      |                  |        |
                   Si     Si                 O        O
                  / \    / \                 |        |
                 O   O  O   O                Si       Si
                /    |  |    \              / \      / \
                     O  O                  O   O    O   O
                     |  |                 /    |    |    \
                                                O    O
                                                |    |

                  (1)                            (2)
```

oxygen atom $O_{(A)}$ becomes more negative, the hydrogen bond between the adjacent OH groups becomes stronger, and therefore the distance between the oxygen atoms $O_{(A)}$ and $O_{(B)}$ is decreased. It is this shortening that gives rise to the contraction effect. It is of interest to note that water, which adsorbs preferentially on adjacent hydroxyl groups (2), cannot give this effect and no contraction is observed.

D. Restricted Rotation of Adsorbed Molecules

When a molecule is adsorbed on the surface, it is clear that it must lose some degree of freedom, and consequently its rotational spectrum must be considerably altered. The amount of restriction is of fundamental interest to any theoretical treatments of the physical adsorption process. Infrared spectroscopic studies of restricted rotation were originally made by Sheppard and his co-workers (49) in Cambridge, and the spectra of methane and methyl bromide physically adsorbed on porous glass were recorded.

1. Methane on Porous Glass

The vibrations of the methane molecule have been discussed in Chapter 2. The five-atom molecule has nine possible vibratory motions of which only four are infrared-active owing to degeneracy of the vibrations. After adsorption on porous glass, Sheppard and Yates (50) observed two bands that could be attributed to the physically adsorbed methane molecule. These were a strong, broad absorption at 3006 cm⁻¹ that corresponds to the triply degenerate v_3 vibration (Fig. 4-11) and a weaker band at 2899 cm⁻¹. The latter band is close to the value of the Raman-active v_1 vibration, and it is clear that the surface fields have caused the relaxation of the normal infrared selection rules and application of Raman selection rules. This effect of external fields was predicted by Condon (*51*) in 1932.

The gaseous methane molecule has three rotational degrees of freedom. Upon adsorption, the molecule could exist in one of three possible forms:

1. It could be adsorbed in such a loosely bound state that no degrees of freedom are lost.

2. It could be so strongly bound to the surface that there is no free rotation whatsoever.

3. It could be weakly held to the surface via three hydrogen atoms so that the molecule exhibits one rotational degree of freedom about an axis perpendicular to the surface.

From a consideration of the rotational energy levels and the relative intensities that would pertain for the three models, Sheppard and Yates were able to calculate the shapes of the band that would be expected in each case. These were then compared with the observed ν_3 band (3006 cm^{-1}). The free rotational model was eliminated immediately because it gave rise to considerable P and R branches. However, no clear conclusion regarding the correctness of model 1 or model 2 could be reached. In order to distinguish between these models, Yates and Sheppard calculated the band shapes that would give an overall intensity equal to that of the observed band. Again there was no clear-cut distinction between the two models, but the experimental results seem to agree better with the calculated results for the model based on the assumption of one rotational degree of freedom.

[handwritten margin note: ERROR ← 2 or 3]

The normally inactive band induced by the surface forces (ν_1) is much sharper and apparently more symmetrical than the ν_3 vibration, the band half-widths being 10 and 28 cm^{-1}, respectively. The effect of the surface field on the methane will be to induce a dipole moment in the molecule in a direction perpendicular to the surface. Since the polarizability ellipsoid of methane is spherical, the magnitude and direction of the induced dipole moment will be independent of the orientation of the methane molecule, and thus rotational motions will not affect the band shape. The spectrum will, therefore, consist only of a symmetrical Q branch. In the case of the ν_3 vibration, however, it must of necessity be broader and less symmetrical than the ν_1 vibration because of the contributions from the P and R branches to the band shape.

2. Methyl Bromide on Porous Glass

An alternative explanation for the increased band width of the ν_3 vibration as compared with the ν_1 vibration is based on the possible effect of the surface on the degenerate vibration. Since the surface forces are able to induce normally inactive Raman vibrations, it is not inconceivable that they could cause the triply degenerate ν_3 vibration to split into three components of slightly different frequency and thus give rise to a broadened, asymmetrical band. These possiblities can be distinguished by investigating the shape of this band as a function of temperature. If the difference in the band width is due to the degeneracy, then this would become more pronounced at lower temperatures when the molecule is more strongly bonded to the surface. If, however, the band width is attributable solely to rotational motion, then the width should be a function of the square root of temperature. In order to obviate experimental difficulties associated with the adsorption of methane, Sheppard et al. (49) studied the adsorption of the analogous methyl bromide on porous glass at room temperature and $-192°C$.

Gaseous methyl bromide exhibits three absorption bands in the region of interest. These are due to the ν_1, ν_4, and $2\nu_5$ frequencies and are observed at 2977, 3070, and 2863 cm^{-1}, respectively. The first and the last of these vibrations appear as doublets. After adsorption on porous glass at room temperature, the spectrum of the methyl bromide exhibits bands at 2970, 3058, and 2847 cm^{-1}. Perturbation of the surface hydroxyl groups is noted during the adsorption process. The half-widths of the methyl bromide bands are approximately 50% of those in the gas phase, and all doublets are removed, thus indicating that rotational motions about axes perpendicular to the threefold axis are effectively quenched. When the sample is cooled to $-78°K$ and the spectrum at a similar surface coverage is recorded, it is observed that the ν_4 band shifts slightly in frequency and sharpens considerably, the half bandwidth decreasing from 53 to 32 cm^{-1}. This result completely negates the hypothesis that band broadening is due to split degeneracy. The observed band shapes correspond very well with those calculated on the assumption that the methyl bromide molecule rotates freely about its threefold axis.

E. Calculation of Surface Charge: Hydrogen on Porous Glass

It is a general rule of thumb that bands due to physically adsorbed species are usually shifted by about 10 cm^{-1} from their positions in the gaseous spectrum. The adsorption of hydrogen on porous glass is an exception to this rule. Sheppard and Yates (50) have examined the infrared spectrum of hydrogen adsorbed on porous glass at an estimated surface coverage of 0.2. The symmetrical diatomic hydrogen molecule does not give rise to an infrared active mode, the single vibration being observed by

Raman techniques at 4161 cm^{-1}. Upon adsorption on the glass surface, this band becomes infrared-active and is observed at 4131 cm^{-1}, a displacement of 30 cm^{-1} from the gas-phase band. The maximum optical density for an effective path length of 0.39 mm was reported to be 0.1, giving an integrated absorption coefficient of 4.5×10^{-20} cm^{-1}, the band half-width being 21 cm^{-1}. Sheppard and Yates then used these values to estimate the charge on the porous glass surface.

As early as 1932, Condon (51) had examined the theoretical implications of the effect of an external electric field on an infrared spectrum. He predicted that the effect would be to cause a relaxation of the normal infrared selection rules with the result that the Raman-active vibrations should become observable in the infrared. Crawford and Dagg (52) further investigated this hypothesis and studied the intensity of the observed induced Q branch as a function of applied fields. A comparison of intensity data for adsorbed hydrogen with Crawford and Dagg's data enabled Sheppard and Yates to estimate the field at the surface of the glass. This was found to be 7×10^6 V/cm (or about 2×10^4 esu). This figure is in reasonable agreement with fields calculated at the surface of simple ionic crystals (CsI = 1.9×10^5 esu). Good agreement could not be expected because of the basic differences in the nature of these materials.

F. Miscellaneous Studies on Porous Glass

1. Chloroform Adsorption

Infrared data on the adsorption of chloroform (CH_3Cl) on porous glass has been published by Folman and Yates (47). The position of the C—H stretching frequency of the adsorbed chloroform is perturbed by only 10 cm^{-1} from the values observed for the gaseous species. The chloroform is evidently physically adsorbed and is completely removed from the surface by evacuation at 150°C. The extinction coefficient of the C—H vibration increases as the surface coverage increases, and this factor is taken as an indication that the chloroform is adsorbed on the porous glass surface via the chlorine atom rather than via one of the C—H groupings. Had the adsorption occurred through the C—H group, the intensity of the absorption due to the vibration of this group would have been considerably perturbed; the greatest perturbation (and hence increase in intensity) would have occurred with the first adsorbed molecule. In this case the adsorbate does not have a lone pair of electrons and cannot form a surface complex with the Lewis acid sites. Complete reversibility is thus observed.

2. Acetone on Porous Glass

When acetone is adsorbed on porous glass, the C—H stretching frequencies are shifted 10 cm^{-1} from their corresponding vibrations in the liquid phase (47), and the extinction coefficient is found to increase with surface coverage. Again the interpretation is that the physical adsorption takes place via the lone pair of electrons on the oxygen of the carbonyl group rather than via a methyl group, and consequently the CH frequencies are relatively unperturbed. In this case the intensity of the carbonyl group would be expected to be a function of surface coverage, but no data have been obtained for this vibrational mode. The lone-pair electrons on the oxygen atom of the acetone molecule might be expected to react with the boron sites in the same manner as ammonia, but it is interesting to note that there is no evidence of acetone remaining on the surface after evacuation at 150°C. The present author (53) has been unable to obtain evidence for the chemisorption of a strong Lewis base such as pyridine or hexachloroacetone on porous glass, and Chapman and Hair were unable to find any evidence of electron abstraction from anthracene adsorbed on porous glass (54). It seems likely that the boron atoms are relatively well hidden and that molecules much larger than ammonia are unable, for steric reasons, to approach the boron atom closely enough to react and form a surface complex. Folman and Yates do note, however, that their desorption data for acetone are indicative of two types of adsorption site on the porous glass surface, the bond with the second type of site being stronger than the bond with the hydroxyl groups.

3. Acetylene and Ethylene on Porous Glass

The infrared spectra of acetylene and ethylene physically adsorbed on porous glass have also been published by Sheppard and Yates (50). Points of interest are that the v_1 stretching vibration of the ethylene molecule (Fig. 2-14), which is inactive in the gas phase, becomes active and is observed when the ethylene is adsorbed on the porous glass. This is again attributed to a change in the ethylene molecule caused by the surface potential. More recently Little (55) has published the spectrum of ethylene adsorbed at 79°K on porous glass and observed a further vibration corresponding to the normally inactive v_5 (C—H stretching) vibration.

When the physically adsorbed ethylene is allowed to stand in contact with the porous glass and excess ethylene for extended periods of time, a saturated chemisorbed species is observed on the surface (56, 57). Major bands at 2922, 2850, and 2970 cm^{-1} are observed. These bands are typical of C—H stretching vibrations of CH_3 and CH_2 groups attached to saturated carbon atoms and show that polymerization has occurred. The adsorbed species is strongly held, and evacuation for 50 min removes only small amounts of the chemisorbed species. The formation of this species has been traced by Yates and Lucchesi (57) to the sodium impurity that is present in the porous glass. A glass sample that had been treated and given a further acid leach did not give rise to a chemically adsorbed ethylene species even after several weeks. Adding back sodium ions in the form of sodium hydroxide caused reappearance of the chemisorbed species. Addition of boric acid to the glass does not give rise to this species, and it seems unlikely, therefore, that the boric oxide impurity in the glass can be blamed for this polymerization reaction.

4. Effect of Gamma Radiation

In recent years gamma-ray bombardment on several oxides has been found to induce catalytic properties, and, in particular, the rate of hydrogen-deuterium exchange reaction on silica is found to be increased considerably if the silica sample is first irradiated. Yates and Lucchesi (57) reported that irradiation of porous glass also increases the rate of ethylene polymerization. Irradiation of porous glass for 16 hr imparts a purplish coloration to the glass that is due to the formation of color centers. Addition of ethylene to the irradiated glass does not remove the color centers. This result is to be compared with work on irradiated silica gel, where the addition of hydrogen and ethylene is known to cause decoloration of the radiation-induced color centers. The degree of ethylene polymerization on the porous glass is found to be a function of the length of preirradiation, and it is observed that the ratio of the optical densities of the bands at 2970 and 2922 cm^{-1} is reduced from 0.94 to 0.15 as the irradiation time is increased from 16 to 48 hr. The band at 2970 cm^{-1} is due to the asymmetric stretching vibration of a $>CH_3$ group, whereas that at 2922 cm^{-1} is due to the asymmetric stretching vibration of a $>CH_2$ group. Thus it is obvious that very few CH_3 groups are present in the final species. This must, therefore, be a long-chain molecule of the type $CH_3(CH_2)_n CH_3$.

Preadsorption of hydrogen and deuterium on the porous glass prior to the adsorption of ethylene caused disappearance of the purple color but did not affect the ethylene adsorption in any way. No OD groups were detected on the surface, and it is concluded that the defects responsible for the formation of the color centers are not responsible for the ethylene chemisorption.

Yates and Lucchesi speculated that the polymerization process involved a free-radical mechanism. Nitric oxide is well known as an inhibitor in free-radical reactions, and addition of this molecule to the porous glass–ethylene system, either before or after ethylene addition, successfully quenched the polymerization. Addition of the nitric oxide caused the purple glass sample to become yellow, but complete decolorization was not obtained. Further support for the free-radical mechanism was obtained by preadsorption of oxygen. In this case a decrease in the rate of ethylene adsorption was noted. The sites responsible for the ethylene chemisorption could not be detected by spin-resonance techniques and were concluded to be due to free radicals formed in the surface of the solid.

5. Butenes on Porous Glass

The spectra of a series of butenes adsorbed on porous glass at room temperature have been reported by Little et al. (58). These molecules are first physically adsorbed and then undergo isomerization and polymerization reactions. In the case of butene, the disappearance of the unsaturated species was monitored by the band at 3020 cm^{-1}, which is attributed to an olefinic $=$C—H vibration. The infrared spectrum of the adsorbed species was similar to that of 2-octene, and solvent extraction followed by gas chromatographic analysis indicated the presence of several complex polymers with between 6 and 12 carbon atoms. Removal of the polymers from the surface at higher temperatures resulted in cracking of the hydrocarbons. Releaching the porous glass with nitric acid reduced the amount of polymerization; and since the surface hydroxyl groups were unaffected by this treatment, the X_2O_3 impurities were blamed, possibly through their effect on the hydroxyl groups.

6. HCN on Porous Glass

HCN is a linear triatomic molecule that gives rise to three infrared-active vibrations ν_1, ν_3, and ν_2 at 3311, 2097, and 712 cm^{-1}. A combination band is also present in the gas-phase spectrum at 4016 cm^{-1}. On adsorption on porous glass, the C—H vibration at 3311 cm^{-1} is shifted by about 40 cm^{-1} and appears at 3271 cm^{-1} at low coverages (59). The exact position and intensity of this band are functions of surface coverage. At larger coverages, the band broadens and moves to lower wave numbers. The comparatively large shift and the change in frequency as the surface coverage is increased are taken as an indication that at least some of the molecules are adsorbed via their hydrogen atoms, probably to surface oxygens. The C—N vibration (2097 cm^{-1} in the gas phase) is shifted to higher frequencies on adsorption.

On standing in contact with the porous glass for a few days, the HCN polymerizes and new bands are observed at 2.94, 3.40, and 4.48 μ (3398, 2943,$^{-1}$ and 2232 cm^{-1}). After desorption of some of the polymer, additional bands can be seen at 2.85 and 3.15 μ (3509^{-1} and 3179 cm^{-1}). These bands remain after all weakly adsorbed HCN molecules have been removed from the surface. Kozirovski and Folman (59) assigned the bands at 2.85 and 2.94 μ to symmetric and asymmetric —NH$_2$ stretching vibrations, the 3.4 μ band to a C—H vibration and the 4.48 μ band to a C—N stretching vibration. A band at 6.1 μ (1638 cm^{-1}) was assigned to the —NH$_2$ bending mode.

Hydrogen cyanide is known to undergo a base-catalyzed polymerization reaction to give structures of the type

$$
\begin{array}{ccccc}
\text{CN} & \text{CN} & \text{CN} & \text{CN} & \\
\diagdown & \diagup & \diagdown & \diagup & \\
\text{C}\!=\!\text{C} & \rightleftharpoons & \text{C}\!-\!\text{C}\!-\!\text{H} & \text{and} & \text{H}\!-\!\text{C}\!-\!\text{C}\!\equiv\!\text{N} \\
\diagup & \diagdown & \diagup & \diagdown & \| \\
\text{NH}_2 & \text{NH}_2 & \text{NH} & \text{NH}_2 & \text{NH} \\
\end{array}
$$

The infrared evidence indicates that both of these polymers are formed on the porous glass surface. Kozirovski and Folman suggest that the initial step in the polymerization involves adsorption of the HCN molecule onto a basic oxygen. The second step is thought to involve a gaseous HCN molecule rather than a reaction between two adsorbed molecules.

4-4. THE REACTIONS OF SURFACE SILANOL GROUPS

Infrared spectroscopy has proved itself to be an important tool in the investigation of chemical reactions between the surface groups and adsorbed molecules. Thus, in the case of siliceous surfaces, it has been found that the surface silanol groups can react chemically as individual species in the same manner as a phenolic or alcoholic hydroxyl group. The silica surface will therefore react with ethyl alcohol to give a surface compound that is analogous to a metal ethoxide. Many stable surface compounds can be produced, and such investigations have shown the potentiality of this type of approach in "tailor-making" surfaces for specific applications (e.g., gas chromatography). Infrared spectroscopy is an essential tool in the investigation of such reactions, since it is the only technique that provides a ready means of accurately identifying the surface species.

A. Surface Esterification

The replacement of the surface hydroxyl groups by an alkyl- or aryloxy group is often called surface esterification (methylation, *etc.*). This type of reaction has been reported by many workers to occur on both silica and porous glass surfaces. The reaction may be written

$$\diagdown\text{Si}\!-\!\text{OH} + \text{ROH} \rightleftharpoons \diagdown\text{Si}\!-\!\text{O}\!-\!\text{R} + \text{H}_2\text{O}$$

Folman and Yates (*47*) give full experimental details following the method of Sidorov (*60*). Essentially, the reaction between the porous glass surface and methanol vapor is carried out in a closed vessel. The sample is heated with methanol at 360°C for 1 hr and is then evacuated in order to remove the by-products of the reaction. The procedure is then repeated until no further reaction occurs. An examination of the spectrum of the glass before and after reaction showed that, after 9 hr methylation at 360°C, the band at 3730 cm⁻¹ was removed or displaced and a new peak occurred at 3690 cm⁻¹. The peak optical density was reduced from 1.35 to 0.66. At the same time, two new bands were observed at 2960 and 2860 cm⁻¹. These are typical of the C—H stretching vibrations of methoxy groups and are so assigned. The shift in the peak maximum probably indicates that the methyl alcohol reacts preferentially with the free surface hydroxyl groups, but this cannot be considered certain in the absence of more definitive intensity data. Folman and Yates found that maximum methylation was obtained after 10 hr, at which stage it appeared that at least 50% of the surface hydroxyl groups had been removed. Sidorov reports that methylation of porous glass at 550°C causes almost complete removal of surface hydroxyl groups. Folman and Yates, however, report that, at this temperature, decomposition of the methyl alcohol occurred.

The work of Sidorov is of further interest in that it also indicates that the single OH groups are methylated in preference to adjacent OH groups. After complete methylation, Sidorov found that addition of water vapor gave rise to an intense absorption band at 3660 cm⁻¹ that had a weak shoulder at 3500 cm⁻¹. Removal of the water by pumping at 400°C shows that a small number of the methoxy groups had been rehydrolyzed to freely vibrating OH groups. No bands due to adjacent OH groups were found, and thus it seems likely that the initial reaction involved only the isolated hydroxyl groups.

Spectra have also been reported for the reaction between butyl alcohol and a silica gel surface that had been dried at 105°C (*61*). The surface hydroxyl groups are replaced, and new bands are observed at 2959, 2933, 2878, 1471, and 1385 cm^{-1}. The bands at 2959 and 2878 cm^{-1} are typical of —CH$_3$ groups, whereas the band at 2933 cm^{-1} can be attributed to a >CH$_2$ group. The bands at 1471 and 1385 cm^{-1} are very useful identifying features in this case and are attributed to the asymmetric and symmetric deformation modes of a —C—CH$_3$ group. The surface species is, therefore,

$$-\overset{|}{\underset{|}{Si}}-O-CH_2-CH_2-CH_2-CH_3$$

B. Diazomethane

Methoxy groups can also be introduced into a silica surface by reaction with diazomethane (62). In this case the reaction with the surface hydroxyl groups proceeds according to the equation

$$-\overset{|}{\underset{|}{Si}}OH + CH_2N_2 \rightleftharpoons -\overset{|}{\underset{|}{Si}}OCH_3 + N_2$$

The reaction must be carried out in the complete absence of water, or a side reaction will take place: the diazomethane will be hydrolyzed to methyl alcohol and nitrogen,

$$CH_2N_2 + H_2O = CH_3OH + N_2$$

The diazomethane may be employed either as a gas or in ethereal solution. The method has been used quantitatively to measure the number of surface hydroxyl groups, but it is susceptible to many errors including that of a side reaction that leads to the formation of polyethylenes:

$$nCH_2N_2 \rightarrow (CH_2)_n + nN_2$$

C. Surface Fluorination

Surface hydroxyl groups are normally only weakly acidic and may be replaced by halogen atoms. Complete dehydroxylation of a surface is difficult to achieve. However, Elmer (63) has shown that treatment of a porous glass surface with 30% ammonium fluoride solution followed by heating to about 700°C causes complete replacement of the surface silanol groups by fluorine. This causes the surface to become hydrophobic. The reaction has been followed spectroscopically (64). Readsorption of water onto the completely fluorinated surface gives rise to a band at 2.76 μ (3628 cm^{-1}) that is very asymmetric and has evidence of a shoulder at 2.8 μ (3570 cm^{-1}). No band attributable to free silanol groups was observed, and it is possible that the bands observed are due to hydrolysis of the Si—F band and reformation of adjacent hydroxyl groups.

By using a similar technique but employing a weaker ammonium fluoride solution ($12\frac{1}{2}\%$), Chapman and Hair (54) showed that only about half the surface hydroxyl groups were replaced by fluorine atoms and that the subsequent surface exhibited high catalytic activity for the cracking of cumene. The enhanced activity due to fluorine substitution was attributed to the inductive effect of the electonegative fluorine atom on an adjacent silanol group, an effect considered analogous to the increase in acidity observed when fluorine is introduced into the acetic acid molecule,

In view of the postulate that strong protonic sites are produced on porous glass by the partial replacement of OH by F, Chapman and Hair examined the infrared spectrum of ammonia adsorbed on this surface (29). Previous work had shown that ammonia adsorption at room temperature gave rise to peaks at 3400 and 3320 cm^{-1}, owing to physically adsorbed ammonia, and peaks at 3365 and 3280 cm^{-1}, owing to ammonia chemisorbed on Lewis acid sites. On the completely fluorinated surface, only the two latter peaks were observed. However, when ammonia was adsorbed on the partially fluorinated surface, a fifth peak appeared at 3450 cm^{-1}. This was attributed to the presence of an NH_4^+ species on the surface. This species is stable up to about 250°C, all physically adsorbed and coordinately bonded NH_3 being removed below 200°C. The exact position of the NH_4^+ peak was found to be slightly dependent upon the degree of fluorination of the surface, moving to higher frequencies as the fluorine content was increased. It is of interest to note that the value found for the position of the NH_4^+ absorption is higher than any value reported previously for ammonium salts. However, a close examination of published values for the NH stretching vibrations of a series of ammonium salts reveals a definite trend in which the frequency of the most intense absorption increases as the strength of the complementary acid increases. Thus, the highest value reported for an ammonium compound (3330 cm^{-1}) corresponds to the salt of perchloric acid, the strongest complementary acid investigated (65).

In view of the high frequency at which the NH_4^+ band appears, it should be noted that Uytterhoeven and co-workers (66) have since reported the formation of a band at 3425 cm^{-1} on the addition of NH$_3$ to an activated molecular sieve. This band was ascribed to the formation of an NH$_4^+$ species, and it seems possible that it is these strong protonic sites that are responsible for the catalytic activity of these surfaces.

Whereas the partially fluorinated glass surface is apparently quite stable toward ammonia, it was found that the fully fluorinated surface tended to react with ammonia at 200°C. At this temperature the intensity of the fundamental OH stretch (3740 cm^{-1}) was observed to increase and a new small band appeared at 3700 cm^{-1}. No bands attributable to an —NH$_2$ group were observed. The position of the new band is suggestive of a new hydroxyl group (perhaps attached to a boron atom), but it could also be due to an NH group formed by reaction of the ammonia with siloxane linkages

$$2\text{—Si—O—Si} \rightarrow \underset{\overset{|}{\text{—Si—O—Si—}}}{\overset{\overset{\text{H}}{|}}{\text{N}}} + \underset{\text{—Si—O—Si}}{\overset{\overset{\text{H}\quad\text{H}}{|\quad|}}{\text{O}\quad\text{O}}}$$

D. Chlorination of Surfaces

It has been found that the surface hydroxyl groups on both silica gel and porous glass can be partially replaced by chlorine atoms if the solid is treated under refluxing conditions with sulfuryl chloride (SO$_2$Cl$_2$). The reaction proceeds according to the equation

$$2\text{—SiOH} + SO_2Cl_2 = 2\text{—Si—Cl} + 2HCl + SO_2$$

The HCl and SO$_2$ are removed as gaseous by-products. The reaction can also be carried out in the vapor phase, and the removal of the OH groups can be monitored by infrared techniques. Folman (67) reports 90% removal of surface hydroxyl by using this technique.

Chlorination of the silica surface can also be accomplished by heating the silica in chlorine gas at 700°–950°C (68) or in carbon tetrachloride at 350°–600°C (34). In both cases weight changes indicate a 1:1 replacement of OH by Cl, and complete dehydroxylation is reported.

E. Surface Ammination

The surface $\geqslant$Si—Cl bond is unstable in the presence of ammonia and undergoes the following reaction:

$$\text{—Si—Cl} + 2NH_3 \rightarrow \text{—Si—N}\overset{\displaystyle \text{H}}{\underset{\displaystyle \text{H}}{}} + NH_4Cl$$

This reaction was studied by using infrared spectroscopy, the appearance of the surface —NH_2 species being identified by the symmetric and asymmetric N—H stretching modes at 3445 and 3520 cm^{-1}. The NH_4Cl was readily identified spectroscopically, and it could be fumed off to leave only the amminated surface. Peri (34) reports that $\geqslant$Si—NH_2 group is relatively stable toward water vapor, but heating in oxygen at 600°C causes oxidation of the surface species and reformation of the surface hydroxyl groups.

F. Grignard Reactions

The Grignard reactions that have proved so useful in organic chemistry have also been successfully applied to the silica surface. Several of these reactions have been discussed by Uytterhoeven and Fripiat (61, 62). The Grignard reagents are organometallic compounds, such as methyl magnesium iodide, CH_3MgI, and methyl lithium, CH_3Li, that undergo specific reactions with many radicals. Hydroxy compounds react according to the equation:

$$X—OH + CH_3Li = X—O—Li + CH_4$$

Thus, on a silica surface the hydrogen atoms are replaced by lithium and methane is quantitatively evolved. The amount of methane produced has been used to estimate the number of surface hydroxyl groups per unit surface area, infrared spectroscopy being employed to monitor the elimination of the hydroxyl groups. For the silica gel examined, the average hydroxyl content was 4.2 units per 100 Å^2, the theoretical value for a completely hydroxylated surface being about 8 units per 100 Å^2.

Lithium can also be introduced into the silica surface by utilizing the ion-exchange properties of the surface group. The silanol group is weakly acidic, and immersion in an aqueous salt solution causes cation exchange to take place:

$$\diagdown\!Si—OH^+ + Li^+ \rightleftharpoons \diagdown\!Si—O^-Li^+ + H^+$$

However, since the "acidity" is very weak, the amount of exchange obtained in the normal pH ranges is very small. No comparisons have yet been made regarding the nature of the lithium-impregnated surfaces prepared by these alternative techniques.

Grignard reagents will also react with the surface $\geqslant$Si—Cl groups produced by prior reaction of the $\geqslant$Si—OH with SO_2Cl_2. In this case direct silicon–carbon bonds are formed:

$$-Si-Cl + CH_3Li \rightarrow -Si-CH_3 + LiCl$$

$$-Si-Cl + \phi Li \rightarrow -Si-\phi + LiCl$$

Uytterhoeven and Fripiat report spectra for the surface species formed by these reactions. They are strictly analogous to the spectra of corresponding organic species.

Surface phenyl groups have also been introduced into a chlorinated surface by a Friedel-Kraft reaction with benzene in the presence of aluminum chloride:

$$-Si-Cl + C_6H_6 \xrightarrow{AlCl_3} -Si-C_6H_5 + HCl$$

G. Carboxylic Acid Derivatives

The hydroxyl groups on silica–alumina and alumina surfaces are reported to react with carboxyl acids and their derivatives according to the reactions:

$$-X_S-OH + CH_3COOH \rightarrow -X_S-O-\overset{\overset{\textstyle O}{\|}}{C}-CH_3 + H_2O$$

$$-X_S-OH + CH_3COCl \rightarrow -X_S-O-\overset{\overset{\textstyle O}{\|}}{C}-CH_3 + HCl$$

These reactions do not occur with pure silica specimens and must be dependent upon the presence of other ions on the surface, an increase in the acidity of the surface hydroxyl group, or both. A more complete discussion appears later in this text in a consideration of the reactivity of alumina surfaces.

H. Reaction with Organosilicon Compounds

Silica, particularly in the form of diatomaceous earth, has proved to be a useful support material in the area of gas chromatography. One of the essential qualifications of such a material is that the surface must be homogenous and nonreactive toward the adsorbing molecules. The high reactivity of many silica surfaces has been traced to the strong specific physical bond formed between the adsorbing gas and the surface hydroxyl groups. It has been found that these reactive surfaces can be deactivated if their surface hydroxyl groups are removed by reaction with organic molecules. Thus, if the hydroxyl groups are replaced by, say, a methoxy group, the adsorptive properties of the surface are completely changed, and no specific adsorption with aromatic molecules or lone-pair compounds can occur. The resultant chromatograms thus show much less evidence of "tailing." A good example of the effect of surface methylation on adsorptive properties has already been given in the discussion of the work of Folman and Yates on the expansion of porous glass during the adsorption process (Fig. 4-12).

Methylated chlorosilanes have been found to be extremely efficient in their ability to dehydroxylate surfaces, and these reactions have been examined, notably by the Russian school (6, 69–71). Many spectroscopic data on the nature of the surface species are now available.

In a typical reaction the silica is freed from adsorbed water by evacuation at about 150°C and reacted with liquid trimethylchlorosilane under reflux conditions. The reaction proceeds according to the equation:

$$\diagdown\!\!\!-SiOH + ClSi(CH_3)_3 = \diagdown\!\!\!-Si\!-\!O\!-\!Si(CH_3)_3 + HCl$$

The infrared spectrum of this surface complex (69) exhibits a characteristic strong absorption at 2968 cm^{-1}, which is due to the asymmetric stretching vibration of the C—H bond in the methyl groups. Complete dehydroxylation of the surface has not been obtained by this technique, though whether this is due to an equilibrium condition or whether the bulky trimethyl chlorosilane molecules are sterically prevented from reaching some surface hydroxyl groups has not been established.

The unreacted hydroxyl groups are available to small molecules such as water. This can be demonstrated by deuterium exchange. Addition of D_2O followed by evacuation at 200° causes replacement of the OH band and the appearance of an OD stretching vibration at 2740 cm^{-1}. This new band is asymmetric and is attributed to interacting OD groups. On heating to 500°C, the band at 2968 cm^{-1}, owing to the trimethylsilane, disappears and the OD stretch appears at 2761 cm^{-1}. At this position the formation of freely vibrating surface O—D groups is indicated. Lygin and Kiselev (70) have shown that the accessibility of the hydroxyl groups that have not reacted with the trimethylchlorosilane is dependent upon the surface coverage of the silane: when 93% of the OH groups had been replaced, deuterium exchange was insignificant.

The spectrum of the aerosil surface after reaction with the silane shows no evidence of free hydroxyl groups, suggesting that these groups react preferentially with the Si—Cl bond. This conclusion is also supported by the spectra published by Davydov et al. (6). These workers suggest that the apparent disinclination of the monochlorosilane to react with the hydrogen-bonded hydroxyl groups may be due to the energy that is required to break the hydrogen bond. The heat of chemisorption of the trimethylchlorosilane is only about 10 Kcal/mole and is approximately the same as the strength of the hydrogen bond.

If the monochlorosilane reacts preferentially with the unperturbed silanol groups, it might be expected that a dichlorosilane would react preferentially with adjacent hydroxyl groups, the steric configurations being apparently well adapted to each other:

The reactions of several substituted dichlorosilanes with the silica surface have been studied spectroscopically by Kiselev et al. (71). The spectra of the reacted surfaces, after a 6-hr reflux with the silanes in dioxane solution, showed that the replacement of surface hydroxyl groups in all cases was less than 50%. The following reactants were studied:

$$Cl_2SiCH_2CH_2COOCH_3 \quad Cl_2Si{-}CH_2CH=CH_2 \quad Cl_2SiCH_2CH_2Cl \quad Cl_2SiCHCl$$
$$\underset{CH_3}{|} \qquad\qquad\qquad \underset{H}{|} \qquad\qquad\qquad \underset{CH_3}{|} \qquad\qquad \overset{CH_3}{|}$$

(1)   (2)   (3)   (4)

In all cases reaction with both free and adjacent hydroxyl groups took place, but the spectra were not unequivocal evidence that the two chlorine atoms were involved in the reaction with the adjacent hydroxyl groups.

The spectrum of the ester-type surface compound [reaction with (1)] was of interest in that extensive hydrogen bonding was observed. This can presumably be attributed to a hydrogen bonding interaction between the unreacted surface hydroxyl groups and the carbonyl groupings of the esterified silane. The carbonyl group, which normally gives rise to a single intense absorption at about 1736 cm^{-1}, was found to be split into two intense absorptions at 1750 and 1723 cm^{-1}, thus lending support to this hypothesis.

The silane containing the unsaturated C=C bond in the side chain (2) did not react completely even with the free hydroxyl groups, as was evidenced by the continued presence of a sharp absorption at 3740 cm⁻¹ in the surface spectrum. No interaction with the double bond occurred, the band at 1638 cm⁻¹ due to the C=C vibration being readily monitored. Upon addition of bromine, however, this band disappeared completely. Evidently, bromination of this group occurred in the usual ways:

$$>C{=}C< + Br_2 \rightarrow -\underset{Br}{\overset{|}{C}}-\underset{Br}{\overset{|}{C}}-$$

I. Reaction with Diborane

One of the earliest efforts to distinguish between adsorbed H_2O and surface hydroxyl groups was reported by Shapiro and Weiss (72) in 1953. These workers argued that surface OH groups would react with diborane to form the species (1)

$$2-Si-OH + H-B\text{—}B-H \rightarrow 2-Si-OB \qquad + 2H_2$$

$$(1)$$

with the elimination of two moles of H_2 per mole of diborane consumed. Bulk water would produce up to 6 moles of hydrogen per mole of diborane

$$6H_2O + H-B\text{—}B-H \rightarrow 2H_3BO_3 + 6H_2$$

In a later paper, this method was used in conjunction with boron exchange studies to determine the ratio of Al—OH and Si—OH groups on a silica–alumina catalyst (73).

This reaction has now been observed in the infrared by Baverez and Bastick (74), Mathieu and Imelik (75), and Fripiat and van Tongelen (76). None of these workers are in agreement with the others, but all are in agreement that the method as proposed cannot be used to distinguish between adsorbed and "bound" water.

The addition of diborane to the surface of silica gives rise to strong absorptions at 2850 and 1375 cm⁻¹. These can be attributed to B—H and B—O stretching vibrations. Additional bands have been noted in all four

papers on this subject, but the lack of uniformity in results makes interpretation difficult. In actual fact, a miscellany of products is probably
produced.

J. Reaction with SiCl$_4$

Peri (*34*) has studied the reaction between silicon tetrachloride and
surface hydroxyl groups quantitatively with the aid of infrared spectroscopy. His results are important in the information they give regarding
the aging process that a gel surface undergoes. Hockey (*9, 77*) and others
have speculated that a freshly formed gel can have a surface that is fully
hydroxylated and in which two hydroxyl groups can be attached to the
same silicon atom i.e.,

Such bonds would not hydrogen-bond with each other, and Hockey has
suggested that the band at 3500 cm^{-1} in the spectrum of some silica
surfaces is due to this species. If it is, then reaction with one SiCl$_4$ molecule
would be expected to result in the elimination of two molecules of HCl,

(1)

Peri found that on freshly prepared aerogel that had been calcined and
predried at 600°C most of the SiCl$_4$ reacted with two, rather than one,
hydroxyl groups. Even after heating to 800°C (at which point the infrared
spectrum showed a symmetric OH stretching band at 3750 cm^{-1}), over
40% of the SiCl$_4$ molecules reacted with two OH groups.

However, when virgin silica was first heated under vacuum at 800°C,
calcined in oxygen at 600°C, or exposed to air for a year, a 1:1 reaction
was observed. Moreover, when the surface species (1) was hydrolyzed and
reheated to 800°C, the spectrum could not be distinguished from that of
the original sample predried at 800°C.

It is thus apparent that even on silica surfaces containing fewer than
two OH groups per 100 Å^2 most of the surface OH groups can be sufficiently close together to react in pairs with one molecule of SiCl$_4$. The

spectrum, however, shows no evidence of hydrogen bonding. Thus, adjacent silanol groups do not necessarily hydrogen-bond and give rise to a band at 3650 cm^{-1}. The freshly prepared gel almost certainly contains geminal silanol groups. Peri speculates that it is possible that these may migrate as $Si(OH)_4$ species over a period of time and thereby cause a reconstitution of the surface in which a more stable $\geqslant$Si—O—H species is favored. In other words, a surface annealing is taking place.

4-5. SURFACE ACIDITY

A. The Frequency of Surface Hydroxyl Groups

The infrared investigations of the physical adsorption process that have been discussed thus far have revealed that a specific interaction between the surface hydroxyl groups and the adsorbent can occur. The nature of this interaction has been related to the electronic nature (ionization potential, polarizability) of the adsorbate. In such an interaction, however, it is clear that the electron distribution in the surface O—H bond must be equally as important as the nature of the adsorbate. Hydroxyl groups can range from the basic OH$^-$ group to the covalent phenolic group to the acidic O$^-$H$^+$ group, and the physical adsorption process can be regarded as an acid–base solvent interaction between the surface hydroxyl groups and the basic adsorbate. The acidity of the surface hydroxyl groups is of some importance in the elucidation of the mechanism of catalytic cracking reactions, and many workers in this area have speculated about the nature of surface acidity. The acid hydroxyl groups have been termed *Brönsted sites* in order to distinguish these protonic acids from the electron-abstracting or Lewis acid sites that exist on many surfaces.

Infrared spectroscopy has been widely used in physical–organic studies to investigate acid–base interactions in solution, and the results obtained warrant some discussion with respect to the application of some of the conclusions to surface interactions. The infrared spectra of many carboxylic acids and phenols have been reported in the literature, and it has been found that several correlations between the frequencies of the OH vibrations and the acid dissociation constants of the materials under investigation can be made. Thus, Goulden (78) has shown that the pK_a values obtained for a series of phenols bear a direct linear relation to the frequency of the hydroxyl stretching vibration. Also, examination of the infrared spectra of about 50 carboxylic acids showed that the OH frequencies fell on one of three straight lines, each line representing a different type of acid. The existence of this type of correlation suggests that the position of a freely vibrating surface hydroxyl group can be related to the acidity of that group. While this supposition cannot be disproved, it must be pointed out that deviations from the above correlations are noted, particularly when unsaturated groups are introduced into the carbon chain.

In Fig. 4-13 the OH stretching frequencies of a number of hydroxides have been plotted as a function of the electronegativity of the atom to

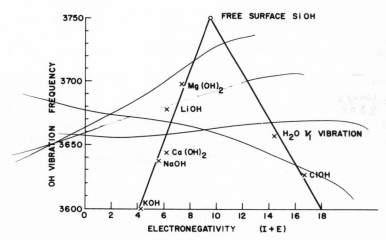

Fig. 4-13. Plot of OH *stretching frequency as a function of electronegativity.*

which they are attached. Although there is no exact correlation between these parameters, it is seen that the frequency of the hydroxyl stretching vibration is very dependent on the electronegativity of the atom to which it is attached, but is not related to the acidity in any definitive way. Thus, both NaOH and HOCl exhibit hydroxyl stretching vibrations at about the same frequency (3637 and 3626 cm^{-1}); yet, in the normal use of the words, one is considered basic, the other acidic. Moreover, in the case of the organic carbinols and the carboxylic acids discussed above, it is found that as the acidity of the carbinol increases (pK_a decreases), the hydroxyl stretching frequency decreases. The frequency of vibration of a silanol group is higher than that of the corresponding carbinol group, and thus it might be argued that the silanol groups are more basic than the corresponding carbinol compounds. All available evidence, however, indicates that silanols are more acidic than their corresponding carbinols, and thus it seems unwise to utilize the stretching frequency of the O—H group by itself as an indication of acidity unless it forms part of a well-defined series of compounds whose pK_a values and O—H stretching frequencies are known.

The increased acidity of the silanol group, as compared with the carbinol group, is to be expected on theoretical grounds, and it has been attributed to a π-bonding interaction between the unshared electrons on the oxygen atom and an empty d orbital on the silicon atom. The resultant drift of electrons away from the oxygen increases the positive character of the hydrogen.

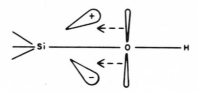

It should be noted that the silanol group in liquid silanols occurs at about 3670–3690 cm^{-1}. The same group, freely vibrating on the silica surface, is observed at 3750 cm^{-1}. Basila (16) has suggested that this increase in frequency might be due to an increased delocalization of the electron pairs on the oxygen due to a π-bonding interaction with the d orbitals of *two* surface silicon atoms, i.e., an interaction of the type

In this case the surface silanol group would be more acidic than the liquid silanol group.

B. Hydrogen-Bonding Interactions

In the extensive studies on the specific physical adsorption of organic molecules on the silica surface, a relationship has been shown to exist between the shift in frequency of the Si—O—H group and the ionization potential (electron-donating properties) of the adsorbate. In any study of surface acidity, the magnitude of these shifts is of some importance, because the shift for any given adsorbate must depend upon the acidity of the surface hydroxyl group.

Lippincott and Schroeder (79) have proposed a one-dimensional model of the hydrogen bond, which allows calculation of O—H frequency shifts during a hydrogen-bonding interaction. An interaction of the type

$$X—O—H \cdots O \diagup_{\diagdown}$$

was considered, the O—H $\cdots$ O bond being assumed to be linear. A potential-energy function of the type

$$V = D[1 - \exp(-n\,\Delta r^2/2r)]$$

was used, and the O—H frequency shift was calculated as a function of the O—O distance. D is the bond dissociation energy, r is the O—H bond length, and $n = k_0 r_0/D$. Some calculated O—H frequency shifts are plotted as a function of the O—H $\cdots$ O distance in Fig. 4-14, together with some experimentally observed values, and it is seen that there is good correlation between the theory and experiment. Use of this relationship enables estimates of the O—O bond distance to be made, provided the frequency shift is known.

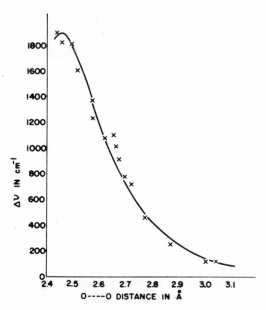

Fig. 4-14. *The relation between OH frequency shift and O $\cdots$ O distance during hydrogen-bonding interaction.* [*Redrawn from Reference (79) by courtesy of the Journal of Chemical Physics.*]

Coggeshall (80) has calculated the frequency shifts that might be expected during hydrogen-bonded interactions by solving the Schrödinger equation. An expression of the form

$$\Delta\nu(\text{cm}^{-1}) = 3qE/4\pi c(2\mu_m)^{1/2}D^{1/2}$$

was obtained, where q is the charge of the dipole, E is the field component along the O—H axis, D is the dissociation energy, and μ_m is the reduced mass. Good agreement between theory and practice was observed for the two cases examined.

TABLE 4-7

Comparison of Hydrogen-Bonded Frequency Shifts of Alcohols, Silanols, and Surface Hydroxyl Groups with Basic Solvents

Acid	pK_a	$\Delta\nu$, cm^{-1}, mesitylene	$\Delta\nu$, cm^{-1}, diethyl ether	$\Delta\nu$, cm^{-1}, benzene	Ref.
Methyl alcohol		47	122		81
Phenol	10	76	280		81
Trimethyl silanol	$\simeq$11	71	238		81
Si$_s$—O—H	—	146	450	120	16
Molecular sieve	—		—	330	83

From the above equation it can be seen that as the O—H bond becomes more acidic, the charge on the dipole (q) must increase, and therefore a greater shift is observed during an interaction with an adsorbate of equal basicity. This prediction is substantiated by the data of West and Baney (81), which are reproduced in Table 4-7. It can be seen that, for the alcohol, phenol, and silanol, the OH shift becomes greater as the strength of either the acid or the basic solvent is increased. A comparison of the shifts obtained for the surface silanol group with the same adsorbates again indicates that the surface hydroxyl group is much more acid than the liquid silanol. Similarly, the shifts observed during water and benzene adsorption on magnesia and molecular sieve surfaces indicate that these hydroxyl groups are more basic and more acidic (respectively) than those on the silica surface (82, 83).

Basila (16) reports that both silica and silica–alumina surfaces have hydroxyl groups that give essentially identical shifts during the adsorption of mesitylene and p-xylene. This has been taken as evidence that both these surfaces contain the same type of hydroxyl group. It seems fairly certain, however, that the silica–alumina surface contains many sites that are more acidic than those on silica, and therefore the evidence obtained from frequency shifts alone must be considered circumstantial.

In addition to the frequency changes that occur during hydrogen bonding, the integrated intensity of the perturbed hydroxyl group is found to be greatly increased by the hydrogen-bonding interaction. The intensity of any infrared band depends upon dp/dr, and thus the initial dipole moment p is of some importance. The effect of hydrogen bonding is to increase the dipole and therefore the intensity. However, no work that relates the intensity changes of a surface hydroxyl group to the adsorbate basicity has yet been published. Such data would be of some importance, particularly in the case of bands that might be attributed to surface hydroxyl groups of varying acidity but coincident frequency. Adsorption of the basic solvent would cause a perturbation of the OH stretching frequency and a broadening of the band. For a solvent of given basicity, differences in the acidity of the surface hydroxyl group should be revealed by intensity measurements.

REFERENCES

1. R. S. McDonald, *J. Phys. Chem.*, **62**, 1168 (1958).
2. N. G. Yaroslavskii and A. N. Terenin, *Dokl. Akad. Nauk. SSSR*, **66**, 885 (1949).
3. N. G. Yaroslavskii, *Zh. Fiz. Khim.*, **24**, 68 (1950).
4. N. G. Yaroslavskii and A. V. Karyakin, *Dokl. Akad. Nauk SSSR*, **85**, 1103 (1952).
5. H. A. Benesi and A. C. Jones, *J. Phys. Chem.*, **63**, 179 (1959).
6. V. Ya. Davydov, A. V. Kiselev, and L. T. Zhuravlev, *Trans. Faraday Soc.*, **60**, 2254 (1964).
7. G. J. Young, *J. Colloid Sci.*, **13**, 67 (1958).
8. J. J. Fripiat, M. C. Gastuche, and R. Brichard, *J. Phys. Chem.*, **66**, 805 (1962).
9. J. A. Hockey and B. A. Pethica, *Trans. Faraday Soc.*, **57**, 2247 (1961).
10. J. B. Peri, *J. Phys. Chem.*, **70**, 2937 (1966).
11. J. A. Hockey, *Chem. Ind.* (*London*), **1965**, 57.
12. A. V. Kiselev, *Structure and Properties of Porous Materials, Colston Papers*, Vol. 10 (D. H. Everett and F. S. Stone, eds.), Butterworth, London, 1958, p. 195.
13. J. H. Anderson, Jr., and K. A. Wickersheim, *Surface Sci.*, **2**, 252 (1964).
14. G. Herzberg, *Infrared and Raman Spectra of Polyatomic Molecules*, Van Nostrand, Princeton, N.J., 1945.
15. G. J. C. Frohnsdorff and G. L. Kington, *Trans. Faraday Soc.*, **55**, 1173 (1959).
16. M. R. Basila, *J. Chem. Phys.*, **35**, 1151 (1961).
17. R. S. Mulliken, *J. Am. Chem. Soc.*, **74**, 811 (1952).
18. G. A. Galkin, A. V. Kiselev, and V. I. Lygin, *Russ. J. Phys. Chem. English Transl.*, **36**, 951 (1962).
19. V. Ya. Davydov, A. V. Kiselev, and V. I. Lygin, *Proc. Acad. Sci. USSR Phys. Chem. Sect. English Transl.*, **147**, 769 (1962).
20. A. V. Kiselev, Ya. Koutetski, and I. Chizhek, *Proc. Acad. Sci. USSR Phys. Chem. Sect. English Transl.*, **137**, 283 (1961).

21. A. V. Kiselev and V. I. Lygin, *Colloid J. USSR English Transl.*, **23**, 478 (1961).
22. A. V. Kiselev, *Surface Sci.*, **3**, 292 (1965).
23. J. H. Anderson, Jr., *Surface Sci.*, **3**, 290 (1965).
24. M. R. Basila, *J. Chem. Phys.*, **35**, 1151 (1961).
25. V. N. Abramov, A. V. Kiselev, and V. I. Lygin, *Russ. J. Phys. Chem. English Transl.*, **37**, 5, 613 (1963).
26. A. V. Kiselev and V. I. Lygin, *Surface Sci.*, **2**, 236 (1964).
27. T. Yoshino, *J. Chem. Phys.*, **23**, 1564 (1955).
28. N. W. Cant and L. H. Little, *Can. J. Chem.*, **43**, 1252 (1965).
29. I. D. Chapman and M. L. Hair, *Trans. Faraday Soc.*, **61**, 1507 (1965).
30. A. W. Smith and J. M. Quets, *J. Catalysis*, **4**, 163 (1965).
31. R. S. McDonald, *J. Am. Chem. Soc.*, **79**, 850 (1957).
32. V. Ya. Davydov, A. V. Kiselev, and V. I. Lygin, *Russ. J. Phys. Chem. English Transl.*, **37**, 243 (1963).
33. R. P. Eischens and W. H. Pliskin, *Advan. Catalysis*, **9**, 662 (1956).
34. J. B. Peri, *J. Phys. Chem.*, **70**, 2937 (1966).
35. E. P. Parry, *J. Catalysis*, **2**, 371 (1963).
36. N. D. Parkyns, *Proceedings Third International Congress of Catalysis*, p. 914. North-Holland, Amsterdam, 1965, p. 194.
37. P. G. Ashmore and W. Hertl, *J. Catalysis*, **3**, 438 (1964).
38. L. J. Bellamy, *Infrared Spectra of Complex Molecules*, Methuen, London, 1960, p. 382.
39. H. P. Hood and M. E. Nordberg, U.S. Pat. 2,215,039.
40. M. E. Nordberg, *J. Am. Ceram. Soc.*, **27**, 299 (1944).
41. M. L. Hair and I. D. Chapman, *J. Am. Ceram. Soc.*, **49**, 651 (1966).
42. A. N. Sidorov, *Opt. Spectry. USSR English Transl.*, **8**, 424 (1960).
43. N. W. Cant and L. H. Little, *Can. J. Chem.*, **42**, 802 (1964).
44. L. H. Little and M. V. Mathieu, *Actes du Deuxième Congrès International de Catalyse, Paris, 1960*, Vol. 1, Editions Technip, Paris, 1961, p. 771.
45. M. J. D. Low and N. Ramasubramanian, *J. Phys. Chem.*, **70**, 2740 (1966).
46. T. H. Elmer, I. D. Chapman, and M. E. Nordberg, *J. Phys. Chem.*, **66**, 1517 (1962).
47. M. Folman and D. J. C. Yates, *Proc. Roy. Soc. (London)*, **A246**, 32 (1958).
48. T. H. Elmer and M. E. Nordberg, preprint, *VII International Congress on Glass, Brussels*, 1965.
49. N. Sheppard, N. V. Mathieu, and D. J. C. Yates, *Z. Electrochem.*, **64**, 734 (1960).
50. N. Sheppard and D. J. C. Yates, *Proc. Roy. Soc. (London)*, **A238**, 69 (1956).
51. E. U. Condon, *Phys. Rev.*, **41**, 759 (1932).
52. M. F. Crawford and I. R. Dagg, *Phys. Rev.*, **91**, 1569 (1953).
53. M. L. Hair, unpublished work, 1965.
54. I. D. Chapman and M. L. Hair, *J. Catalysis*, **2**, 145 (1963).
55. L. H. Little, *J. Phys. Chem.*, **65**, 342 (1961).
56. L. H. Little, *J. Phys. Chem.*, **63**, 1616 (1959).
57. D. J. C. Yates and P. J. Lucchesi, *J. Am. Chem. Soc.*, **86**, 4258 (1964).
58. L. H. Little, H. E. Klauser, and C. H. Amberg, *Can. J. Chem.*, **39**, 42 (1961).
59. Y. Kozirovski and M. Folman, *Trans. Faraday Soc.*, **60**, 1532 (1964).
60. A. N. Sidorov, *Russ. J. Phys. Chem. English Transl.*, **30**, 995 (1956).
61. J. Uytterhoeven and J. J. Fripiat, *Report of the International Geological Congress XXI Session, Norden, 1960*, Copenhagen.

62. J. J. Fripiat, M. C. Gastuche, and G. Van-Compernolle, *V*e *Congrès international Sc. du Sol.*, *Leopoldville, 1954*, Vol. 2, p. 401.
63. T. H. Elmer, U.S. Pat. 2,982,053.
64. T. H. Elmer, I. D. Chapman, and M. E. Nordberg, *J. Phys. Chem.*, **67**, 2219 (1963).
65. F. A. Miller and C. H. Wilkins, *Anal. Chem.*, **24**, 1253 (1952).
66. J. B. Uytterhoeven, L. G. Christner, and W. K. Hall, *J. Phys. Chem.*, **69**, 2117 (1965).
67. M. Folman, *Trans. Faraday Soc.*, **57**, 2000 (1961).
68. T. H. Elmer and M. E. Nordberg, patent applied for.
69. G. A. Galkin, Sp. Zhdanov, A. V. Kiselev, and V. I. Lygin, *Kolloidn. Zh.*, **25**, 1, 123 (1963).
70. V. I. Lygin and A. V. Kiselev, *Colloid J.*, **23**, 250 (1961).
71. A. V. Kiselev, V. I. Lygin, and I. N. Solomonova, *Kolloidn. Zh.*, **26**, 3, 324 (1964).
72. I. Shapiro and H. G. Weiss, *J. Phys. Chem.*, **57**, 219 (1953).
73. H. G. Weiss, J. A. Knight, and I. Shapiro., *J. Am. Chem. Soc.*, **81**, 1823 (1959).
74. M. Baverez and J. Bastick, *Bull. Soc. Chim. France*, **1964**, 3226.
75. M. V. Mathieu and B. Imelik, *J. Chim. Phys.*, **59**, 1189 (1962).
76. J. J. Fripiat and M. Van Tongelen, *J. Catalysis*, **5**, 158 (1966).
77. J. A. Hockey, *Chem. Ind. (London)*, **1965**, 57.
78. J. D. S. Goulden, *Spectrochim. Acta*, **6**, 129 (1954).
79. E. R. Lippincott and R. Schroeder, *J. Chem. Phys.*, **23**, 1099 (1955).
80. N. D. Coggeshall, *J. Chem. Phys.*, **18**, 978 (1950).
81. R. West and R. H. Baney, *J. Am. Chem. Soc.*, **81**, 6145 (1959).
82. P. J. Anderson, R. F. Horlock, and J. F. Oliver, *Trans. Faraday Soc.*, **61**, 2754 (1965).
83. C. L. Angell and P. C. Schaffer, *J. Phys. Chem.*, **69**, 3463 (1965).
84. R. P. Eischens and W. A. Pliskin, *Advan. Catalysis*, **10**, 1 (1958).

5

Acid Oxide Surfaces

5-1. THE ALUMINA SURFACE

A. Surface Hydroxyl Groups

Although it has great commercial importance, the alumina surface has not been nearly as well identified as the silica surface. This difference can be traced to two factors. The first is that the surface of alumina is inherently more complicated than the surface of silica, and the second is that the alumina is a more difficult material to deal with experimentally. As it is normally obtained, it is a hard material that is often difficult to grind into small particle sizes and to press into thin discs suitable for infrared spectroscopy. The difficulties encountered in reducing the particle size results in a large percentage of the incident light being lost due to scattering effects.

The first major spectroscopic investigation of the alumina surface was carried out by Peri and Hannan (1) in 1960. These workers were able to prepare a highly transparent porous plate of γ-Al_2O_3 by using the slow evaporation procedure (2) described in Chapter 3, and they investigated the spectra of several samples in the region from 4000 to 1500 cm^{-1}. For an undried sample, bands near 3300 and 1650 cm^{-1} were observed and, in accordance with prior spectroscopic data on silica gel, these were attributed to the stretching and bending frequencies of molecular water adsorbed on the alumina surface. Evacuation at 400°C caused desorption of the bulk water, and the resultant spectrum showed the presence of several distinct bands in the 3700-cm^{-1} region. After evacuation at 700°C the spectrum was well defined, three peaks being observed at 3698, 3737, and 3795 cm^{-1}. These bands are essentially symmetric

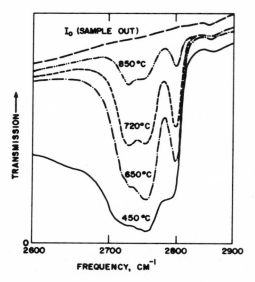

Fig. 5-1. Deuteroxyl groups on an alumina surface. [Redrawn from Reference (1) by courtesy of The Journal of Physical Chemistry.]

and are attributed to the stretching vibrations of isolated surface hydroxyl groups. Deuteration causes these three bands to disappear and be replaced by three equivalent bands at 2733, 2759, and 2803 cm^{-1} (Fig. 5-1). All the bands are shifted by a constant factor (0.738) that is close to the theoretical value for the isotope shift. This provides good evidence that the original absorptions were due to stretching vibrations of surface hydroxyl groups and not to combination bands.

On heating to 850°C, the surface hydroxyl groups are slowly removed. The rate of removal of these OH groups at high temperatures, however, is not identical, and it was observed that the intensity of the band at 2759 cm^{-1} ($\equiv$ 3737 cm^{-1}) was reduced more rapidly than that of the other two bands. This independent behavior of the surface hydroxyl groups was also observed by Peri and Hannan during isotopic exchange of the surface hydroxyl groups with deuterium and in the reaction of butene with a deuterated sample. In the first case, when deuterium gas was added to the alumina surface between 250° and 500°C, the central OH band changed in intensity more slowly than the other two bands and is thus the least susceptible to this exchange reaction. The hydroxyl group responsible for the lowest-frequency hydroxyl vibration was able to exchange its H for D faster than the other two groups, and since this low-frequency band was the only one to undergo an exchange reaction when butene was added to the completed deuterated surface, this can be taken as an indication that this hydroxyl group is the most acidic of the three types that exist on the alumina surface.

Peri and Hannan used the exchange reaction between deuterium gas and surface aluminol groups to determine the number of such groups present on their sample. The average absorptivity of the isolated OH groups was calculated to be about 8×10^4 cm²/mole. Readsorption of water at room temperature onto a sample of alumina that had been baked at 800°C gave rise to a spectrum characteristic only of adsorbed water. No increase in the number of surface hydroxyl groups was noted unless the water and alumina were heated together at 300°C, at which temperature preferential formation of the highest-frequency (3698-cm⁻¹) OH group was observed. During the adsorption process, only one of the surface hydroxyl bands (at 3795 cm⁻¹) was perturbed by the water adsorption.

In a later paper, Peri (3) reports the spectrum of alumina recorded at temperatures up to 800°C. At this temperature all bands were broadened and moved to lower wavelengths, the displacement being about 30 cm⁻¹. However, even at this temperature, the bands were distinct, indicating that the surface hydroxyl groups are not in random motion but are localized on distinct surface sites. With this particular sample of alumina, additional surface hydroxyl groups were identified at 3780 and 3733 cm⁻¹.

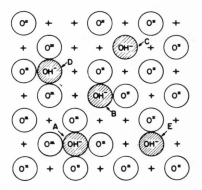

Fig. 5-2. Computer model of a dehydroxylated alumina surface; + denotes Al³⁺ in lower layer. [From Reference (4) by courtesy of the Journal of Physical Chemistry.] The five types of hydroxyl groups are assigned the frequencies in Table 5-1.

The presence of these five types of hydroxyl groups has been explained by Peri (4) on the basis of a computer model of the alumina surface. This model is obtained by considering the dehydration of a fully hydroxylated, 100 crystal face of alumina. A square lattice, initially filled with hydroxyl ions, was assumed (Fig. 5-2), and four arbitrary rules were

TABLE 5-1

Hydroxyl Groups on Alumina[a]

Band	Wave number, cm^{-1}	No. of nearest oxide neighbors
A	3800	4
B	3744	2
C	3700	0
D	3780	3
E	3733	1

[a] Assignment of frequencies by Peri (4) with reference to Fig. 5-2.

established for the dehydration process. The resultant computer model predicted a surface containing five different types of hydroxyl groups. These various types of hydroxyl site are shown in Fig. 5-2. The assigned vibrational frequencies are shown in Table 5-1.

B. Surface Reactions of Alumina

1. With Carbon Tetrachloride

The hydroxyl groups on the alumina surface undergo chemical reaction in much the same way as those on the silica surface. Many additional reactions are observed, however, owing to the presence of the so-called Lewis acid sites that exist on the alumina surface and that can affect the reactions of the hydroxyl groups. That the three (or five) different hydroxyl groups have slightly different chemical reactivity is evidenced by their reaction with carbon tetrachloride.

Peri and Hannan found that carbon tetrachloride was physically adsorbed on alumina, at room temperature, in much the same manner as on silica. Perturbation of the surface hydroxyl groups was observed, but pumping at room temperature caused restoration of the original spectrum. On evacuation at progressively higher temperatures, however, the hydroxyl peaks were gradually eliminated, the bands at the higher frequencies being preferentially removed. After evacuation at 750° the hydroxyl bands were completely removed from the spectrum. The final product is black, presumably because of carbon formation. The initial chemical reaction probably proceeds according to the equation

$$Al_s{-}OH + CCl_4 = Al_s{-}O{-}\overset{\displaystyle Cl}{\underset{\displaystyle Cl}{C}}{-}Cl + HCl$$

$$(1)$$

the black residue arising as a result of the instability of the intermediate (**1**).

2. Chlorination of Alumina Surface

The hydroxyl groups on the surface of alumina can be replaced by chlorine in the same manner as those on silica. Thus, Peri has shown that hydrogen chloride gas will react with surface aluminol groups according to the equation

$$Al_s{-}OH + HCl \rightarrow Al_s{-}Cl + H_2O$$

The resultant $Al_s{-}Cl$ groups will further react with NH_3 to give a surface amide group that is very strongly held:

$$Al_s{-}Cl + 2NH_3 \rightarrow Al_s{-}N\overset{\displaystyle H}{\underset{\displaystyle H}{\diagup}} + NH_4Cl$$

Intensity data indicated that at 800°C the number of $-NH_2$ groups on the surface was the same as the number of hydroxyl groups held by the surface under identical conditions. The spectrum of the $-NH_2$ formed in this manner is almost identical with that formed by direct reaction of ammonia with nonchlorided surface in that two N—H stretching bands are observed at 3386 and 3335 cm^{-1}. These are due to the asymmetric and symmetric stretching vibrations. The interaction of ammonia with a dried, untreated alumina surface will be discussed later.

3. Lewis Acidity

From catalytic studies it has long been known that alumina has a much more reactive surface than silica. Since both surfaces contain hydroxyl groups, the greater activity has been attributed to the presence of a second type of acid site of the electron-abstracting or Lewis acid kind. At the surface of the alumina the normal crystallographic restraints do not apply, and these sites can generally be considered as being due to exposed aluminum ions held in a tetrahedral configuration but attached to only three oxygen atoms.

$$
\begin{array}{ccc}
& \text{Al} & \\
& | & \\
\text{O} \quad \text{O} \quad \text{O} & \quad \text{cf.} \quad & \text{Cl} \quad \text{Cl} \quad \text{Cl} \\
& | & \\
\end{array}
$$

If this species exists, it is exactly analogous to the aluminum halides and would be expected to undergo reaction with Lewis bases to give surface complexes. Thus pyridine, ammonia, and other lone-pair molecules should react with an alumina surface to give a chemisorbed species; i.e.,

$$
\begin{array}{ccc}
\text{O} & \text{O} & \text{H} \\
\backslash & \backslash & | \\
-\text{O}-\text{Al} + \text{NH}_3 \rightleftharpoons -\text{O}-\text{Al} \leftarrow \text{N}-\text{H} \\
/ & / & | \\
\text{O} & \text{O} & \text{H} \\
\end{array}
$$

Ammonia does not react with the alumina surface solely via this chemisorption process. The adsorption is complicated by interactions of the ammonia with surface hydroxyl groups and surface oxide ions and does not provide immediate evidence of these Lewis acid sites. The spectrum of adsorbed pyridine, however, can be interpreted as showing the presence of these sites, and details of this system have been given by Parry (5).

4. Pyridine on Alumina

Pyridine (Py), C_5H_5N, is a nitrogenous aromatic base that can react with either Lewis acids or acidic protons to give either a coordination complex or a pyridinium ion. In both cases the interaction is via the lone pair of electrons associated with the nitrogen atom. The spectra of both types of complex are well known from studies in the inorganic field, but, unfortunately, many of the vibrations that might be expected to be specific to each type of species (e.g., $\geqslant \text{N}-\text{H}^+$) are poorly defined. However, Parry found that considerable information could be obtained about the form of the adsorbed pyridine from a study of the changes in the positions of the bands due to the vibrations of the aromatic ring (5). These occur between 1700 and 1400 cm^{-1}.

The spectra of pyridine, Py—BH_3, and Py—H^+Cl^- in chloroform solution in this region are shown in Fig. 5-3. All the absorptions in this region are due to C—C ring vibrations, so the spectra are similar, but some major differences can be observed. These allowed Parry to identify and distinguish between coordinated pyridine, protonated pyridine, and physically adsorbed pyridine on alumina-silica surfaces. Examination of Fig. 5-3(c) shows that pyridinium chloride, $Py—H^+Cl^-$, exhibits a very strong absorption band at 1540 cm^{-1} that cannot be found for either the

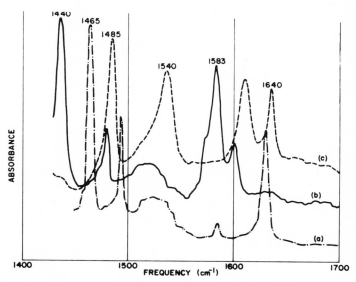

Fig. 5-3. *Infrared spectra of (a) pyridine, (b) pyridine—BH₃, and (c) pyridinium chloride in chloroform solution. [From Reference (5), by courtesy of the Journal of Catalysis (Academic Press).]*

free molecular pyridine or the coordinated pyridine. The position of this band is essentially independent of the anion and thus may be used as a means of identifying the protonated species. Similarly [Fig. 3(b)], the Py—BH₃ complex gives rise to an absorption at 1465 cm^{-1} that is specific to the coordinately bonded pyridine. It can be clearly distinguished from either the 1485-cm^{-1} band that appears in the spectrum of the pyridinium ion or the 1440-cm^{-1} band that appears in the spectrum of the free pyridine. The position of the 1465-cm^{-1} band is slightly dependent upon the nature of the Lewis acid to which it is attached, the band being observed at somewhat lower frequencies as the strength of the Lewis acid is decreased.

The adsorption of pyridine on an alumina surface gave rise to the spectrum shown in Fig. 5-4. At room temperature, bands due to physically adsorbed pyridine are observed, together with additional absorptions at 1496 and 1621 cm^{-1}. On evacuation at successively higher temperatures, the spectrum changes considerably, and, after complete re-

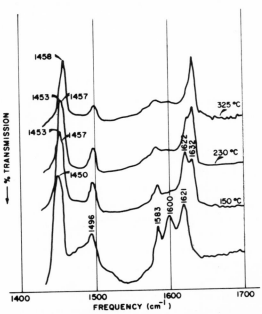

Fig. 5-4. *Infrared spectrum of pyridine adsorbed on alumina. Only Lewis acid sites can be distinguished.* [*Redrawn from Reference (5), courtesy of the Journal of Catalysis (Academic Press).*]

moval of the physically adsorbed pyridine at 150°C, the spectrum that is revealed shows considerable resemblance to that of the Py—BH$_3$ adduct in Fig. 5-3(b). A band at 1453 cm^{-1} is readily observed and is attributed to pyridine coordinated to a surface Lewis acid site. The band at 1453 cm^{-1} has a shoulder at 1457 cm^{-1} that is attributed to a second distribution of Lewis acid sites that are stronger than those giving rise to the major band at 1453 cm^{-1}.

As the temperature of evacuation is raised to 565°C, the 1453-cm^{-1} band is slowly removed and the second band is shifted to 1459 cm^{-1} Both the shift to higher frequencies and the higher temperature that is necessary to produce the stable compound are indicative of the presence of stronger Lewis acid sites on the surface. This result finds support in the work of Hair and Chapman (6) on hexachloroacetone adsorption. No evidence whatsoever is observed for the presence of strong protonic sites on the surface of alumina.

Previously, it had been proposed that a water molecule could interact with a surface Lewis acid site and give rise to a strong protonic site (7).

$$\underset{\diagup | \diagdown}{Al} + H_2O \rightleftharpoons \underset{\diagup | \diagdown}{\overset{\overset{\displaystyle H}{\underset{\displaystyle |}{O \cdots H^+}}}{Al}}$$

Parry found that preadsorption of water on the alumina surface did not give rise to a spectrum characteristic of the pyridinium ion, and it must be concluded that this reaction does not occur.

5. Hexachloroacetone on Alumina

The use of nitrogenous bases in the study of surface acidity suffers from the serious disadvantage that the spectra that are obtained show only small perturbations that can be attributed to differences in the strength of the acid sites or that give information regarding the number of sites of differing acidity. Recently Hair and Chapman (6) have shown that certain halogenated ketones may be used to determine both the number and strength of the Lewis acid sites that exist on alumina-containing surfaces.

It is well established in the literature that ketones will form stable complexes with inorganic Lewis acid halides such as $AlCl_3$ and BCl_3. Complex formation takes place via the oxygen atom of the carbonyl group, and the donation of electrons from the oxygen atom into the vacant orbital of the Lewis acid leads to a delocalization of the electrons in the double bond and a consequent shift of the carbonyl stretching frequency to lower wave numbers. Lappert (8) has argued that the amount of this shift should be a measure of the acidity of the coordinating halide and has published supporting spectral data on a number of complexes of ethyl acetate. This work was extended by Cook (9), who examined the spectra of a series of metal-halide complexes that employed xanthone as the basic ligand. For the boron halides, the shift in the $>C{=}O$ stretching frequency corresponded to data on the heats of formation of similar complexes (6), and the order of Lewis acidity was shown to be $BI_3 > BBr_3 > BCl_3 > BF_3$, the reverse of that predicted from electronegatively concepts. The shift in frequency of the $>C{=}O$

vibration was shown by Hair and Chapman to be almost a linear function of the electronegativity of the substituent halide (Fig. 5-5).

In order to be useful as a means of measuring the Lewis acidity of a surface site, the selected ligand must fulfill the following criteria:

1. The ligand should not be easily protonated. This becomes even more important in dealing with surfaces on which strong protons may exist. Strong protons would react with the donor molecule in the same manner as the Lewis acid sites.

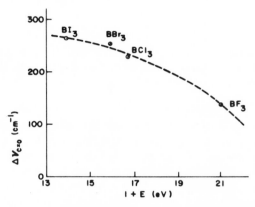

Fig. 5-5. *The shift in* >C==O *stretching frequency of a series of xanthone–boron halide complexes plotted as a function of the electronegativity of the halogen atoms.* [*Reproduced from Reference (6), courtesy of the Journal of Physical Chemistry.*]

2. The complex formed should be stable and nonhygroscopic. This assumes importance if the technique is to be adapted to a routine estimation of surface acidity.

3. Steric hindrance should be minimized. Again, this assumes greater importance in dealing with catalytically active solids in which the pores may be small, rendering the sites inaccessible to large molecules.

4. The carbonyl group should possess a large polarizability—the larger the polarizability, the greater will be the shift for any given Lewis acid.

5. There should be an absence of mechanical effects on the carbonyl group.

6. The ligand should not be easily oxidized. This point is especially important, because several potential ligands such as acetone, cyclohexanone, benzylnitrile, and benzaldehyde have been found to be wholly or partially oxidized by the alumina surface (*10*).

A suitable ligand that appears to fulfill all these criteria is hexachloroacetone, and spectra obtained for the γ-alumina-hexachloroacetone
system at 22°, 150°, and 250°C are shown in Fig. 5-6. At room temperature, on the particular sample studied, three types of sites that gave
rise to peaks at 1692, 1680, and 1585 cm^{-1} were observed. On heating
to 150° [Fig. 5-6(b)], the peaks due to the weaker acid sites at 1692 and

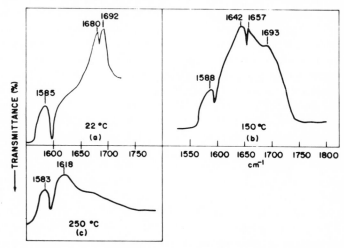

*Fig. 5-6. The adsorption of hexachloroacetone on an alumina surface followed by
heating at (a) 22°C, (b) 150°C, (c) 250°C. [Redrawn from Reference (6), courtesy of the
Journal of Physical Chemistry.]*

1680 cm^{-1} are lost and are replaced by a more symmetrical distribution
that centers at about 1657 cm^{-1}. However, it is seen that this in turn is
split into three distributions, the peaks of which occur at 1642 and 1657
cm^{-1} and as a shoulder at 1693 cm^{-1}. The peak at 1588 cm^{-1} due to the
strong acid sites has been relatively unaffected by the heat treatment.
At 250° [Fig. 5-6(c) the weaker Lewis acid complexes are again decomposed, and two peaks are apparent at 1618 and 1583 cm^{-1}. The peak at
1583 cm^{-1} changes little, if at all, in intensity during this series of heat
treatments, whereas the other Lewis acid-carbonyl complexes are largely
decomposed.

These results can be compared with those of Parry for the pyridine-
alumina system, and it is seen that the two sets of results are in agreement
that:

1. More than one type of Lewis acid site exists on the alumina surface.

2. As the temperature of interaction is raised, the weaker sites are decomposed and stronger sites are created.

The number of different types of sites present on the alumina surface appears to be completely dependent upon the method of sample preparation. Thus, whereas Hair and Chapman report three types on the sample they studied, recent results show that a sample of Cabot Al_2O_3 (Alon C) had three types of site distribution that were so close together that they were difficult to distinguish except by controlled desorption studies (11). The mull technique employed in this work does not readily lend itself to quantitative investigations, and there is a possibility of water contamination if the sample is not doused quickly into fluorolube. Moreover, it is now apparent that some samples of alumina do not react with hexachloroacetone at room temperature but need to be heated to about 150°C. Since the hexachloroacetone is difficult to manipulate in a vacuum, Hair and Chapman selected a partially fluorinated ketone, trichlorotrifluoroacetone (3FK†), for quantitative measurements (11).

The results obtained in these experiments showed that the 3FK is chemisorbed by a sample of Alon C at room temperature. The strongest Lewis acid sites are the first to be occupied, and the chemisorption follows Elovich kinetics (15). About 10^{13} sites/cm² of surface were found for an alumina surface that had been preheated to 600°C. This value is close to that observed by Misono et al. (12) for pyridine adsorption and by Peri (13) for HCl adsorption on α sites. It is considerably greater than the number of active acid sites (3×10^{16} sites/m²) estimated by Amenomiya et al. (14) from the kinetics of ethylene polymerization on alumina. Probably only the strongest acid sites can be considered to be catalytically active, and it is thought that the 3FK adsorption measures the total number of sites present. At elevated temperatures a small interaction between the 3FK and the surface hydroxyl groups was noted, and about 10% of the adsorbed ketone could not be desorbed.

A further point of interest that arises from these results is the observation that the 3FK was physically adsorbed in two forms: a weakly held species that could be removed by pumping for 5 min at room temperature and a more strongly held species that could be removed only by prolonged evacuation at room temperature (Fig. 5-7). The strongly physically adsorbed species was perturbed by about 10 cm⁻¹ from the gas-phase value. As the physically adsorbed 3FK was removed, it was

† Allied Chemical.

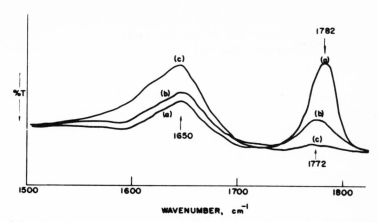

Fig. 5-7. *The adsorption of* 3FK *on an alumina surface at* (a) *room temperature. Pumping for* (b) *30 sec and* (c) *for 1 hr.*

observed that there was an increase in the amount of the chemisorbed material. Apparently some of the physically adsorbed ketone had sterically hindered access to some of the Lewis acid sites. The desorption process presumably allowed reorientation of the material, and only after this treatment were the chemisorption sites completely filled. As might be expected, the extinction coefficient of the chemisorbed $>C{=}O$ group varied with coverage, higher integrated intensities being observed at lower coverages (i.e., on the strongest Lewis acid sites).

6. Ammonia on γ-Al$_2$O$_3$

From our knowledge of the alumina surface it would be expected that the spectrum of ammonia adsorbed on alumina would give rise to four bands: two bands due to the N—H stretching vibrations of physically adsorbed ammonia and two bands due to a species chemically adsorbed at the Lewis acid sites. This picture seems to be essentially correct, and at 50°C Peri (*16*) reports that the spectrum of NH$_3$ adsorbed on a sample of Al$_2$O$_3$, predried at 800°C, shows major bands at 3400, 3355, and 1620 cm^{-1}. These are attributable to the two stretching vibrations and to the bending vibration of an ammonia molecule coordinately bonded to the surface. Other bands, however, were observed in the 3100–3200-cm^{-1} regions and near 1560 and 1510 cm^{-1}.

During the adsorption of ammonia on the alumina surface, all three hydroxyl bands were perturbed, but a 1:1 relationship between the amount of ammonia adsorbed and the disappearance of OH stretching frequency did not exist. At about 14% surface coverage, only 25% of the ammonia had interacted with the surface hydroxyl, whereas 10% had reacted to form a new hydroxyl species at 3725 cm^{-1}.

$$NH_3 + O_s^{2-} \rightarrow NH_{2s}^- + OH_s^-$$

Complete disappearance of the hydroxyl stretching frequencies was not observed until a surface coverage of about 30% had been achieved. Above this coverage the adsorbed ammonia was weakly held and could be removed by evacuation for half an hour at room temperature. The positions of the N—H stretching frequencies for the initially adsorbed ammonia suggest that the ammonia is physically adsorbed (compare with data on porous glass), but the strength of the bond confirms the presence of a chemisorbed species.

During the adsorption of the ammonia at 50°C, the intensities of the three surface hydroxyl groups were all affected equally. On desorbing the NH$_3$ at elevated temperatures, however, it was observed that at 200°C the type C hydroxyl band (Fig. 5-2) reappeared at a much-increased intensity, whereas the N—H bands all decreased in intensity and moved to lower frequencies. Desorption at 400°C caused the type A hydroxyl band (Fig. 5-2) to increase markedly in intensity, the two major N—H vibrations again moving to lower frequencies. During this process, a band at 1510 cm^{-1} due to a N—H deformation vibration remained and suffered only about a 50% reduction in intensity. After desorption at 600°C, the NH$_3$ was essentially completely removed from the surface and the spectrum resembled the original, except that all three hydroxyl groups were more intense. After reheating at 800°C the spectra became identical with the originals.

The temperature at which the alumina had been predried was found to affect the relative intensities of the spectral bands markedly, particularly those in the N—H bending region. Thus, alumina that had been predried at only 400°C showed no band at 1510 cm^{-1} and all ammonia could be removed by evacuation at 400°C. This correlation between degree of dehydration and ammonia adsorption suggests that the ammonia is most strongly adsorbed on those parts of the surface that have proved most difficult to dehydroxylate. From these results it is clear that ammonia adsorption is not a good technique to use in the study of surface acidity. Above 50°C the ammonia is virtually always undergoing reaction with the surface, presumably with a surface oxide ion. However, since ammonia adsorption data often correlate with catalytic activity, Peri's results on the poisoning of alumina with ammonia are of some interest. These results showed that the addition of enough ammonia to give about 5% monolayer coverage at 400° was sufficient to deactivate 90% of the sites that were active in the isomerization of butene. These results led Peri to speculate on the participation of what he calls "ion-pair" sites in this catalytic process. These will be considered in detail later together with further experimental evidence.

7. The Oxidative Properties of Alumina-Containing Surfaces

In discussing the use of hexachloroacetone in the determination of Lewis acidity, it was pointed out that the donor molecule must not oxidize easily on the surface. In their search for a suitable ligand, Chapman and Hair (10) reported that many carbonyl-containing compounds were easily oxidized by alumina-containing surfaces to give stable surface compounds. The oxidation proceeded very rapidly if the ketone was able to undergo the keto–enol transformation; and thus benzaldehyde, which seemed to be a suitable molecule for the determination of surface Lewis acidity, was found to be readily oxidized by alumina and silica–alumina surfaces at 200° and 120°C, respectively.

Prior to this work, it had been shown by Greenler (17) that methyl and ethyl alcohols reacted with an alumina surface to give surface species whose spectra were indicative of formate and acetate radicals, respectively. At low temperatures, the hydroxyl groups on the surface of alumina will react with alcohols to form a surface alkoxide in a manner analogous to the reaction that occurs on a silica surface (18). Thus, Greenler found that the reaction between methyl alcohol and alumina at 35°C gave rise to a surface species whose infrared spectrum was almost identical with that of aluminum methoxide.

$$Al_s\!-\!OH + CH_3OH \rightarrow Al_s\!-\!OCH_3 + H_2O$$

or

$$
\begin{array}{c}
 H \\
 | \\
 H\!-\!C\!-\!H \\
 | \\
H\!-\!C\!-\!H O +H \\
| | \\
 O + Al_s\!-\!O\!-\!Al_s\!-\!O \rightarrow Al_s\!-\!O\!-\!Al_s\!-\!O\!- \\
| \\
 H
\end{array}
$$

Unfortunately, no spectral data were obtained in the OH stretching region, and thus the mechanism cannot be distinguished at this stage.

Approximate calculations carried out by Greenler indicate that approximately one methoxy group was formed for every surface aluminum ion. Since data on the dehydration of alumina (3) indicate that, at this stage, the alumina surface has approximately 40% monolayer coverage of hydroxyl groups, a 1:1 correspondence between surface hydroxyl groups and methoxy groups is suggested.

On heating of the methylated sample to successively higher temperatures, the spectrum changes and three new absorption bands appear in the $1700-1300\text{-cm}^{-1}$ region. These are at 1597, 1394, and 1377 cm^{-1}, and comparison with the published spectra of various metal formates indicates that the surface methoxy group has decomposed and produced a surface formate.

$$\left[H-C\begin{array}{c} \diagup\!\!\diagup\ O \\ \diagdown\!\!\diagdown\ O \end{array} \right]^{-}$$

The formate ion may be treated as a simple XZY_2 molecule that gives rise to a symmetric and an asymmetric C—O stretching vibration. For aluminum formate these are found at 1370 and 1600 cm^{-1}, respectively. Consequently, the bands found at 1377 and 1597 cm^{-1} in the spectrum of the surface species are attributed to those modes. The third absorption in this region is found at 1390 cm^{-1} in aluminum formate and at 1394 cm^{-1} for the surface species and is attributed to a C—H bending vibration. The interpretation of the nature of the surface species is thus satisfactory, even if unexpected. Further confirmation of the nature of this species was obtained by isotopic substitution of C^{13} for C^{12} in the reactant alcohol. The resultant spectrum showed isotopic shifts that were in good agreement with calculated values, and Greenler speculated that the carboxylate structures might be produced by the following reaction:

$$\begin{array}{ccc} H & & H \\ | & & \diagdown \\ H-C-O-H + Al_s-O-Al_s-O \rightarrow & & C{=}O \qquad + 3H \\ | & & | \\ H & & Al_s-O-Al_s-O \end{array}$$

Approximately one formate ion was formed for every 20 surface oxygen atoms, and one acetate ion for every 11 surface oxygen atoms.

Chapman and Hair (10) have shown that aldehydes will react with alumina-containing surfaces to form the corresponding carboxylate ion. Thus, benzaldehyde gives a surface benzoate, and formaldehyde and acetaldehyde give surface formates and acetates, respectively. Mass spectroscopic data showed that hydrogen was not eliminated during the reaction with the aldehydes. When alcohol was used, however, hydrogen was eliminated (*19*). Moreover, since the free acids themselves will react to give spectroscopically identical surface species, the following reaction scheme is suggested:

$$\text{1.} \qquad CH_3OH \rightarrow \begin{array}{c} H \\ \diagdown \\ C=O + 2H\uparrow \\ \diagup \\ H \end{array}$$

$$\text{2.} \qquad \begin{array}{c} H \\ \diagdown \\ C=O \\ \diagup \\ H \end{array} + [O]_s \rightarrow H - C \begin{array}{c} O \\ \diagup\diagup \\ \diagdown \\ OH \end{array}$$

$$\text{3.} \qquad H-C \begin{array}{c} O \\ \diagup\diagup \\ \diagdown \\ OH \end{array} + \begin{array}{c} H \\ | \\ O \\ | \\ -Al-O-Al-O \\ | \qquad | \end{array} \rightarrow \begin{array}{c} H \\ | \\ C \\ \diagup\diagdown \\ O \qquad O \\ \downarrow \qquad | \\ -Al-O-Al-O \\ | \qquad | \end{array} + H_2O\uparrow$$

This scheme is highly tentative, because no evidence that indicates reaction of the surface hydroxyl group has yet been produced.

The nature of the active oxygen postulated in step 2 is not defined and is highly speculative. However, there is an increasing amount of evidence that alumina surfaces may contain a labile reactive oxygen species that is not removed by hydrogen reduction at 500°C (*20*).

The reaction of formic acid with alumina to give a surface formate has also been noted by Hiroto and co-workers (*21*) and Scholten et al. (*22*). Magnesium oxide reacts with formic acid in the same manner, and unpublished work by Hair indicates that all surfaces containing Lewis acid sites appear to give rise to this oxidation effect and the ability to form surface carboxylate species. It should be remembered that the silica surface does not react with these acids, nor does it exhibit the oxidation effect. The oxidizing properties seem, therefore, to be intimately connected with the presence of the surface Lewis acid sites.

Above about 280°C the surface formate decomposes nearly exclusively to give carbon monoxide and water, the latter being largely retained by the surface at that temperature. Aluminum formate also decomposes into CO and H_2O and, since the rate of surface formate decomposition is of the same order of magnitude as the rate of the catalytic decomposition of formic acid, the formate ion is presumed to be the rate-determining catalytic intermediate in that reaction.

8. Carbon Monoxide on Alumina

The spectra produced by carbon monoxide adsorbed on an alumina surface have been recorded by Little and Amberg (23) in a study that was primarily concerned with the chromia–alumina surface. At room temperature the adsorbed carbon monoxide gives a dominant band at 2200 cm^{-1} and weak bands at 1750 and 1570 cm^{-1}. On heating of the CO with the alumina, the band at 2200 cm^{-1} suffered a large reduction in intensity, and new bands appeared at 1620, 1590, 1380, and 1230 cm^{-1}.

The band at 2200 cm^{-1} was attributed to a weakly adsorbed carbon monoxide species on the surface and will be discussed later in connection with similar observations on metal surfaces. It is possible that it is due to a coordination complex formation via a weak, unstabilized σ bond (see Section 6-6). The bands at $1620–1230 \text{ cm}^{-1}$ are ascribed to "carbonate-type" species. Bands in similar positions are observed when carbon dioxide is adsorbed on alumina, and it is clear that the monoxide is oxidized to the dioxide during the formation of the surface carbonate. The exact nature of these species is not known, but they are probably of the "carboxylate" or "carbonate" type that are discussed more fully in a later section.

9. Carbon Dioxide on Alumina

Parkyns (24) has shown that carbon dioxide is strongly chemisorbed on alumina at room temperature and gives strong bands at 1770, 1640, 1480, and 1232 cm^{-1}. Little and Amberg (23) report bands at 1750, 1635, 1500, and 1235 cm^{-1} due to surface carbonate formation. The physically adsorbed species is observed at 2350 cm^{-1} as on silica. Peri (13) has noted additional bands at $1800–1870 \text{ cm}^{-1}$ that are due to a weakly held species and are probably connected with the physically adsorbed CO_2. In addition, Peri notes that one form of adsorbed carbon dioxide causes perturbation of the surface hydroxyls and is evidenced by the appearance of a new band at 3610 cm^{-1}. A small number of the adsorbed CO_2 molecules, which give rise to the absorption in the 2350 cm^{-1} region, are tightly held to a select type of site that Peri has termed an α site. This form of adsorbed carbon dioxide cannot be removed completely from the surface, even by a 30-min evacuation at $100°C$. There are approximately 5.2×10^{12} of these α sites per square centimeter of surface on an Al_2O_3 sample that has been predried at $800°C$. They are thought to have considerable importance catalytically. The number of these sites depends on the temperature of pretreatment, the more dehydroxylated surfaces containing more α sites. These sites are not Lewis acid sites of the type previously discussed but must instead be considered as a "strained" oxide link of the type

$$Al_s \diagdown O \diagup Al_s \quad \text{or} \quad Al^+O^{2-}Al^+$$

10. Adsorption of Butene

Peri (13) has found that 1-butene is selectively adsorbed on α sites and has used the intensity of the band at 2370 cm^{-1}, which is due to CO_2 adsorbed on these sites, to monitor or "titrate" the adsorption of butene. Initially ($\theta \ll 0.04$), the butene remains olefinic in character (25) and the adsorbed species is characterized by a band at 3020 cm^{-1}. At this stage all the α sites are filled and the spectrum of the adsorbed species resembles that of 2-butene. On standing, and at higher coverages, polymerization occurs and is evidenced by the growth of the infrared bands due to saturated C—H groups and the disappearance of the olefinic band at 3020 cm^{-1}. During this polymerization, some of the α sites become reavailable, as must be expected. The rate and degree of reaction are strongly dependent upon the temperature of predrying, a greater activity being observed in samples that have been dehydroxylated at higher temperatures. The degree of catalytic activity thus correlates, at least qualitatively, with the number of α sites present.

Hydrogen chloride also reacts with the α sites on an alumina surface. In this case, the reaction involves the formation of Al–Cl and additional Al–OH groupings. At higher coverages of hydrogen chloride, interaction with the surface hydroxyl groups takes place, and molecular water is observed in the recorded spectrum.

The introduction of the comparatively large quantities of chlorine into the surface of the alumina causes little change in the number of α sites if the samples have been preheated to 800°C, but the number is diminished if the alumina is not adequately dehydroxylated and is not reheated to 800°C. In that case the CO_2 band is also observed at a slightly higher frequency. Complete removal of the surface hydroxyl groups does not decrease the rate of butene isomerization. Indeed, Peri (48) found that the effect of the chlorination was to increase the rate of isomerization. Peri points out the complexities that can be involved in interpreting the observations made on the chlorided alumina owing to possible formation of aluminum chloride or oxychloride, and he comments that "further study is, of course, needed."

11. Acetylene on Alumina

The species formed when acetylene, ethylene, and other unsaturated molecules are adsorbed is of considerable interest, and various configurations for the adsorbed species have been proposed. They include both associative and dissociative reactions and "end-on" and "parallel" species. Yates, Lucchesi, and Carter have published a series of papers concerning the infrared spectra of acetylene, ethylene, and some acetylenic derivatives adsorbed on alumina and silica surfaces (26–28). The interpretation of the spectra obtained by these workers is complicated, controversial, and subject to detailed arguments, and the reader is referred to the original articles for the detailed interpretations.

The gas-phase spectrum of acetylene is well known, and the vibrational modes have been illustrated in Chapter 2. The two most prominent bands in the spectrum occur at 3287 and 1328 cm^{-1} and are due to a C—H stretching vibration (v_3) and a combination band ($v_4 + v_5$), respectively. The —C≡C— stretching vibration is observed at 1974 cm^{-1} in the Raman spectrum but is forbidden in the infrared.

Adsorption of acetylene on alumina gives a spectrum in which two species can be identified. One species is completely removed from the surface by a 5-sec evacuation at room temperature, is observed only at pressures above 0.5 cm, and is characterized by bands at 3220 and 1950 cm^{-1}. The first band is attributed to the (v_3) C—H stretching vibration, and the second, by analogy with the gaseous spectrum, is identified as an induced v_2 (C≡C stretch) mode. The assignment of the 3220-cm^{-1} band to the v_3 vibration is not unreasonable in view of the easy desorption of this species from the surface, though the shift of 67 cm^{-1} from the gas-phase frequency (3287 cm^{-1}) is much greater than the perturbations normally observed for a physically adsorbed species. On silica the perturbation is 35 cm^{-1}, and the greater difference is attributed to the increased heterogeneity of the alumina surface. Moreover, since it is suspected that the acetylene molecule is physically adsorbed parallel with the surface, a greater perturbation of the C—H groups might be expected than for a species physically adsorbed in an end-on position.

The strongly adsorbed acetylene is stable up to 300°C and shows a ≡C—H stretching vibration at 3300 cm^{-1} and a —C≡C— stretch at 2007 cm^{-1}. The $v_4 + v_5$ combination band is missing from the spectrum. The value of the v_3 vibration (3300 cm^{-1}) is intermediate between the value for gaseous acetylene (3287 cm^{-1}) and monosubstituted acetylenes (methylacetylene, $v_3 = 3334$ cm^{-1} gas, 3305 cm^{-1} liquid), and this, in conjunction with the assymetry implied by the presence of the —C≡C— vibration and the lack of the $\nu_4 + \nu_5$ combination band, is attributed to the acetylene being adsorbed in an end-on position:

```
    H                    H
    |                    |
    C                    C
    |||        or        |||
    C                    C
    |                    |
    H                    X_s
    ⋮
    X_s
```

Some confirmation of this end-on assignment is derived from a spectral investigation of the adsorption of methyl acetylene and dimethyl acetylene on alumina. It has been found that methyl acetylene is strongly adsorbed on the alumina surface, giving a species in which the C—H stretching frequencies of the methyl group are very close to those found for liquid methyl acetylene. It was thus concluded that the adsorption must again be end-on and via the unsubstituted acidic hydrogen.

In the case of dimethyl acetylene, the molecule contains no acidic hydrogen, and it seemed reasonable to suppose that this molecule would be adsorbed parallel with the surface, interacting via its triple bond in the same manner as the weakly held acetylene. The spectrum of the adsorbed species is very similar to that of gaseous dimethylacetylene, and thus this explanation seems in order. However, it was noticed that the dimethyl acetylene was strongly adsorbed on the alumina surface and was not desorbed until a temperature of about 400° was reached. This observation implies that the acetylene and the dimethylacetylene are adsorbed on different sites, a conclusion that was confirmed when Yates and Lucchesi (26) showed that acetylene and dimethyl acetylene could each be adsorbed on the alumina surface independently of the presence of the other.

A deuterated surface of the alumina used by Yates and Lucchesi exhibited OD bands at 2790, 2755, and 2735 cm^{-1}, which are similar to the frequencies reported by Peri (3). During the adsorption process, the acetylene interacted strongly with the high-frequency band (2790 cm^{-1}) and produced a broad absorption between 2680 and 2500 cm^{-1}. At higher pressures, a band at 2650 cm^{-1} became obvious. Evacuation for 5 sec removed a considerable quantity of the 2650 cm^{-1} band and caused the band at 2755 cm^{-1} to increase in intensity. The 2790-cm^{-1} band, with which the acetylene originally interacted, did not reappear even on evacuation at 600°. It was assumed that this apparent anomaly was due to an isotopic effect in which the high-frequency —OD group interacted with the acetylene: On desorption of the acetylene an —OH group was produced (3780 cm^{-1}) together with a partially deuterated acetylene. Unfortunately, however, no confirmation of this is available. That hydrogen-deuterium exchange does take place between the surface aluminol groups and adsorbed acetylene was shown by the addition of C_2D_2 to a hydroxylated surface. In this case the OH band at the highest frequency grew much weaker and was replaced by a single OD band at 2785 cm^{-1}. This exchange may be represented by the following equation:

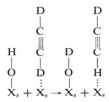

The surface O—D groups could be removed by evacuation at 900°C, but this treatment had little effect on either the nature or the amount of acetylene adsorption. It can be concluded, therefore, that the sites responsible for acetylene adsorption are not hydroxyl groups, although the observed perturbations indicate that they must be closely associated with them.

12. Ethylene on Al_2O_3

Lucchesi et al. (28) report that the species formed when ethylene is adsorbed on alumina is dependent upon the source of the alumina. Whereas they found that with one alumina (A) the ethylene adsorption was very slow and a time interval of 24 hr was necessary before good spectra could be obtained, with a second sample (B) good spectra were produced in 15 min. For sample A all the frequencies observed for the adsorbed ethylene were very similar to those found for saturated hydrocarbons. Good correlation was found for both the stretching and bending modes of the CH_3 and CH_2 groups, and, since the absorbance ratio $CH_3/CH_2 = A_{2970}/A_{2932}$ for the adsorbed species was very similar to that obtained for some liquid molecules containing C_2H_5 groups, it was proposed that self-hydrogenation of the ethylene molecules had taken place during the adsorption process with the consequent formation of a surface ethyl group, X_s—CH_2—CH_3, or propyl group X_s—$(CH_2)_2$—CH_3.

Although perturbation of the hydroxyl stretching frequencies again indicated some hydrogen-bonding interaction between the adsorbed ethylene and the surface hydroxyl groups, it was shown that the hydroxyl groups did not enter into the self-hydrogenation reaction: The addition of ethylene to a fully deuterated alumina surface gave no bands that could be attributed to C—D vibrations, and thus the surface species could not have been formed by interaction with the surface deuteroxyls.

In the case of the second sample of alumina, Lucchesi et al. (28) found that the adsorbed ethylene gave a spectrum that showed no evidence of CH_3, —C≡C—, or >C=C< vibrations. Three bands were observed at 2928, 2855, and 1468 cm⁻¹—frequencies which are very close to those reported for >CH₂ groupings in saturated hydrocarbons. On hydrogenation of this species at 450°C, most of the adsorbate was removed, but some was converted into a second surface species whose spectrum was identical with that observed when ethylene was adsorbed on the first sample of alumina. The species formed initially was attributed to an associatively adsorbed ethylene of the type (1), and the following reaction sequence was suggested:

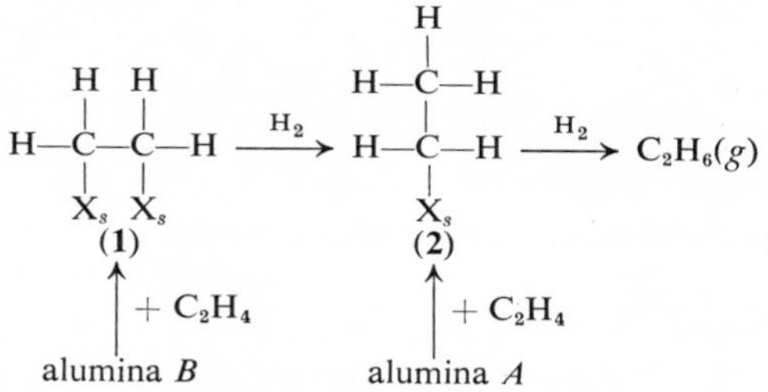

Despite the similarity of the two molecules, it is clear that ethylene and acetylene adsorb on the alumina surface in completely different ways. It is not clear, however, whether the separate reactions occur on the same or different sites. This point was cleared up in a later paper by Yates and Lucchesi (27), who, in a series of competitive coverage experiments, showed that the two adsorptions were essentially independent of each other. Thus, preadsorption of acetylene had but little effect on the self-hydrogenation of ethylene, and vice versa. Moreover, preadsorption of deuterioacetylene on the alumina, followed by addition of ethylene, did not cause any deuteration of the adsorbed ethylene species. Interaction between the two species must, therefore, be negligible.

It should be pointed out that Peri (107) is in disagreement with Yates in the interpretation of the spectra of ethylene adsorbed on alumina samples. He prefers to interpret the observed bands as being due to low-molecular-weight polymers and cites the flash-desorption results of Amenomiya (*14*) in support of his claims.

C. Some Metal–Aluminas

1. *Ethylene on* Pt–Al$_2$O$_3$

The chemistry of the surfaces of metal catalysts supported on acidic oxides has achieved some importance because of the use of these materials in the hydrocracking process. The catalysts have a dual function, and the metal and acidic oxide probably act independently of each other.

The hydrogenation of ethylene on an alumina surface and on a platinum-impregnated alumina has recently been investigated in conjunction with infrared spectroscopy (*29*). The infrared spectra of ethylene adsorbed on these samples are identical, but the hydrogenation behaviors are totally different. The presence of the platinum greatly facilitates the removal of the chemisorbed species. Since the spectra are the same in both cases, it is reasonable to conclude that the ethylene is adsorbed on the alumina and that the function of the platinum is to help in the hydrogenation. Unpublished work (*29*) indicates that the platinum may cause the hydrogen to dissociate into atoms which then migrate to the chemisorbed ethylene. This interpretation, however, is hypothetical, and it is possible that the hydrocarbon species can migrate to the platinum.

2. *Chromia–Alumina*

Chromia–alumina catalysts are used extensively for dehydrogenation or hydrogenation of hydrocarbons, but their surface properties have received little attention from the infrared spectroscopist. Somewhat more information has been obtained from spin-resonance experiments. Like silica–alumina catalysts, they are prepared by precipitation of a co-gel, and their surface properties might be expected to be complicated. In the single infrared study of their surface properties, Little and Amberg (*23*) revealed that even the background spectrum of the bulk sample was dependent upon the activation procedure, spurious bands being observed at 1580 and 1370 cm^{-1}. Addition of carbon monoxide at room temperature produced the usual band at 2200 cm^{-1}, together with bands at 1490–1500, 1590–1610, and 1230 cm^{-1} due to oxidized "carbonate" species. Carbon dioxide similarly gave bands at 2350 (physically adsorbed), 1620, 1580, 1480, and 1230 cm^{-1}.

3. Nickel Carbonyl on Alumina

Nickel carbonyl occurs in (British) town gas, and since its reaction with oxygen is explosive, it must be removed by prior catalytic oxidation. Alumina may be used as the catalyst, and the oxidation reaction has been studied spectroscopically by Parkyns (24). As has already been described, the physically adsorbed nickel carbonyl (on silica) gives a spectrum analogous to that of the gaseous molecule with bands at 2575, 2490, and 2060 cm^{-1}. The last band is the most intense. Adsorption on alumina at room temperature gives a more complicated spectrum, the 2060 cm^{-1} band being considerably broadened and a new band appearing at 1835 cm^{-1}. Desorption of the nickel carbonyl reduces the intensity of all bands considerably, with the exception of the band at 1835 cm^{-1}, which is almost unaffected. During the desorption process, a further new band is revealed at 2090 cm^{-1}. The bands at 2090 and 1832 cm^{-1} correspond to positions found for carbon monoxide chemisorbed on metallic nickel and are so attributed. It is apparent that the nickel carbonyl decomposes during the desorption process, giving metallic nickel and carbon moxoxide. Some of the latter is retained on the nickel surface as a chemisorbed species.

D. Lewis Acidity

From the experimental data accumulated on the nature of the alumina surface, it is apparent that the surface possesses an electron-abstracting type of site, an oxidative type of site, and an acid–base or α site. However, it has not yet been shown whether or not all these sites are concerned with the same aluminum ions or must be considered as separate species. Analogies have been drawn between surface complexes on alumina and the coordination complexes of the aluminum halides (6), but the two systems are not strictly comparable. The surface complex cannot be isolated as a single molecule, and the oxygen atoms are more ionic than the halogen atoms in the analogous compounds. Unfortunately, very few oxides are sufficiently covalent to exist in a molecular form and act as good analogues for the proposed surface Lewis acid sites. Two little-known examples do exist, however, and some of their complexes have been studied in recent years. These are the tetroxides of ruthenium and osmium, and their properties are of some interest in this discussion.

Both ruthenium and osmium tetroxides are easily prepared and distilled in greasefree, evacuated systems, but since the latter is much more stable, its more complex compounds are better identified. The tetroxides are

covalent and tetrahedral and, like the aluminum halides, have a vacant
orbital that can accept a lone pair of electrons and form a coordinate
complex. Thus, with ammonia, a 1:1 addition complex can be isolated
(30).

(1)	**(2)**	**(3)**
complex	intermediate	acid

The atomic structure of the complex (1) is unknown. On heating, it
readily decomposes with loss of water to give a stable solid acid, osmiamic
acid (3). An intermediate such as (2) can be envisioned in this process,
and thus a clear similarity with the results obtained by Peri (1) for
ammonia adsorption of the alumina surface can be seen.

Although the final N—H grouping has not been clearly observed on
an alumina surface, it has been shown that ammonia will react with porous
glass at high temperature to give a structural >N—H group that can be
correlated with the amount of *boron* in the glass (31).

Osmium tetroxide will dissolve in water to give a dibasic acid, osmic
acid H_2OsO_5, presumably with the structure (4).

(4)	**(5)**

The hydroxyl groups formed in (4) correspond to the geminal surface
groups proposed by many workers. An intermediate of the form (5) can
again be postulated to account for the adsorption of molecular water.

Since aluminum is known to form a suboxide and a monofluoride at
higher temperatures, it is not inconceivable that the alumina surface
could contain terminal groups of the type

$$\text{Al}{=}\text{O} \quad \text{or} \quad {-}\text{Al}{=}\text{O}$$

in which the Al=O bond is essentially covalent.

A series of reactions with ammonia, water, HCl, and CO_2 can then be envisioned.

$$-Al{=}O + NH_3 \rightarrow -Al{=}O \rightarrow -Al{-}OH$$

with NH$_3$ coordinated below the first product and NH$_2$ below the second.

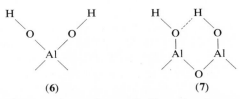

bidentate carbonate

These reactions adequately account for both α sites and Lewis acid sites, as well as some hydration and oxidation reactions. In the case of water adsorption, the formation of the aluminol groups would give rise to unperturbed OH vibrations. This can be qualitatively seen from a comparison of structures (**6**) and (**7**), where it is seen that hydrogen-bonding interaction is most unlikely to occur owing to the increased distance between the H and O atoms. It has been estimated that a five-membered ring (at least) is required before such intramolecular reactions can occur (*32*).

(6)   (7)

If Lewis acid sites on the surfaces of silica–alumina can be considered as being due to trivalent aluminum ions held in tetrahedral coordination to three oxygen atoms, then the effect of this site on adjacent silanol groups must also be considered. The surface Lewis acid sites are electron-deficient, and it seems likely that in the surface layer there would be an overlap of the nonbonding *p* orbitals associated with the oxygen atom with the empty *sp*³ hybrid orbital on the aluminum. An overlap of this type has been proposed by Brown and Holmes (*33*) to account for the fact that BI_3 is a stronger Lewis acid than BF_3. The fluorine orbitals are assumed to give a greater overlap with the vacant boron orbital than the iodine atoms. The coordinating ability of the boron atom is thus reduced as we go from $I \rightarrow Br \rightarrow Cl \rightarrow F$, and the Lewis acidity of the trihalides is, therefore, in the reverse order of their electronegativity.

The effect of this double bonding in a surface species would be to create an inductive effect along the surface. This type of effect has been suggested as occurring on a porous glass surface (*34*). The introduction of an electronegative fluorine atom into the surface led to an increased protonic acidity, and was attributed to an inductive effect on adjacent hydroxyl groups. The double-bonded interaction caused by orbital overlap would have a similar effect on adjacent silanol groups, and the presence of a Lewis acid site adjacent to a silanol group could cause enhancement of the acidity of that grouping.

In order to maintain electrical neutrality, the gel from which the silica-alumina catalysts are formed must contain a number of protons (or H_3O^+ ions) equal to the number of aluminum ions (**1**).

During the dehydration process, both Lewis acid sites (**2**) and surface hydroxyl groups (**3**) will be formed. If the gel structure consists of a random mixture of silica and alumina tetrahedra, then at least four types of hydroxyl group and Lewis acid site can be envisioned; in them the aluminum or silicon atom is attached to zero, one, two, or three tetrahedra of the opposite type. The most acidic silanol group would be that surrounded by three Lewis acid sites, because it would suffer the greatest inductive effect. Since the effect of the orbital overlap in the Al—O bond is to reduce the effective acidity of the central atom, the strongest Lewis acid sites would be those alumina sites that endure the least amount of orbital overlap, i.e., those that are attached to three other Lewis acid sites.

Unfortunately, the evidence gathered so far does not allow differentiation between these hypotheses. The O—H shifts observed by Basila (*35*) during the physical adsorption of xylene and mesitylene on silica and silica-alumina argue in favor of identical surface silanol groups: the evidence of Parry (*5*) on pyridine adsorption shows quite clearly that strong protonic acidic sites do exist on silica–alumina, but not on silica or alumina surfaces. The controversy, raging for more than a decade, remains unresolved.

5-2. SILICA–ALUMINA

A. Preparation and Surface Properties

Dried co-gels of silica and alumina are of immense importance in the petroleum industry, where these materials form the basis of the process used for the cracking of crude oil and the preparation of high-quality fuels. Despite this importance, and despite the efforts of many researchers, both the bulk structure and surface properties of these materials are imperfectly understood. Bearing in mind that these materials are prepared by a co-gelation of silica and alumina, this is perhaps understandable. Sodium silicate and an aluminum salt are usually selected as the starting materials, and the silica and alumina are carefully coprecipitated in a gelatinous form. The alkali is removed from the gel by continued washing (and/or ion exchange with an ammonium salt), followed by drying, dehydration, and activation at 500°C. The resultant powder has a surface area of about 450 m²/g and is highly active. In the laboratory, the co-gel is preferentially prepared by the hydrolysis of a mixture of aluminum isopropoxide and ethyl orthosilicate. The use of this method reduces the possibility of contamination by alkali-metal ions.

Catalytic studies have shown that the efficiency of these cracking catalysts depends on the ratio of silica to alumina in the co-gel. Thus, in Fig. 5-8, a plot of catalytic activity against $SiO_2–Al_2O_3$ ratio clearly demonstrates that, whereas silica by itself is almost inactive and alumina is only partially active, a synthetic co-gel containing about 25 wt % of alumina is highly efficient for the polymerization reaction under study. The optimum ratio of $SiO_2:Al_2O_3$ appears to be somewhat dependent upon the method of preparation but is usually between 13 and 25 wt %. The crystalline structure of the catalytic gel is unknown, and the gel is apparently amorphous. X-ray fluorescence spectroscopy, however, has given some idea of the coordination environment of the cations, and application of this method by Léonard and others (*36*) indicates that for gels containing less than 33% of alumina, 95% of the aluminum ions are tetrahedrally coordinated.

Titration experiments (*37*) indicate that the surface of silica–alumina is acidic in nature, and kinetic data on the cracking mechanisms are fully consistent with the concept of an acid-catalyzed reaction. However, for over two decades controversy has existed as to the specific nature of the

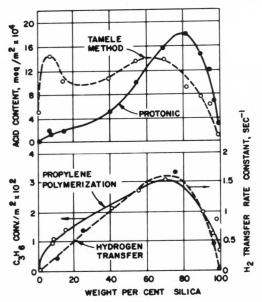

Fig. 5-8. *A comparison of surface acidity and catalytic activity with* SiO_2–Al_2O_3 *ratio.* [*Redrawn from Reference (104), courtesy of the Journal of Physical Chemistry.*]

acid sites involved in these reactions, and workers in this area have essentially been divided into two schools of thought: those who consider proton addition to be the primary step in the catalytic reaction, i.e.

$$X_s—H^+ + C_xH_y \rightarrow X_s(C_xH_{y+1})^+ \rightarrow products + X_s—H^+$$

and those who consider hydride ion abstraction to be the primary step, i.e.,

$$X_s + C_xH_y \rightarrow X_s—H^-(C_xH_{y-1})^+ \rightarrow products + X_s$$

In the first case the presence of a Brönsted acid is necessary and is tacitly assumed to be connected with the surface hydroxyl groups. In the second case a Lewis acid site is required. Many publications on this subject have appeared and, although they have shed considerable light on the nature of the silica, alumina, and silica–alumina surfaces, they have not defined the nature of the sites responsible for catalytic cracking.

The application of infrared spectroscopy to this problem has met with partial success in that some unique differences between the three types of surface have been noted in conjunction with an alarming number of similarities. Perhaps the most cogent observations in this area have derived from the work of Parry (5), who, for the first time, was able to show that strong protonic groups exist on the silica–alumina surface and that they are not present on either silica or alumina.

B. Surface Hydroxyl Groups

If protonic acidity is an important property of the silica–alumina surface, then the hydroxylic nature of the surface is of some concern. From the work already reviewed, it is known that the silica surface exhibits only one type of freely vibrating hydroxyl group, whereas the alumina surface contains at least three different types of surface hydroxyl in addition to the Lewis acid sites. An interesting problem thus arises: What is the nature of a mixed silica–alumina surface?

Answers to this question were first supplied by Roev, (38) who, on the basis of infrared studies, concluded that the silica–alumina surface contained only one type of hydroxyl group. This was confirmed by Basila (35), who reported that the infrared spectrum of a commercial silica–alumina cracking catalyst containing 25 wt % alumina showed only one absorption in the OH stretching region of the spectrum. This band, which is observed at 3745 cm^{-1}, is easily deuterated and shifted to 2762 cm^{-1}. Although it is possible that accidental degeneracy could give rise to a single hydroxyl stretching frequency in place of the three vibrations observed on alumina, the close similarity in both frequency and band half-widths for the OH group on silica–alumina (12 cm^{-1}) and silica (10 cm^{-1}) favors the assumption that the hydroxyl groups are attached to silicon atoms in the surface rather than aluminum atoms. This assignment also finds support from Basila's observations that the hydrogen-bonded frequency shifts, which occur when paraxylene and mesitylene are physically adsorbed on the silica–alumina surface, are almost identical with those observed when the same molecules are adsorbed on silica.

The dehydration of the silica–alumina surface also follows a pattern similar to that of the silica surface. During the elimination of water, the band at 3745 cm^{-1}, due to the free surface hydroxyl groups, increases in intensity, whereas those at 3500 and 1633 cm^{-1}, due to physically absorbed water, decrease in intensity and eventually disappear. Most of the physically adsorbed water is removed between 150° and 200°C. The increase that occurs in the 3745-cm^{-1} band is indicative that at least some of the physically absorbed water is hydrogen-bonded to the free surface hydroxyl groups. One major difference between the silica surface and the silica–alumina surface is that the latter does not appear to contain any hydrogen-bonded internal groups. This is shown by the absence of any band at 3650 cm^{-1}. This conclusion, however, has been questioned recently by Peri (13).

Reexposure of dehydrated silica–alumina to water vapor (1 hr at 150°C), followed by evacuation at the same temperature, has been shown to have a considerable influence on the catalytic activity of the material (39). The water retained by this procedure has been termed "fixedly adsorbed water" and greatly increases the activity. Spectroscopic observation of this process is of interest in that the adsorption of the water had no effect on the intensity of the band due to the free hydroxyl groups (3745 cm^{-1}). It can, therefore, be concluded that the adsorbed water is essentially immobile on the surface and is located sufficiently far away from the silanol groups that hydrogen bonding with them is impossible.

1. Catalyst Poisoning

Adsorbed alkali-metal ions are notorious for their ability to deactivate silica–alumina catalysts, and contact with potassium acetate solution has been found to be a particularly effective way of deactivating the surfaces. Basila (35) found that the addition of fixedly adsorbed water to a K$^+$-poisoned catalyst was almost the same as water addition to the non-poisoned catalyst. However, the intensities of the bands due to molecular water (3500 and 1633 cm^{-1}) were not so great in the case of a poisoned catalyst, thus indicating the presence of fewer adsorption sites. The implication of this experiment is that the water adsorbs on sites that are catalytically active and that are deactivated by the potassium acetate treatment.

One further point of interest to arise from Basila's work was the observation of a band at 1394 cm^{-1} that was present on the active catalyst but was not present in the spectrum of either dehydrated silica or K$^+$-poisoned silica–alumina. Moreover, it appeared only after the silica–alumina had been dehydrated above 300°C. It is not connected with a surface hydroxyl group, because it did not shift upon deuteration. However, its connection with some surface species seems clear from the fact that it disappeared when either water vapor or pyridine was adsorbed on the surface, yet reappeared during the desorption of the material. Basila suggested that it might be due to a vibration of a surface Al—O group, possibly an overtone or combination band. The presence of this band has been neglected by many workers in their discussion of the silica–alumina surface, and in view of recent results pertaining to oxidizing properties of silica–alumina surfaces, it would seem to be worthy of further investigation.

C. Surface Reactions of Silica–Alumina

1. Ammonia Adsorption

In early attempts to establish and differentiate between Lewis and Brönsted acid sites on silica–alumina surfaces, it seemed logical that an infrared study of ammonia adsorption would give the necessary information. The NH_3 would be adsorbed either by coordinate bond formation with the Lewis acid sites or by reaction with a surface proton to give an NH_4^+ species. However, as has been seen from work on the NH_3–Al_2O_3 system, a chemical interaction with the surface occurs and species that are not necessarily related to the acidic sites are formed. Initial work on the adsorption of ammonia upon silica–alumina was described by Mapes and Eischens (40) in 1954, and a surface NH_4^+ ion was identified by the presence of the N–H stretching and bending vibrations at 6.9 and 3.3 μ (1450 and 3028 cm^{-1}). These bands increased in intensity when water was adsorbed onto the silica–alumina, and it was suspected that the ammonium ion was formed by interaction with a proton that in turn had been formed by reaction of a water molecule with a Lewis acid site, i.e.,

$$
\underset{\diagup\,|\,\diagdown}{Al} + H_2O \rightleftharpoons \underset{\diagup\,|\,\diagdown}{\overset{\displaystyle \overset{\textstyle H}{O\cdots H^+}}{\underset{\displaystyle |}{Al}}}
\tag{5-1}
$$

Coordinately bonded ammonia can be identified by its N—H stretching vibration, and, in particular, by the frequency of its bending mode. The latter occurs at about 1640 cm^{-1} and is well separated from that of the NH_4^+ ion at 1450 cm^{-1}. Bands at 3.0 and 6.1 μ (3335 and 1638 cm^{-1}) were observed by Mapes and Eischens and were therefore attributed to this species. The intensities of the bands due to the coordinated ammonia were much greater than those due to the NH_4^+ ion, and it was concluded that many more Lewis acid sites than Brönsted sites were present on the surface.

It is important to note that Mapes and Eischens published a spectrum of their catalyst prior to any activation treatment, and since the sample had presumably been washed in NH_4^+ solution, bands due to this species can be seen in the spectrum. In particular, a strong band at 6.9 μ (1450 cm^{-1}) is very obvious. During activation, this band is completely removed together with most of the water. However, it is clear that in the original preparation the surface hydroxyl groups have behaved as ion-exchange sites in the usual manner:

$$\diagdown\!\!\!\!\!\diagup Si-OH + NH_4^+ \rightleftharpoons \diagdown\!\!\!\!\!\diagup Si-O-NH_4 + H^+ \tag{5-2}$$

All hydroxylated surfaces can behave in this manner in aqueous solution; therefore all surfaces containing hydroxyl groups can give a spectrum showing the presence of adsorbed NH_4^+ ion. However, not all surface hydroxyl groups can react with dry ammonia gas to give an NH_4^+ species, and thus the presence of the NH_4^+ species must be taken as evidence of strong protonic groups *only* when it is observed under dry conditions with no water present. In the presence of molecular water, the reaction scheme

$$H_2O + NH_3 \rightarrow NH_4OH \tag{5-3}$$

$$\diagdown\!\!\!\!\!\diagup Si-OH^+ + NH_4OH \rightarrow \diagdown\!\!\!\!\!\diagup Si-O-NH_4^+ + H_2O \tag{5-4}$$

can occur and give rise to spectra identical with those that would be observed assuming the reaction scheme normally considered (5-1).

Nicholson (*41*) reports that he has investigated the adsorption of NH_3 on SiO_2–Al_2O_3 and obtained spectra that were different from those published by Mapes and Eischens. Apparently a series of bands that could be attributed to "a minimum of three discrete energy-levels of Lewis acids and four definite energy levels of Brönsted sites" were observed. No spectra were published, however.

French and co-workers (*42*) have also published data on ammonia adsorption on silica–alumina and report the presence of NH_4^+ ions. However, since their samples undoubtedly contained water (silica also produced an NH_4^+ species under the conditions of their experiment), it seems probable that the main reaction was due to ion exchange. This suspicion seems warranted in view of the diminution in intensity of the hydroxyl bands observed after adsorption of the ammonia.

The position of the bending mode for the adsorbed NH_4^+ was reported by French and co-workers to be at 7.2 μ (1390 cm^{-1}), in contradistinction to Mapes and Eischens, who reported this band at 6.9 μ (1450 cm^{-1}). Pliskin and Eischens (*43*) were able to show that this difference was due to the disc technique used by French et al. Pliskin and Eischens found that ions on the catalyst surface were able to undergo ion exchange with the potassium bromide, so that the NH$_4^+$ in the catalyst was replaced by the alkali ion of the salt,

$$\text{—Si—ONH}_4 + \text{KBr} \rightleftharpoons \text{—Si—O—K} + \text{NH}_4\text{Br} \qquad (5\text{-}5)$$

The spectrum observed by French, therefore, was that of the ammonium bromide and not that of adsorbed NH$_4^+$.

Recently, studies of the adsorption of ammonia onto well-dried silica–alumina surfaces have been published by Cant and Little (*44*) and by Basila and Kantner (*45*). These workers observe bands due to ammonia chemisorbed both on surface Lewis acid sites and on Brönsted sites. Cant and Little's data indicate that the coordinately bonded ammonia gives bands at 3335, 3280, and 1610 cm^{-1} and the adsorbed NH$_4^+$ gives bands at 3270 and 1440 cm^{-1}. Addition of water causes apparent conversion of Lewis acid sites to Brönsted sites. Basila and Kantner estimate that one out of every five chemisorbed ammonia molecules is adsorbed as an NH$_4^+$ ion and correlate the adsorption with the disappearance of the surface OH vibration. It is to be noted that the band attributed to the NH$_4^+$ (3270 cm^{-1}) is considerably higher than the band found by Mapes and Eischens for the NH$_4^+$ chemisorbed on the surface by exchange from aqueous solution (3028 cm^{-1}).

2. Trimethylamine Adsorption

In order to try to circumvent the chemical reaction between the silica–alumina surface and nitrogenous adsorbates, Basila et al. (*46*) investigated the adsorption of a substituted ammonia, trimethylamine, on SiO$_2$–Al$_2$O$_3$. The infrared spectrum, however, indicated that the trimethylamine was dissociatively adsorbed. The exact nature of the adsorbed species could not be determined, but it seemed probable that it was of the secondary, possibly primary, amine type.

3. Pyridine Adsorption

Just as NH$_3$ might adsorb on the silica–alumina surface to give coordinated ammonia and ammonium ion, one might expect pyridine, a slightly weaker base, to chemisorb upon this surface and give either a pyridinium ion, a coordinately bonded species, or both. In this case, however, spurious reaction with the surface is unlikely to occur.

Both the spectrum of coordinately bonded pyridine and that of pyridinium ion are well known from studies of inorganic complexes. The N—H+ stretching vibration in the pyridinium salts occurs at approximately 2450 cm⁻¹, but, unfortunately, it is poorly defined and has not been detected on any surfaces. Parry (5), however, has found that considerable

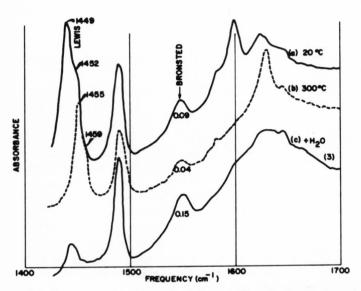

Fig. 5-9. *Infrared spectrum of pyridine adsorbed on a silica–alumina cracking catalyst (a) at 20°C, (b) after evacuating at 300°C, and (c) after addition of 0.05 mole if water. Note the presence of both Lewis and Brönsted forms of adsorbed pyridine and the increase in Brönsted form on the addition of water. [Redrawn from Reference (5), courtesy of the Journal of Catalysis (Academic Press).]*

information can be obtained about the form of adsorbed pyridine by a study of the ring vibrations, and his results with silica and alumina have already been discussed. With silica only physical adsorption is observed (bands at 1447 and 1599 cm⁻¹), whereas with alumina a coordinately bonded species is identified by a characteristic vibration at 1455 cm⁻¹. No trace of pyridinium ion formation (characteristic vibration at 1540 cm⁻¹) was observed with either of these materials.

When pyridine was added to a silica–alumina cracking catalyst, however, Parry obtained the spectrum shown in Fig. 5-9. The band at 1540 cm⁻¹ is clearly indicative of the presence of pyridinium ions formed by addition to a surface proton. Evacuation at 300°C reduces the quantity of pyridinium ion on the surface and reveals the presence of coordinately bonded pyridine (band at 1455 cm^{-1} and shoulder at 1459 cm^{-1}). The addition of 0.05 mole of water to the sample that had been evacuated at 300°C caused an increase in the intensity of the 1540-cm^{-1} band, indicating the formation of a considerable quantity of pyridinium ion, and this increase was accompanied by a reduction in the amount of coordinately bonded pyridine. This result can be interpreted as indicating a conversion of some Lewis sites into Brönsted sites via Eq. (5-1); but it should be remembered that the method of formation makes it equally possible that the water is preferentially adsorbed on the Lewis acid site, replacing a pyridine molecule and causing the latter to be readsorbed on a Brönsted site that had previously been energetically less acceptable. Alternatively, of course, the ion-exchange mechanisms indicated in Eqs. (5-3) and (5-4) could also pertain to this adsorption. Basila and his co-workers (46) report that the water addition is completely reversible and that pumping for 1 hr at 150°C returns the sample to its original state. The pyridine is not desorbed at this temperature.

Parry also investigated the effect of K$^+$ poisoning on the pyridine adsorption, and his spectra are of interest in that they show quite clearly that both Lewis and Brönsted sites are affected by the potassium acetate treatment. The protonic sites are not completely removed, although the band at 1540 cm^{-1} is much reduced in intensity. The main effect on the Lewis acid sites is an apparent weakening of the adsorption sites, which is evidenced by the appearance of the characteristic absorption at 1444 instead of 1460 cm^{-1}.

Parry's work on the pyridine–SiO$_2$–Al$_2$O$_3$ system has been confirmed and extended by Basila et al. (46). These workers were able to completely eliminate the Brönsted sites by base exchange, and yet their examination of the hydroxyl stretching region showed that very few surface hydroxyl groups had been removed by this procedure. Thermogravimetric studies indicated that pyridine absorbed on the K$^+$-poisoned catalyst was held much less tenaciously than on the original silica–alumina, thus providing further evidence for Parry's interpretation of the shift of the Lewis–pyridine band from 1460 to 1444 cm^{-1}.

In an effort to estimate the relative proportions of Lewis and Brönsted acid sites on a silica–alumina surface, Basila and his co-workers were faced with the problem of assigning absorption coefficients for the bands at 1450 and 1545 cm^{-1}. If these bands are assumed to have equal absorption coefficients, then the ratio of the number of Lewis acid sites to Brönsted acid sites would be simply the ratio of the observed intensities, i.e., 10.5:1. However, this was not found to be the case, and an original estimate was made by assuming that the intensity of the 1490-cm^{-1} band was the same for both the chemisorbed and the physically adsorbed species. This assumption was also shown to be incorrect, and Basila and Kantner (47) have since proposed a corrected value that indicates that there are between three and six Lewis acid sites for every Brönsted site on the silica–alumina surface.

4. Hexachloroacetone

The concept of using a ketone as an indicator molecule in order to obtain spectroscopic evidence of ranges of Lewis acidity has been discussed in connection with the alumina surface. The ketone chemisorbs via the carbonyl oxygen atom, and the consequent shift in the vibration frequency of the $>C=O$ bond is taken as a measure of the strength of the surface Lewis acid sites. The infrared spectra of hexachloroacetone adsorbed on SiO_2–Al_2O_3 at various temperatures have been obtained by Hair and Chapman (6) and their results are reproduced in Fig. 5-10. At

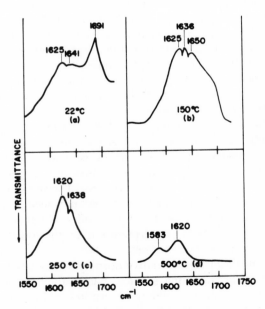

Fig. 5-10. *The adsorption of hexachloroacetone on a silica–alumina surface followed by heating to (a) 22°C, (b) 150°C, (c) 250°C, (d) 500°C. [Redrawn from Reference (6) by courtesy of the Journal of Physical Chemistry.]*

room temperature it can be seen that there is a considerable quantity of physically absorbed hexachloroacetone (1780 cm^{-1}) on the surface, but, on heating to 150°, this is completely removed and a broad band that has peaks at 1625, 1636, and 1650 cm^{-1} is observed. This is interpreted as a site distribution curve in which the intensity ordinate is a measure of the number of sites and the frequency is a measure of the strength of these sites. Lower frequencies correspond to stronger Lewis acid sites. It can be seen that as the temperature is increased the distribution changes, and at 500°C only two small peaks remain at 1583 and 1620 cm^{-1}. Similar results have been published for hexachloroacetone adsorption on an alumina surface, and the results show that, although the fine structure of the distribution curves is somewhat different, the overall Lewis acidity of the surfaces is very similar. Comparison of the spectra taken on SiO$_2$–Al$_2$O$_3$ and Al$_2$O$_3$ at 150°C indicate that the Lewis acid sites on the SiO$_2$–Al$_2$O$_3$ are slightly stronger, because the peak of the site distribution curve occurs at 1636 cm^{-1} in the case of the SiO$_2$–Al$_2$O$_3$ as compared to 1657 cm^{-1} in the case of the alumina. However, the alumina surface shows a peak at 1588 cm^{-1} (corresponding to very strong acid sites) that accounts for about 10% of the total number of sites.

For a given series of ketone–inorganic halide complexes, it is known that the shift of the carbonyl stretching frequency is a function of the electronegativity of the substituent halogen atom. Thus, in the case of the boron halides, the $>C=O$ stretching frequency is shifted to lower wave numbers as we go from the BF$_3$ complex to the BI$_3$ complex, i.e., as we go from weaker to stronger Lewis acids. Hair and Chapman published data for a series of aluminum halide–hexachloroacetone complexes, and these data are reproduced in Fig. 5-11. Insertion of the value for the electronegativity of oxygen into Fig. 5-11 indicates that, for any aluminum ion tetrahedrally coordinated to only three oxygen atoms, one might expect a shift in the carbonyl stretching frequency of about 170 cm^{-1}. Moreover, the shift in this stretching frequency should be primarily a function of the electronegativity of the oxygen atoms and should thus be approximately the same for both silica–alumina and alumina. Comparison of Figs. 5-6 and 5-10 shows that the results are in good agreement with this forecast, the actual shift observed at 150°C being 160 cm^{-1}.

5. Oxidative Properties of Silica–Alumina Surfaces

Silica–alumina, like alumina, will react with alcohols, aldehydes, and acids to give surface species that are spectroscopically similar to the ion

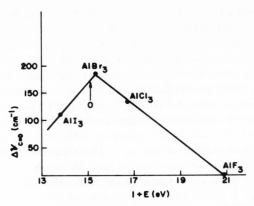

Fig. 5-11. *The shift in* $>$C$=$O *stretching frequency of a series of hexachloroacetone–aluminum halide complexes plotted as a function of the electronegativity of the halogen atoms.* [*Reproduced from Reference (6), courtesy of the Journal of Physical Chemistry.*]

of the parent acid. Thus, Chapman and Hair (*10*) were able to observe the formation of a surface benzoate on silica–alumina by reaction with benzaldehyde, despite the fact that the catalyst had been heated to 500°C in hydrogen prior to reaction. Silica does not react in this manner.

In many carboxylic salts the position of the asymmetric stretching frequency is dependent upon the electronegativity of the ion to which it is attached, and in some cases a linear relationship has been established. Chapman and Hair found that the position of the asymmetric stretching frequency of the adsorbed benzoate ion was a function of the composition of the SiO_2–Al_2O_3, the alumina surface being apparently more electronegative than the silica–alumina surface. If an increase in electronegativity is accepted as indicative of an increase in Lewis acidity, then an apparent inverse relationship exists between Lewis acid strength and Brönsted acid strength.

6. α Sites on Silica–Alumina

Peri (*13, 48*) has shown that α sites occur on silica–alumina surfaces in about the same concentration as on alumina ($3 - 9 \times 10^{12}$ sites/cm²). These sites are similar in properties to those on alumina (see preceding section), and reaction with CO_2 and HCl is again observed. No exact correlation with catalytic activity is noted, and indeed the blocking of all α sites by chemisorption of HCl actually was found to increase the activity for butene polymerization.

Both ammonia and water react with α sites on silica–alumina and are able to prevent carbon dioxide adsorption, although about 10 times as much NH_3 as CO_2 is needed. Other molecules such as acetylene, benzene, carbon disulfide, ethyl bromide, nitrous oxide, and butene also react with the α sites. In the last case Peri again postulates polymerization of the butene and notes the disappearance of the $=C—H$ stretching vibration at 3020 cm^{-1} during the process. Leftin (49) has commented on this and has pointed out the difficulties encountered in interpreting the spectra of adsorbed hydrocarbons. As an example, Leftin and Hobson (50) have obtained the spectrum of compounds (1) and (2) by the reaction of compounds (3) and (4) with fused $SbCl_3$.

$$CH_3—CH_2—\underset{\underset{(3)}{\overset{|}{Cl}}}{CH}—CH_3 + SbCl_3 \rightarrow CH_3—CH_2—\overset{\oplus}{CH}—CH_3 + SbCl_4^-$$

(3)   (1)

$$CH_2{=}CH—\underset{\underset{(4)}{\overset{|}{Cl}}}{CH}—CH_3 + SbCl_3 \rightarrow CH_2—\overset{H}{\underset{\underset{\oplus}{|}}{C}}—\overset{H}{\overset{|}{C}}—CH_3 + SbCl_4^-$$

(4)   (2)

The spectrum of compound (2) is identical with that observed when 1-butene was adsorbed on silica–alumina and is slightly different from that of compound (1).

7. Ethylene Oxide

Naccache and his co-workers (51) have used infrared spectroscopy to identify the polymeric product formed when ethylene oxide is exposed to a silica–alumina surface at 50°C. Whereas the organic oxide is only weakly physically adsorbed on silica, it is decomposed on the acidic silica–alumina, and a polymeric material is produced. Extraction of this polymer and examination of its spectrum showed it to be very similar to that of polyoxyethylene glycol, the spectrum of the adsorbed species exhibiting additional bands at 1620 and 1735 cm^{-1}. These are assigned to fundamental stretching vibrations of $—CH{=}CH_2$ and $C{=}O$ groups, respectively. The presence of a band at 2720 cm^{-1}, typical of an aldehydic $—C—H$ stretching vibration, in conjunction with the $C{=}O$ band at 1735 cm^{-1}, is taken as evidence of the presence of an aldehydic group at the end of the chain.

The spectrum of ethylene oxide is never observed on the silica–alumina. Apparently, the first stage in the polymerization is an interaction with the surface hydroxyl groups and the opening up of the ring, giving an

O—CH$_2$—CH$_2$—OH species on the surface. The presence of strong acid sites on the surface is necessary for the polymerization reaction to occur, and prior adsorption of ammonia on the Lewis acid sites caused deactivation of the surface. In this case no reaction occurs, and the spectrum is characteristic only of physically(?) adsorbed ethylene oxide. This is completely desorbed from the surface by heating to 180°.

Just as the silica–alumina surface can be deactivated by the preadsorption of ammonia, so the silica surface can be activated by addition of boron trifluoride. In this case polymer formation was readily observed to occur.

5-3. MOLECULAR SIEVES (ZEOLITES)

A. Structure

The molecular sieve materials have been of great interest to surface chemists because, for the first time, materials became available that had high surface activity, large surface area, and controlled pore size coupled with a supposed regularity of crystal form. The well-defined crystallinity of the molecular sieves has been taken as evidence of known surface constitution (52), and, although this may well be true of the interior of the crystals, infrared spectroscopy has shown that these materials contain hydroxyl groups that may or may not be limited to the exterior crystalline surface.

The molecular sieves consist of essentially three types—A, X, and Y. The type A zeolite [Fig. 5-12(a)] has a structure in which about 48 SiO$_2$ type tetrahedra are arranged to form a truncated cubo-octahedron. The inner cavity can be entered via six octahedral holes, the diameter of these holes being approximately 4 Å. Only small molecules such as O$_2$, H$_2$O, NH$_3$, and H$_2$S can enter the inner cavity, and thus this type of material finds application as a molecular sieve rather than as a catalyst. About 29 molecules of water can be held in each cavity.

The type X and Y molecular sieves are based on the Faujasite structure, which is shown in Fig. 5-12(b). These skeletons are again truncated octahedra, but, in this case, access to the inner cavity is via four 12-sided holes, the diameter of the holes being about 9 Å. The more open structure of the Faujasite-type sieves allows their use as a catalyst. About 32 molecules of water can be held in each cavity.

The zeolites are aluminosilicates, and the silica tetrahedra shown in Figs. 5-12(a) and 5-12(b) are partially replaced by a tetrahedral alumina species, the electrical neutrality being maintained by the presence of a

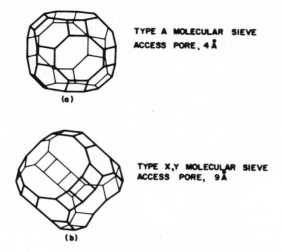

TYPE A MOLECULAR SIEVE
ACCESS PORE, 4 Å

(a)

TYPE X,Y MOLECULAR SIEVE
ACCESS PORE, 9 Å

(b)

Fig. 5-12. Skeleton structures of molecular sieves. [Redrawn from Reference (105), courtesy of R. M. Barrer and Endeavour.]

charged cation in the usual way. Thus, the Linde 13X molecular sieve has the general formula

$$(Na_2O)_{40}(Al_2O_3)_{40}(SiO_2)_{112}$$

per unit cell. It has been found that the unit cell is often deficient in Na_2O to the extent of about 8 %. The cations can be readily ion-exchanged, and thus the catalytic and adsorption properties can be altered by this process. In particular, it is known that exchange of NH_4^+ for Na^+ ion, followed by thermal decomposition of the NH_4^+ complex, produces a highly active cracking catalyst (53).

B. Water Adsorption, Surface Hydroxyl Groups

The first infrared data on molecules adsorbed in a type *A* zeolite were obtained by Frohnsdorff and Kington (54). These workers examined the infrared spectrum of water present in the cages at points in excess of 34 % of the saturation value. At this 34 % adsorption point, the water exhibited bending and stretching vibrations at 1660 and 3486 cm^{-1}. Increasing the amount of water in the cages caused these bands to shift until final values of 1650 and 3377 cm^{-1} were observed. These values can be compared with those observed for liquid water at 22°C (1646 and 3390 cm^{-1}).

Kiselev et al. (55, 56) report that the frequencies of the adsorbed water vibrations are also a function of the exchanged cation and have noted an approximately linear relationship between the OH stretching frequency and the radius of the cation.

Szymanski et al. (57) employed a mull technique and examined the spectrum of water adsorbed on a type X zeolite at coverages below the 34% adsorption value. On reducing the water content of the molecular sieve, these workers found that the bands originally observed at about

TABLE 5-2

Frequencies of Residual Hydroxyl Groups on Near-Faujasites[a]

Cation	Band positions, cm⁻¹			
Li (OH)	3740		3660	
Na (OH)	3750	3695	3655	
K (OH)	3750	3715	3650	
Ag (OH)	3750	3685	3630	
Ba (OH)	3750	3695	3620	
Ca (OH)	3750	3695	3590	
Sr (OH)	3750	3700	3660	3605
Cd (OH)	3750	3690	3600	

[a] Taken from Reference (59).

3400 and 1650 cm⁻¹ shifted to 3550 and 1690 cm⁻¹ during the desorption process. When the water content was reduced below 15% of the saturation value, a sharp band became obvious at 3550 cm⁻¹ together with a weak band between 1700 and 1600 cm⁻¹. It was originally postulated that these bands corresponded to surface hydroxyl groups and did not represent physically adsorbed water. However, quantitative repetition of this work in a closed vacuum system [Bertsch and Habgood (58), Carter et al. (59)] showed that these bands were due to molecular water that could substantially all be removed from the surface by evacuation at 450°C.

The presence of surface hydroxyl groups on the molecular sieves was first definitely established by Carter et al. (59), who published a series of well-resolved spectra that clearly showed that three types of hydroxyl groups existed on the surface of all the 13X sieves examined, with the exception of that which had been subjected to Li⁺ ion exchange. The positions of the bands at the two highest frequencies were found to be relatively independent of the exchangeable cation (Table 5-2) and were observed in all cases at about 3750 and 3605 cm⁻¹. The lowest frequency band, however, occurred in the region 3660 to 3590 cm^{-1} and showed a strong dependence upon the nature of the cation. In addition to the changes in frequency, the relative intensities of the hydroxyl stretching frequencies were found to vary considerably with changes in the cation. Thus, whereas on the Ca–X sieve the 3590-cm^{-1} band was very strong, ion-exchanging to the chemically similar Ba–X compound caused the analogous 3620-cm^{-1} band to appear only weakly.

The range of ion-exchanged zeolites that have been studied has been extended by Angell and Schaffer (60). These workers have shown that the relative intensities of the various —OH bands are dependent upon the rate of sample activation and that, after flash activation, the band at 3640 cm^{-1} is much smaller than after the more usual, prolonged activation treatment. This effect is attributed to the "self-steaming" process noted by Peri (3) during the desorption of water from alumina; if it is not immediately removed, the desorbing water is apparently able to attack the surface and cause more surface hydroxyl groups to form than were present initially.

In view of the aluminosilicate constitution of the sieves, Carter et al. compared the frequencies of the hydroxyl groups found on the sieve surfaces with those previously found on silica and alumina. The band at 3740 cm^{-1} correlates with the free Si—OH vibration found on silica gel; but since this band is not perturbed by physically adsorbed materials, it cannot be functioning as a true surface hydroxyl group. Its exact identification is not known, but it is possibly due to an occluded impurity such as silica gel. The band at about 3690 cm^{-1} is close to the band of lowest frequency that is observed on alumina (3710 cm^{-1}) and is therefore attributed to an aluminol grouping. The third vibration, at 3590–3660 cm^{-1}, is much lower in frequency than any band yet reported for a "free" surface hydroxyl. In view of its strong dependence on the nature of the cation, it is probably closely associated with the cation, although the frequency shifts are not large enough to suggest direct attachment.

Bertsch and Habgood (58), and Habgood (61) examined the spectral changes that occur when water is added at low concentrations to predried samples of Li–X and K–X sieves. Sharp bands are observed at 3720 and 3648 cm^{-1}, respectively, together with a bending mode in the vicinity of 1650 cm^{-1}. Lithium hydroxide and potassium hydroxide exhibit O—H stretching vibrations at 3678 and 3611 cm^{-1}, respectively, and the close agreement of the relative frequencies suggests that these bands can be attributed to water molecules directly adsorbed on the cations. The addition of water to Ca–X, however, caused the appearance of a band at 3480 cm^{-1}, and this can be attributed to molecular water. It is of interest to note that no workers have observed bands ascribable to the presence of an H_3O^+ ion.

The optical density of the 3690-cm^{-1} band on the Na^+–X sieve after evacuation at 600°C was determined to be 0.30. Comparison of this value with the optical density of the 3720-cm^{-1} band on alumina led Carter et al. to speculate that the hydroxyl coverage on the surface of the sieve was about one-seventh that of the alumina surface.

Uytterhoeven et al. (62) have since examined the question of the concentration of hydroxyl groups on the surface of the type X and Y sieves by using a combination of infrared spectroscopy, deuterium-exchange, and thermogravimetry, and they have shown that the number of hydroxyl groups present is in good agreement with the number of hydroxyl groups that would be necessary to terminate the ultimate crystal faces of the zeolites. It was calculated that particles 1 μ in diameter would require 0.15×10^{20} OH/g to complete the crystal faces, whereas 0.1-μ-diameter crystals would require 1.4×10^{20} OH/g. An experimental value of 0.57×10^{20} OH/g was found for the Na^+–X sieve, which is in good agreement with the calculated values. The methods used in estimating the theoretical hydroxyl content have been criticized by Kerr and co-workers (63), but the corrections proposed fall within the experimental error of the original data.

C. Surface Acidity

1. Ammonia Adsorption

Decationation of the zeolites gives rise to products that are highly active cracking catalysts and are therefore presumed to have highly acidic surfaces similar to those of the silica–alumina gels. There is therefore considerable interest in this material and in the nature of its surface acidity. Decationation of the Na^+–X sieve is achieved by completely ion-exchanging NH_4^+ for Na^+ in aqueous solution; followed by thermal decomposition of the NH_4^+ ion. It is suspected that this treatment partially destroys the crystal lattice. Uytterhoeven and co-workers (62) showed that the NH_4^+–X zeolite exhibited major bands at 3250, 2950, and 1450 cm^{-1} prior to its thermal decomposition, and these are ascribed to two stretching vibrations and the deformation vibration of the NH_4^+ ion. In addition, a weak deformation vibration is observed at 1682 cm^{-1}.

On heating to 475°, all traces of the N–H vibrations are removed from the spectrum and the O—H vibrations at 3670 and 3580 cm^{-1} are found to increase in intensity. Above 415°C, the OH bands start to diminish in intensity, but the 3670-cm^{-1} band remains the most intense and, indeed, is the only band readily observable after heating to 555°C. Kjeldahl determinations were used to confirm the complete removal of NH_4^+ from the material, and deuterium-exchange experiments indicated that the hydroxyl content had increased by a factor of 50, i.e., to about 10^{21} OH/g. The increase in intensity of the band at 3670 cm^{-1} was taken as evidence that the proton formed by elimination of gaseous ammonia had interacted with the lattice to form a trigonal alumina species and an adjacent SiOH group. This is shown in Eq. (5-6):

$$
\begin{array}{c}
NH_4^+ \qquad\qquad\qquad H^+ \\[2mm]
\text{structure with } Al^{iv} \text{ and } Si \quad \rightarrow \quad \text{structure with } Al \text{ and } Si \quad + NH_3\uparrow \\[2mm]
\text{(Al—O bonded)} \qquad\qquad \text{(with H on O, and Al, Si and)}
\end{array}
\tag{5-6}
$$

A mechanism similar to this had been proposed earlier by Szymanski et al. (57). In the activated species, the aluminum ion is surrounded by three oxygen ions and can be considered to be a conventional Lewis acid site, the adjacent silanol group acting as a Brönsted acid. Thus, it is clear that the surface of the decationated zeolite is probably very similar to that of an amorphous silica–alumina catalyst, and the crystallinity can no longer be used as evidence of surface perfection. Indeed, it provides an excellent example of the care that must be exercised in extrapolating bulk properties in surface considerations.

The protonic nature of the —SiOH group is confirmed by the series of spectra observed during the adsorption of ammonia on the decationated species. On the addition of ammonia, a sharp band at 3423 cm^{-1} is immediately observed, and this is followed by the appearance of broader bands at 2990 and 3200 cm^{-1}. Bands were also observed in the bending region of the spectrum at 1435, 1487, and 1680 cm^{-1}. The bands at 3200, 2990, 1435, and 1680 cm^{-1} correspond quite closely to the bands attributed to the original NH_4^+ ion present in the NH_4^+–X sieve before the thermal decomposition, and a partial reformation of the original NH_4^+-X sieve structure is indicated. The bands at 3423 and 1485 cm^{-1}, although readily identified as being due to an NH_4^+ ion, are clearly due to a different species.

The band at 3423 cm^{-1} is of great interest in that it is higher than any band previously found for an ammonium ion in a simple salt. Previously, the adsorption of ammonia on a partially fluorinated porous glass surface has been shown to give rise to a band at 3450 cm^{-1}, and this also was attributed to a stretching vibration of an NH_4^+ ion. The partially fluorinated glass surface had previously been shown to exhibit strong catalytic activity, presumably attributable to Brönsted sites. In view of the fact that both of these materials are catalytically active, it is tempting to postulate that the catalytically active sites are those strong protonic groups that are capable of chemisorbing NH_3 and giving an NH_4^+ ion that exhibits a stretching frequency at about 3450 cm^{-1}. In the case of the molecular sieve, it is interesting to note that very little ammonia was observed to be coordinately bonded to the surface, despite the high catalytic activity of the material. Indeed, Lewis-bonded NH_3 was not observed at all in samples that had been pretreated at temperatures lower than 300°C.

2. Perturbation of Hydroxyl Groups

Angell and Schaffer (60) have examined the shifts in stretching frequency of the surface hydroxyl groups on the molecular sieve during the physical adsorption of benzene. It will be remembered that, when benzene is physically adsorbed on silica, there is a preferential adsorption on the surface hydroxyl groups, the weak hydrogen-bonding interaction causing a shift of about 120 cm^{-1} in the O—H stretching frequency. Considerable broadening is also noted, and there is an increase in the integrated intensity of the band. On the addition of benzene to samples of Ni–Y and Mg–Y zeolites, it was found that the band at 3744 cm^{-1} was completely unchanged by the process, whereas the band at 3640 cm^{-1} was shifted to 3310 cm^{-1} and broadened considerably. The magnitude of this shift (330 cm^{-1}) cannot be explained on the basis of a simple silica-type hydroxyl group. However, as was seen from the discussion on surface acidity, if the hydroxylic group giving rise to the 3640-cm^{-1} band was strongly acid, then the much larger perturbation would be expected in this interaction with a weak base.

The perturbing effect of the surface forces of the molecular sieve on the benzene molecule is also appreciable and has been studied by

Abramov et al. (65). Certain distinct changes can be noticed in the spectrum of the adsorbed benzene, the most obvious of which is the great increase in intensity experienced by the C—C stretching vibration at 1486 cm^{-1}. It will be recalled that in the case of adsorption of benzene on silica, the intensity of this band was increased by a factor of 1.7. When the absorption was on the molecular sieve, however, a tenfold increase in intensity was noted.

D. Adsorption of Other Molecules

1. Ethylene

Carter and co-workers (64) have shown that ethylene is adsorbed on a series of ion-exchanged molecular sieves via direct coordination to the cation. As was expected, a direct relationship existed between the heats of adsorption and the changes in the frequency of the $>C=C<$ vibration of the adsorbed ethylene. One of the most unique features of this work, as yet unexplained, was the lack of intensity of the C—H vibration of the adsorbed ethylene in coordination with some ions. Thus, for Cd^{2+}–X, no C—H bands at all could be detected despite the fact that bands in the 1300–1600-cm^{-1} region were readily observable; with Ag^+–X the C—H bands were readily detected.

2. Hydrogen Chloride

Hydrogen chloride is known to react with both Mg–X and Na–X zeolites with the production of new hydroxyl bands (60). In the first case, two bands are produced at 3643 and 3533 cm^{-1}. These values are identical with those obtained for the surface hydroxyl groups when the sample is decationized. In the case of the Na–X sieve, a single new band is produced at 3658 cm^{-1}. Here again, the molecular sieves are behaving analogously to the silica–aluminas and, presumably, reaction with a strained surface Si—O—Al group can again be postulated.

3. Carbon Dioxide

Carbon dioxide also reacts with Li^+–, Na^+–, and K^+–X zeolites in the same manner as with the alumina surface. At 20°C the rate of adsorption is slow, but it is markedly accelerated by the preabsorption of a small quantity of water (58). Several bands are observed in this system, and the intensities of these bands are dependent upon both the cation and the length of time that the reaction has been allowed to proceed. The observed bands are reproduced in Table 5-3. The band at about 2350 cm^{-1} is attributed to the ν_3 vibration of physically adsorbed carbon dioxide held linearly to the surface, and the 1380-cm^{-1} band is tentatively assigned to the ν_1 vibration of this same species. This vibration is normally inactive in the infrared. In a second communication (66) Ward and Habgood were able to show that the frequency of the band between 2350 and 2375 cm^{-1} was a function of the electrical field of the cation and was accom-

TABLE 5-3

Observed Bands for Carbon Dioxide Adsorbed on X—Zeolites[a]

Observed bands, cm^{-1}, when cation is

Li$^+$	Na$^+$	K$^+$	CO$_2$ gas
2368	2355	2348	2349
		1690	
1728[a]	1715[a]	1670[a]	
1660		1640	
	1580	1570	
	1485		
1446	1425		
1380	1380	1380	
1302[a]	1365[a]	1340[a]	
		(1235)	

[a] From Reference (58).

panied by two weaker bands that were equally spaced from the major band. No satisfactory explanation, however, is yet available to account for the presence of these bands. Since higher frequencies were observed with higher cationic fields, an ion–dipole interaction was held to be the most likely bonding mechanism for the species giving rise to the central band.

The bands marked with an asterisk at about 1715 and 1365 cm^{-1} (Na$^+$–X zeolite) appear to behave in an interdependent manner and have been ascribed to a relatively unsymmetrical carbonate structure. The band at 1365 cm^{-1} develops more slowly than the 1715-am^{-1} band and is not always readily observed. The bands at 1485 and 1425 cm^{-1} also vary in a dependent manner, and they are tentatively assumed to be due to a "carbonate"-type species of a more symmetrical nature. Once again, however, the presence or absence of a given species is dependent on the nature of the cation. The divalent cations, with the exception of Mg^{2+}, are comparatively inactive in their "carbonate" formation.

5-4. CLAY SURFACES

A. Kaolinite

The bulk structures of clay and mineral silicates have, in general, been well examined by infrared spectroscopy, and many structure correlations have been made. However, work on the true surface of these minerals is somewhat scanty; most of the adsorption data reported refer to adsorp-

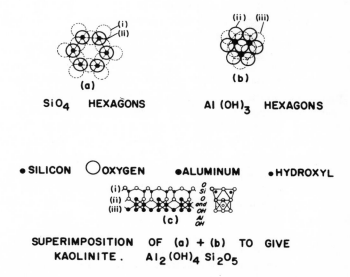

Fig. 5-13. The structure of kaolinite clays: (a) SiO_4 hexagons; (b) $Al(OH)_3$ hexagons; (c) superimposition of (a) and (b) to give kaolinite. [Redrawn from Reference (106) by courtesy of Clarendon Press, Oxford.]

tion from aqueous solution. The clay that appears to have been subjected to the most serious study is kaolinite, and a discussion of the work on this substance should exemplify the difficulties that must be overcome in determining the true nature of the surfaces of clays and other minerals.

In kaolinite, the silica tetrahedra form sheets of a structural unit, of composition Si_2O_5, by linking together three out of the four tetrahedral oxygen atoms. The silicon atoms thus form a hexagonal ring with the remaining oxygen atoms pointing vertically upward. This is shown in Fig. 5-13(a). The aluminum portion of the structure is derived from $Al(OH)_3$, and this also forms a ring structure [Fig. 5-13(b)] in which the hydroxyl groups lie at the corners of a hexagon. The kaolinite is then formed by superimposition of the silica rings on top of the alumina rings to give the layer structure shown in Fig. 5-13(c). The final composition is $Al_2(OH)_4Si_2O_5$. The hydroxyl groups are an integral part of the composition and are thus a considerable nuisance in an examination of surface hydroxyl groups. Elimination of these groups by heat treatment causes a collapse of the structure, and, presumably, an amorphous silica–alumina type surface is then produced. Moreover, from Fig. 5-13(d) it can be seen that at least four types of hydroxyl groups will be observed in the spectrum of kaolinite, and these have been defined by Ledoux and White (67) according to the following classification:

1. Outer hydroxyl groups. Type A: Those hydroxyl groups that occur at the surface of the microcrystals and at broken edges—in other words, our conventional surface hydroxyl groups. Type B: The hydroxyl groups belonging to the octahedral layer that is exposed to the surface.

2. Inner hydroxyl groups. Type C: Hydroxyl groups belonging to the octahedral layer but opposite to the tetrahedral oxygens of the adjacent silica layer. Type D: The hydroxyl groups between the octahedral and tetrahedral sheets.

The infrared spectrum of a kaolinite sample preheated to 110°C shows strong bands at 3695 and 3620 cm^{-1} and weaker bands at 3650 and 3670 cm^{-1}. All these are attributed to hydroxyl vibrations. It seems reasonable to assign the strongest bands to the inner surface hydroxyl groups and the weaker bands to the surface species, which must be fewer in number. Evidence for this type of assignment was obtained by Ledoux and White by the insertion of potassium acetate between the layers of the clay structure. This caused a reduction in intensities of the bands at 3695 and 3650 cm^{-1} and the complete disappearance of the band at 3670 cm^{-1}. A new hydroxyl band was produced at 3600 cm^{-1} together with bands attributable to the acetate ion (3000 cm^{-1}) and molecular water (3470 cm^{-1}). An interlayer expansion of between 7 and 40 Å is reported for this process. The use of hydrazine rather than potassium acetate in this intersalation process causes similar spectroscopic changes to occur, and the 3695-cm^{-1} band is again much reduced in intensity and replaced by a new band at 3600 cm^{-1}.

From these results Ledoux and White concluded that both the 3695- and 3620-cm^{-1} bands were due to vibrations of inner hydroxyl groups. The band that was not affected by the intersalation (3620 cm^{-1}) must correspond to the type D groups, and thus the 3695-cm^{-1} band is assigned to type C groups. Infrared data on urea, formamide, and hydrazine

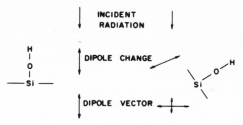

Fig. 5-14. *The interaction of radiation with a dipole: dependence of intensity on angle of incidence.*

inclusions have been published recently (*68*), and details on the deuteration of these hydroxyl groups have also been published (*67,69*).

In recording the infrared spectrum of a single crystal of a clay with definite layer structure, it is clear that both the intensity and frequency of the absorption bands will depend on the angle at which the incident radiation strikes the crystal plane. The intensity depends on the vector of the dipole-moment change, and thus, from Fig. 5-14, it can be seen that the intensity of a hydroxyl group vibration will depend on both the angle the hydroxyl group makes with a crystal plane and the angle of incidence of the infrared radiation. Fripiat and Toussaint (*70*) have utilized this effect and studied the variations in frequency and intensity of the four deuteroxyl groups in kaolinite as the angle of incidence is altered. The deuteroxyl groups are observed at 2724, 2713, 2700, and 2673 cm^{-1}, and the changes reported for different film orientations are given in Fig. 5-15. It can be seen that, as the clay lattice rotates, the intensity of the

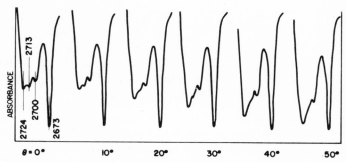

Fig. 5-15. *Spectra showing the changes in the relative intensities of the kaolinite hydroxyl groups as the angle of incidence of the infrared beam is altered. [Redrawn from Reference (70), courtesy of the Journal of Physical Chemistry.]*

low-frequency component remains fairly constant, but the higher-frequency bands become more pronounced. From a consideration of the probable orbital structures of the oxygen atoms in the unit cell, Fripiat and Toussaint concluded that the high- and medium-frequency bands were due to hydroxyl groups parallel to the c axis, whereas the low-frequency band was probably due to a hydroxyl group tilted at about 110° to that axis. The low-frequency component can therefore be attributed to hydroxyl groups in the inner octahedral layer, whereas the medium- and high-frequency values are attributed to hydroxyls in the upper octahedral layer.

The band intensities are also a function of the temperature of the sample, but it was found that above about 360° the spectra did not change as the temperature was increased. Since this temperature correlates with a significant change in the surface conductivity of the kaolinite, Fripiat and Toussaint attribute the frequency changes up to this point to a proton delocalization that, at 360°C, gives rise to a "prehydroxylation state." Above 360°C, dehydroxylation of the clay becomes measurable, and the kinetics have been recorded (71). Destruction of the octahedral sheet is found to be essentially complete before the tetrahedral sheet is affected (72).

B. Other Silicate Structures

The infrared spectra of nearly fifty silicate structures have been published by Saksena (73,74), and the intensities and positions of the OH stretching frequencies have been discussed. Considerable variations in the intensity of the bands due to the hydroxyl groups have been noted, particularly as the cation is changed. An interesting example of this effect is in the structure of the muscovite minerals. Here it has been shown that, whereas the Al^{3+} and Mg^{2+} muscovites exhibit strong OH bands which are easily observed, the substitution of Fe^{3+} causes only a weak hydroxyl band to appear. The varying angle of incidence method discussed above has also been used to determine the orientation of the OH bond axes in muscovite and other minerals (75).

C. Montmorillonite

Montmorillonite clays are known to have catalytically active surfaces, particularly after they have been acid-washed and activated. The dehydration of both montmorillonite and vermiculite clays has been followed by Fripiat and his co-workers (76) by using a combination of X-ray diffraction and infrared spectroscopy. A study of the intensity of the 6.1 μ (1638-cm^{-1}) H_2O bending frequency as a function of the dehydration temperature enabled these workers to show that free water still existed in all samples at temperatures up to 400°C. This is a much higher temperature than is required for complete desorption from alumina or silica–alumina surfaces. The temperature required for a given degree of dehydroxylation was found to be independent of the cation in the clay, and it was found that dehydroxylation of structural hydroxy groups took place before the molecular dehydration was complete. The montmorillonite clays are characterized by a large surface area; and it is noteworthy that the kaolinite clays, which do not have internal surfaces are dehydrated at much lower temperatures.

D. Adsorption Studies on Clays

1. Ammonia Adsorption

Clay surfaces, particularly those of acid-treated montmorillinite clays, like other alumina-containing surfaces, have considerable acidity (77). This has been shown colorimetrically by the use of indicator dyes and by the determination of the cation exchange capacity (78). It would be expected, therefore, that the infrared spectrum of ammonia adsorbed on these materials would give some evidence of the presence of surface Lewis or Brönsted acid sites. The spectra observed, however, are somewhat complicated because of the variety of reactions that can occur, and few studies on completely dehydrated surfaces appear to have been carried out. Bands ascribable to species adsorbed on true Lewis acid sites have not been observed.

Adsorption isotherms of ammonia on clay minerals have been reported by many workers, and it is found that the amount of ammonia adsorbed is dependent on the exchangeable cation. The adsorption follows the same order as the hydration properties of the respective ions, namely,

$$H^+ > Ca^{2+} > Na^+ > K^+$$

As was seen from the reaction between kaolinite and potassium acetate, the adsorption process on clays is not limited to the external surface, and adsorption of ammonia on the montmorillonite clays causes an expansion of the 001 spacing. Combined adsorption–desorption experiments show that a hysteresis loop is followed as the pressure is increased and reduced.

By studying the infrared spectra of ammonia adsorbed on a montmorillonite clay, Mortland and co-workers (77) determined that an inverse linear relationship existed between the formation of the NH_4^+ bending frequency (1450 cm^{-1}) and the disappearance of the hydroxyl stretching frequency. The frequency of both the stretching and bending N—H vibrations was a function of the exchangeable cation. A hydrogen-substituted montmorillonite, for instance, gave rise to NH_4^+ stretching and bending frequencies at 3311 and 1433 cm^{-1}, as compared to values of 3333 and 1459 cm^{-1} obtained for the Na$^+$ clay. In view of these results it was proposed that the adsorbate gas interacted with preadsorbed water to give the NH_4^+ ion,

$$NH_3 + H_2O \rightleftharpoons NH_4^+ + OH^-$$

The water molecules are presumably close to the exchangeable cation—hence the dependence of both the NH_4^+ and H_2O frequencies on the nature of the cation. This reaction proceeds very colorfully when a Cu^{2+} clay is used (79). The first stage in the reaction is the replacement of the coordinated H_2O by NH_3 with the formation of a Cu(NH$_3$)$_4^{2+}$ species. This has the usual deep blue color of the copper ammonium complexes.

When ND$_3$ was added to a Ca^{2+} montmorillonite, an OD stretching frequency was observed at 2632 cm^{-1} (77). This extremely low value possibly indicates considerable perturbation of the normal frequency, presumably owing to particular environmental conditions. Russell (80) has commented on this proposal and suggested an alternative explanation. He suggests that, during the reaction of ammonia with the clay, the exchangeable cations can be precipitated as basic hydroxides in the interlayer space. Ammonium ions then replace the exchangeable cations at the exchange sites, i.e.,

$$\text{clay—}Ca^{2+} + 2NH_3 + 2H_2O = \text{clay—}(NH_4^+)_2 + Ca(OH)_2$$

Pure calcium hydroxide gives an OH stretching frequency at 3644 cm^{-1} (OD $\simeq$ 2680 cm^{-1}), and since a completely hydroxylated form would give a somewhat lower value, this explanation seems very reasonable.

2. Amine Adsorption

The adsorption of butyl- and propylamines and ethylene- and propylene-diamines onto clay surfaces from benzene solution has been reported in a series of three papers by Servais et al. (81–83). Protonation occurs in all cases, the infrared spectra showing the presence of alkylammonium, or diammonium, cations. Addition of monoamines to H$^+$, Al^{3+}, Na$^+$, and Ca^{2+} montmorillonites gives rise to a species that is characterized by the perpendicular orientation of the aliphatic chain with respect to the 001 plane. Two deformation vibrations attributable to the RNH$_3^+$ grouping are observed at the same frequency as in the corresponding pure chloride. When the diamines are added to the acid montmorillonite, however, the aliphatic chain is found to be oriented parallel to the 001 plane and in this case an appreciable shift in frequency of the symmetrical RNH_3^+ deformation band is observed. When an excess of the diamine is added to the H^+ (or Na^+) montmorillonite, a second type of adsorbed species is formed. In this case, the aliphatic chain is perpendicular to the 001 plane, and an NH_2 deformation band can be recognized. Similar observations with a different interpretation have been made in the case of ethylamine adsorption (79).

The strong acidity of acid-washed montmorillonite has an interesting extension in its reaction with cobalt(III) hexammine chloride (84). The $Co(NH_3)_6^+$ ion reacts immediately with surface protons to form an adsorbed NH_4^+ species and precipitate cobalt hydroxide. The NH_4^+ is the ion removed by further exchange.

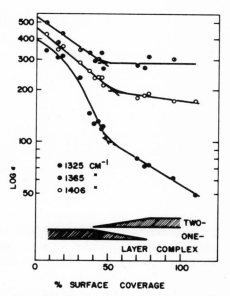

3. Ketone Adsorption

The infrared spectra of 2,5-hex-anedione and 2,5,8-nonanetrione adsorbed on Ca^{2+} montmorillonite have been published by Hoffmann and Brindley (85,86) together with data on the extinction coefficients of the various vibrations as a function of surface coverage. The ketones were adsorbed on the clay from aqueous solution, and the infrared spectra were studied by differential techniques. Only small changes in frequency were noted as the organic molecule was adsorbed on the surface, indicating that the adsorption is physical in nature. Preadsorbed water was

Fig. 5-16. Changes in the extinction coefficient of the C—H bending vibrations of 2,5-hexanedione as a function of surface coverage. [Redrawn from Reference (86), courtesy of the Journal of Physical Chemistry.]

removed from the surface as coverage of the organic material was increased, and the original H_2O bending vibration at 1632 cm^{-1} became shifted to 1653 cm^{-1} during this process. A plot of the extinction coefficient of the C—H bending vibrations (1300–1400 cm^{-1}) as a function of surface coverage showed a sharp break at $\theta = 0.5$. This was interpreted as being due to the initial formation of a one-layer complex followed by the formation of a two-layer complex (Fig. 5-16).

In the adsorbed state, the carbonyl stretching frequency is observed at the same position as in the crystalline state, and this leads to a picture of the one-layer complex in which the ketone molecules lie flat between the clay plates with the carbonyl groups providing bonding to adjacent molecules. The configuration of the molecules in the two-layer arrangement is not so specific. Interaction between the organic molecules must be presumed and is in fact evidenced by the considerable broadening of the observed peaks and the changes in relative intensities.

5-5. MAGNESIUM OXIDE

A. Surface Hydroxyl Groups

The thermal decomposition of magnesium hydroxide and the subsequent rehydration of the oxide thus formed has been studied by using infrared spectroscopy (*87, 88*). The magnesium hydroxide initially exhibits a broad absorption band between 3650 and 3700 cm^{-1} that is due to the antisymmetrical OH stretching vibration of the lattice hydroxide and a small band at 3770 cm^{-1} that is a combination band also characteristic of the bulk material. Thermal decomposition at 300° in vacuo causes these bands to be gradually removed, and new bands are produced at higher frequencies. A band at 3710 cm^{-1} is first observed, and this in turn slowly disappears, leaving a sharp peak at 3752 cm^{-1} together with a broad band at 3610 cm^{-1}. In conformity with the interpretation of similar bands observed in the spectrum of silica and other oxides, the sharp peak at 3752 cm^{-1} is attributed to a free surface hydroxyl group and the band at 3610 cm^{-1} is attributed to a hydrogen-bonded hydroxyl group.

After a 2-hr heat treatment at 300°C, molecular water is no longer present on the surface, and this is evidenced by the absence of a bending vibration in the 1600–1650 cm^{-1} region of the spectrum. Further heating causes the bands at 3610 and 3652 cm^{-1} to disappear slowly until, at 750°C, only the free surface hydroxyl grouping can be seen. Further heating to 900°C causes the onset of the sintering process, and the hydroxyl groups become broadened and shifted to 3725 cm^{-1}. As with the silica surface, the species formed during the readsorption process are dependent upon the prior thermal history of the oxide sample.

Readsorption of water, at less than monolayer coverage, onto a completely dehydrated surface causes replacement of the 3752-cm^{-1} band and formation of a broad hydroxyl band at 3550 cm^{-1}. This latter frequency is to be compared with the value of 3610 cm^{-1} observed in the original sample. Above a surface coverage of 0.11 molecules/Å^2 (9H$_2$O/100 Å^2), molecular water becomes adsorbed on the surface and all the hydroxyl bands are broadened and shifted to lower frequencies. The 3725-cm^{-1} band, for instance, appears at 3675 cm^{-1}, a shift of 77 cm^{-1}. This shift is much less than that observed for H$_2$O on silica ($\Delta \nu = 200$ cm^{-1}) and is interpreted in terms of a more basic surface hydroxyl group. This is in conformity with the ideas already expressed on the acidity of surface hydroxyl groups and provides further evidence that the frequency of a surface hydroxyl group cannot be taken as evidence of the acidity of the group in surface studies. The magnesium oxide is much more ionic than silica, and it would therefore be expected that the surface hydroxyl groups would be more like OH$^-$ ions than the phenolic-type hydroxyl groups that are formed on the more covalent silica lattice. It is interesting to note, therefore, that the OH—OD exchange reaction is slow and difficult to accomplish (87), a result that also agrees with the basic nature of the hydroxyl group.

The readsorption of water onto the dehydrated magnesium oxide surface is thought to involve reaction with a surface Mg$^+$—O^{2-}—Mg$^+$ grouping, with the consequent formation of two Mg$^+$OH$^-$ groups. Evidence for this supposition is provided by the adsorption of H$_2$S on the dehydrated surface. In this case a single sharp —SH band and a single broad OH stretching band are produced. By considering the magnesium oxide surface to comprise the crystal face of lowest energy (110 plane), Anderson et al. were able to calculate that all the terminal valencies would be satisfied when a surface adsorption of nine molecules of water per 100 Å^2 of surface had occurred. A plot of the water retention as a function of outgassing temperature showed a distinct break at this coverage, and as has already been mentioned, the infrared spectra revealed the presence of molecular water only at surface coverages higher than the 9 molecules/100 Å^2.

The band that is observed at 3710 cm^{-1} during the initial stages of the dehydroxylation is of interest in that it is apparently due to a metastable state. Once removed, it can be reformed only by a drastic rehydration involving multilayer adsorption of water and redrying. That it is due to a surface species is shown by its perturbation during the adsorption of water. Complete removal of the band is never observed, and apparently only about 50% of these groups are available as adsorption sites.

B. Surface Activity

The surface of magnesia has been shown to react with formic acid with the production of surface formates, but no interaction with the hydroxyl groups was noted (*89*). The infrared spectrum of ethylene oxide and its polymeric products on magnesia has also been reported. (*90*)

5-6. TITANIUM DIOXIDE

A. Surface Hydroxyl Groups

Titanium dioxide occurs in two well-known crystallographic forms, anatase and rutile. It has enjoyed some popularity as an adsorbent in physical adsorption studies, owing to the fact that it appears to have a chemically stable, reproducible surface at low temperatures. Industrially, its use as a pigment in the paint industry give it considerable commercial value, and it is indeed surprising that only two spectroscopic studies on the nature and chemistry of its surface have appeared so far. The original work on this system was carried out by Yates (*91*), but since a recent study (*92*) indicates that the extent of surface reduction is an important parameter in the dehydroxylation process, the spectral details of the latter work only (on rutile) will be considered. The rutile, as obtained by Lewis and Parfitt (*92*), showed the presence of bands at 3300, 1620, 1440, 1400, and 1270 cm^{-1}. The first two bands are probably due to adsorbed water and the last three to surface carbonate impurities. Heating to 200°C causes removal of the molecular water, and a small band is observed at 3660 cm^{-1} together with a broad band at 3350 cm^{-1}. At 300°C three sharp bands become visible at 3730, 3690, and 3660 cm^{-1} and the 3350 cm^{-1} band is reduced in intensity.

On further heating to 400°C, the 3730-cm^{-1} band moves to higher frequencies (3740 cm^{-1}) and has a lower-frequency tail. The 3660- and 3690-cm^{-1} bands are gradually eliminated. The "carbonate" bands at 1440 and 1400 cm^{-1} are removed at 400°C, but the 1270-cm^{-1} band remains unaffected. Further heating to 610°C for 2½ hr gradually reduces the intensity of the 3740-cm^{-1} band and at this stage gives a symmetrical absorption peak. Comparison of these results with those obtained for silica and alumina shows that the behavior of the titania surface is intermediate between that of the other two oxides. Three distinct types of hydroxyl bands are observed, but at this stage it cannot be stated that they are due to separate species rather than to separate hydrogen-bonding interaction. The gradual disappearance of the two lower-frequency bands with increasing temperature and the appearance of the low-frequency assymetry on the 3740-cm^{-1} group are very reminiscent of the spectra reported during the dehydroxylation of silica and suggests the hydrogen-bonding interpretation.

Lewis and Parfitt found that the hydroxyl vibrations were observed only if the titania had been exposed to oxygen after sample activation. If the surface was not well oxidized, the hydroxyl absorptions were strongly perturbed and appeared to be hydrogen-bonded. An extreme example of this is reproduced in Fig. 5-17, where it is apparent that there is no evidence whatsoever of the surface hydroxyl groups until oxygen is added to the system. No real explanation of this effect is available, although a "geometric" reorganization associated with the removal of surface impurities or surface defects has been suggested. This reorganization is thought to move the hydroxyl groups farther away from each other, thus removing the hydrogen-bonding interaction. This explanation, however, can hardly cover the extreme example shown in Fig. 5-4, because the effect of hydrogen bonding is to cause a considerable increase in intensity as well as frequency perturbation. If Lewis acid sites are produced adjacent to the surface Ti—OH groups during the heating process, it seems wildly possible that the filled orbitals on the hydroxyl

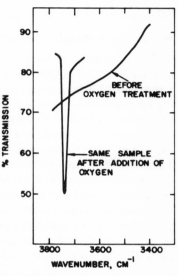

Fig. 5-17. *The effect of oxygen adsorption on the observability of the hydroxyl vibration on the titania surface.* [*Redrawn from Reference (92), courtesy of the Transactions of the Faraday Society.*]

oxygen atom could interact with the vacant orbitals associated with the Lewis acid site. This could give rise to a species that is completely changed in symmetry and no longer gives the characteristic OH stretching frequency. An interaction can be envisaged of the type

On rehydration at low surface coverages, the intensity of the band due to the isolated hydroxyl group (3740 cm^{-1}) is unaffected, except that a low-frequency tail is produced together with a band at 3660 cm^{-1}. The latter band is attributed to hydrogen-bonded hydroxyl groups that are possibly formed by interaction with strained Ti—O—Ti linkages. Hydrogen-bonded water molecules, however, could give a similar band, and thus a definite conclusion cannot be drawn.

B. Carbon Monoxide on Titania

The adsorption of carbon monoxide on a (deuterated) sample of anatase (91) has been shown to give rise to a major band at 2205 cm^{-1} and a shoulder at 2190 cm^{-1}. On increase of the carbon monoxide pressure, the lower-frequency band increases in intensity until, at a pressure of 5.88 cm, it dominates the spectrum. With rutile, only one band is observed. This occurs at 2195 cm^{-1} at low pressure and shifts to lower frequencies as the CO pressure is increased. A maximum shift of 13 cm^{-1} was noted at a pressure of 35 cm. No interaction with the surface deuteroxyls was noted during this adsorption, and the results are essentially independent of the degree of oxidation of the sample. The carbon monoxide is only weakly adsorbed, and since the position of the C—O vibration is very close to that observed during carbon monoxide adsorption on other oxide surfaces, it is attributed to a species held linear to the surface, possibly by a weak σ bond or by dipole interaction.

C. Carbon Dioxide on Titania

Carbon dioxide is chemisorbed on the anatase surface to form a species that exhibits two strong peaks at 1580 and 1320 cm^{-1} in its infrared spectrum. The intensities of the peaks depend on the carbon dioxide pressure. A weak shoulder that is detected at about 1500 cm^{-1} is easily removed by evacuation. During both the adsorption and desorption process, the band at 1580 cm^{-1} is the more intense. By analogy with the bands reported by other workers for ionized carboxylic acids (1610–1550 cm^{-1} and 1420–1300 cm^{-1}), Yates (91) tentatively classified the adsorbed species as a CO_2^- group formed by an electron–transfer reaction with the surface. The broadness of the bands was taken as an indication of surface heterogeneity.

The adsorption of carbon dioxide on rutile was found to be different from that on anatase, and, in this case, two strong bands were observed at 1330 and 1485 cm^{-1} with a shoulder at 1580 cm^{-1}. This shoulder corresponds to the strongest absorption in the spectrum of carbon dioxide on anatase, whereas on rutile it is the weakest. Conversely, the 1330-cm^{-1} band, which was the weaker of the two bands on anatase, is the most intense on the rutile. Assignment of these bands cannot definitely be made, but the present writer favors assignment to a bidentate carbonate complex,

$$
\begin{array}{c}
\quad\quad\quad O \\
\quad\quad\diagup\quad\diagdown \\
M\quad\quad\quad C{=}O \\
\quad\diagdown\quad\diagup \\
\quad\quad\quad O
\end{array}
$$

in the case of the anatase and a monodentate carbonate complex,

$$
\begin{array}{c}
\quad\quad\quad\quad O \\
\quad\quad\quad\diagup \\
M{-}O{-}C \\
\quad\quad\quad\diagdown \\
\quad\quad\quad\quad O
\end{array}
$$

in the case of the rutile.

5-7. BERYLLIUM OXIDE

A. Surface Hydroxyl Groups

The infrared spectrum of beryllium oxide that has been exposed to water vapor at 20°C shows the presence of four absorption bands at 3300, 1630, 1550, and 1390 cm^{-1}. (93). The 1390-cm^{-1} band is unaffected by the adsorption–desorption processes and is associated with the beryllium oxide structure. The bands at 1630 and 3300 cm^{-1} are clearly indicative of adsorbed molecular water. They are removed from the spectrum by evacuation at room temperature. After evacuation at 350°C, the band at 3300 cm^{-1} is much reduced in intensity, although it remains very broad. It is completely removed from the system only by prolonged heating at 550°C. In view of the fact that the 1630-cm^{-1} band is completely removed at room temperature, the band at 3300 cm^{-1} must be attributed to surface hydroxyl groups that are hydrogen-bonded very strongly with each other. "Free" surface hydroxyl groups are apparently not formed on this surface.

The band at 1550 cm^{-1} is of some interest, because it is removed on heating at 350°C and replaced by a band at 1580 cm^{-1}. Readsorption of either water or methanol causes replacement of the 1580-cm^{-1} band and reformation of the 1550-cm^{-1} band. The band is not exchanged by D$_2$O, and thus, although it is clearly related to the surface adsorption process, it cannot be attributed to a hydroxyl group. Stuart and Whateley (93) attribute this band to a defect phenomenon, and it is suggested that the chemisorption process increases the number of defects present in the bulk crystal. A similar band has been reported in single crystals of beryllium oxide and has been attributed to this defect structure.

Bands of a similar type have been noted by Basila (*35*), Matsushita and Nakata (*94*), and Little and Amberg (*23*) during adsorption studies on alumina, zinc oxide, and chromia–alumina, and they also are attributable to defect formations.

B. Carbon Dioxide on Beryllia

The infrared spectrum of carbon dioxide chemisorbed on beryllium oxide samples that have been uniformly degassed at 450°C shows the presence of three bands at 1630, 1440, and 1220 cm^{-1}, in addition to the band, already discussed, that is present at 1580 cm^{-1}. All three bands are observed at temperatures below 200°C, but above this temperature only one band, at 1440 cm^{-1}, is observed. Both the rate of growth and decomposition of these bands follow Elovich kinetics (*15*)

$$dx/dt = ae^{-bx}$$

and show a transition at 200°C. Clearly, two surface species are present, the low-temperature species producing the bands at 1640 and 1220 cm^{-1} and the high-temperature species producing the 1440-cm^{-1} band. These species are defined as a bidendate carbonate complex and a symmetrical carbonate ion, respectively.

It is of some interest to note that the rate of growth of the 1580-cm^{-1} defect band also follows the same Elovich kinetics as the carbonate bands. This is not true during the desorption process, however, when a temperature of 450°C is found necessary to remove the defects.

5-8. SURFACE CARBONATES

From the discussions on the reactions of carbon monoxide and carbon dioxide on oxide surfaces presented thus far, it is clear that several species that give rise to infrared absorptions in the 1300–1600-cm^{-1} region of the spectrum can be formed. Since these species are of importance as possible intermediates in the catalytic oxidation of carbon monoxide, their nature and structure are of some concern. Although many data have now been collected, there are as yet no definitive assignments that can be made. It would, however, seem wise at this stage to digress and discuss some of the structures that have been proposed and their correlation with the spectra of known inorganic complexes of a similar nature. A listing of the frequencies observed for various surface species during carbon monoxide and carbon dioxide adsorption is given in Table 5-4. The frequencies observed for certain types of coordinated carbonate species are given in Table 5-5.

TABLE 5-4

Carbonate Bands Observed on Oxide Surfaces

Surface	Adsorbate	Bands						Ref.
Rutile	CO_2			1580	(1500)w	1320		91
Anatase	CO_2			(1580)w	1485	1330		91
BeO								
20°C	CO_2		1630		1440		1220	93
200°C	CO_2				1440			93
ZnO								
20°C	CO_2		1640		1430			99
200°C	CO_2			1570		1380	(1010)	99
200°C	CO			1575		1342		95
FeO	$CO + O_2$			1560		1330		96
NiO	CO		1615 or 1575		1425			110
NiO	CO_2		1615			1360		110
NiO	CO_2			1550	1408			109
Ni	CO_2		1640			1374		109
Ni	CO		1650		1450		1230	108
Na–X zeolite	CO_2	1715			1485, 1425	1365		58
Al_2O_3		1770	1640		1480		1232	24

TABLE 5-5

Infrared Spectra of Some Carbonate Complexes[a]

Compound	Frequencies, cm^{-1}					
Monodentate carbonate complexes, e.g., $[Co(NH_3)_5CO_3]Br$	1453	1373	1070	850	756	678
Bidentate carbonate complexes, e.g., $[Co(NH_3)_4CO_3]Cl$	1593	1265	1030	834	760	673
Covalent bidentate carbonate, e.g., $(CH_3O)_2CO$	1870	1260				
CO_3, e.g., $MgCO_3$	1460		1096		735	
CO_2^- ion[b]	1550–1610	1410				

[a] All data except ([b]) taken from Nakamoto (103).
[b] From reference (96).

Starting with a surface that contains metal ions, oxygen ions, and hydroxyl groups, it seems logical that one of the following species will be formed. (Interaction with hydroxyl groups has not been observed during carbonate formation.)

(1)	(2)	(3)	(4)
carboxylate	carbonate	monodentate carbonate	bidentate carbonate

Species (1) can be envisioned as forming on a surface by direct adsorption of carbon dioxide onto a metal ion by the transfer of an electron from the adsorbent to the adsorbate. The resultant species is similar to the ionized salts of the carboxylic acids (formates, etc.). As an XY_2 type of structure, it should give rise to both symmetric and asymmetric C—O stretching vibrations. These are typically found in the 1350–1400 and 1560–1580-cm^{-1} regions. The

torsional vibration is usually observed at about 650 cm^{-1} and is beyond the range usually available to surface chemists. The *most* important feature of this structure is that it does *not* give rise to any bands in the 1000-cm^{-1} region.

The carbonate-type species that can form on the surface can be due to the free ion (2), the monodentate form (3), or the bidentate form (4). The free CO_3 ion is a planar XY_3 species and, of the six possible vibrations, a maximum of four can be observed owing to degeneracy. Of these, the symmetrical C—O stretching mode (found at 1080 cm^{-1} in the Raman spectrum) is inactive in the infrared, and only three bands can be observed in the spectrum of this ion. One of these usually occurs at about 1440 cm^{-1}, and the others below 900 cm^{-1}. Again, *no* bands are observed around 1000 cm^{-1}.

The asymmetry that is introduced into the simple XY_3 structure by either mono- or bidentate ligand formation causes the ν_1 vibration (1080 cm^{-1}) to become infrared-active and the doubly degenerate ν_3 symmetric vibration (1440 cm^{-1}) to split into its two components. The degree of splitting is dependent upon the type of ligand formation and upon the covalent character of the metal–oxygen bond. The splitting is less in the case of the monodentate complex as compared with the bidentate complex, and the difference between C—O_I and C—O_{II} force constants is therefore greater in the bidentate complex than in the mono-dentate complex. This effect is reflected in the typical frequencies found for some Co^{3+} complexes containing these ligands (Table 5-5). The difference between ν C—O_I and ν C—O_{II} is only about 100 cm^{-1} for the monodentate complexes but is over 300 cm^{-1} for the bidentate complexes.

A further factor to be considered in studying the separation of these frequencies is introduced by the covalent character of the metal–oxygen bond. It has been found that a completely covalent bond, such as occurs in dimethyl carbonate, causes a further increase in the separation up to about 600 cm^{-1}. In this particular case, it should be noted that the main effect of the covalency is on the C—O_{II} bond. The C—O_I bond is very little affected by this process despite the fact that it is attached directly to the covalent species.

In determining the nature of the chemisorbed "carbonate" species, the most important point of departure is in differentiating between the carbox-ylate (1) and carbonate (2, 3, 4) possibilities. A glance at Table 5-5 shows that the single most distinguishing feature between these species is the presence or absence of a band at about 1070 cm^{-1}. Unfortunately, this is a difficult spectral region to observe because of the general background absorption due to the oxide samples themselves, and few workers have examined this region in any detail. Amberg and Seanor (95), however, have reported observation of a band in this region for adsorption on zinc oxide, and Blyholder (96), by using a flash evaporation–mull technique, has been able to observe the spectrum of carbon monoxide and oxygen adsorbed together on a nickel surface from 3500 to 750 cm^{-1}. Bands were found at 1560, 1330, 1040, and 830 cm^{-1}, and since they are in excellent agreement with those found for bidentate CO_3 complexes, they clearly eliminate the presence of a carboxylate-type species. It is felt by this writer that all the surface carbonates reported in the literature will have bands in the 1070-cm^{-1} region. The real problem in the assignment of observed frequencies in the 1200–1600-cm^{-1} region lies in distinguishing between mono- and bidentate species and accounting for other various species which are observed.

From Table 5-4 it can be seen that there are in general three types of carbonate species. These give bands at the following frequencies.

1. 1560–1580 cm^{-1} and 1320–1380 cm^{-1}
2. 1630–1640 cm^{-1} and 1220 cm^{-1}
3. About 1440 cm^{-1}

A single band at 1440 cm^{-1} can be attributed to the symmetrical carbonate ion. The work of Stuart and Whateley (*93*) shows that this is a relatively stable species that exists, at any rate on the beryllium oxide surface, at temperatures above 200°C. At this temperature, the species giving bands at 1630 and 1220 cm^{-1} has completely decomposed. The bands at 1630 and 1220 cm^{-1} are probably due to a bidentate complex, and since Blyholder has shown that the bands at 1560 and 1330 cm^{-1} are also due to this type of complex, it seems clear that the bidentate form is the preferred species. While it is obvious that minor variations in surface composition (preoxidation effects, etc.) can produce some variation in the positions of the characteristic frequencies, it is not clear way two types of adsorbed bidentate carbonate should exist under different circumstances on the same surface. Thus, why should carbon dioxide on zinc oxide give species (2) at room temperature and species (1) at 200°C? A possible explanation can be seen from a reexamination of structure (4). It is clear that the bidentate species is not of a single type, but can be the structure (4) or (5)

(4)   (5)

It seems likely, therefore, that a surface rearrangement can occur with the formation of (5) and (4) and vice versa. Intuitively, one might expect that the two metal atoms concerned in structure (4) will exert a greater influence on the splitting of the degenerate vibrations than the single metal atom postulated in (5). The bands at 1630 and 1220 cm^{-1} are therefore attributed to (4), and those at 1570 and 1330 cm^{-1} to (5).

5-9. ZINC OXIDE

A. Background Absorption

Zinc oxide is an *n*-type semiconductor that owes its conductivity to an excess of zinc atoms in the crystal lattice. The zinc ionizes to give interstitial zinc ions and free electrons according to the following equation:

$$Zn_i \rightleftharpoons Zn_i^+ + e$$

Oxygen is chemisorbed on the surface of zinc oxide, interacting with the interstitial zinc and with the consequent formation of zinc oxide. The adsorption may be summarized as follows:

$$O_2 + 2e \rightarrow 2O_{ads}^-$$

$$2O_{ads}^- + 2Zn_i^+ \rightarrow 2ZnO$$

This adsorption causes a decrease in the number of free electrons in the solid, and, since these electrons cause a considerable background absorption in the spectral region of interest, the degree of surface oxidation controls the background. This should be kept as small as possible in a study of surface species, and the best spectra of a surface species are obtained when a fully oxidized sample is employed.

When prepared in a high-area form, the zinc oxide has a tendency to sinter on heating. Under normal conditions, exposure to the atmosphere apparently causes the surface to react with the carbon dioxide and water in the air, giving rise to surface carbonates. These can be decomposed by heating and outgassing, but this procedure causes an increase in the background adsorption, and reoxidation is often necessary in order to secure sufficient transmission to observe the spectra of adsorbed species.

Taylor and Amberg (97) report that the zinc oxide shows strong background absorptions at 1527 and 1333 cm^{-1} and a weak band at 1350 cm^{-1}. These bands remain even on evacuation at 570°C for 19 hr. They are not present in single-crystal zinc oxide, but since their intensity is somewhat increased by the oxygen pretreatment, Taylor and Amberg speculate that they may be associated with the defect structure of the material.

Outgassing of the zinc oxide at elevated temperatures removes the adsorbed water from the surface, revealing the presence of some surface hydroxyl groups. The resolution of the spectrum is not, however, sufficient to support speculation regarding the number of these groups or their distribution on the surface.

B. Carbon Monoxide Adsorption

The adsorption of carbon monoxide on zinc oxide surfaces has been well investigated by Amberg and his co-workers (95, 97, 98) and also by Matsushita and Nakata (94, 99). Amberg and Seanor (95) report that carbon monoxide adsorbs on a highly oxidized Kadox sample (New Jersey Zinc Company) to give three strong bands at 2212, 1575, and 1342 cm^{-1}, together with two weak bands at 2135 and 2065 cm^{-1}. The adsorption process also causes an increase in the background absorption. The band at 2212 cm^{-1} is removed by pumping at 30°C, and, in view of the easy removal, the bonding is assumed to be physical in nature. The carbon monoxide molecule is a dipole of the type

$$\overset{\delta+}{C}\!=\!\overset{\delta-}{O}$$

the positive end being associated with the carbon atom. In view of this, Seanor and Amberg suggest that the adsorption process occurs by inter-action of this carbon atom with a negatively charged surface oxygen ion, thus giving a weakly held species. Adsorption by σ-bond complexation can also be considered, as will be seen in Section 6-6.

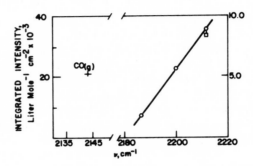

Fig. 5-18. *Change in integrated intensity of* CO *adsorbed on zinc oxide as a function of change in frequency.* [*Redrawn from Reference (95), courtesy of North-Holland Publishing Company, Amsterdam.*]

In the presence of carbon monoxide at 30°C, the bands at 1575 and 1342 cm^{-1} grow slowly and at approximately equal rates. These bands are attributed to a surface carbonate complex that is probably of the bidentate type. In some samples a band at 1470 cm^{-1} that may be due to a different carbonate species has been noted.

The rate of growth of the bands attributed to the "carbonate" structures was found to depend on the presence of the weakly adsorbed CO species (2200 cm^{-1}). Thus, removal of the weakly held species completely pre-vented the growth of the bands in the 1300–1600-cm^{-1} region. Amberg and Seanor have speculated that the weakly held species is an intermediate in the formation of the surface carbonate complex. The adsorption can be written according to the equation

$$CO_{ads} + Zn_i^+ + O_{2ads}^- \rightarrow ZnOCO_2^+ + e^-$$

This type of equation is supported by the facts that the background absorp-tion increases with time throughout the adsorption process and that the number of free carriers, as measured by electron spin resonance experiments, increased under the same conditions. The rate at which the transmission was decreased was independent of the carbon monoxide pressure, and this suggests that the rate-determining step could be the diffusion of the interstitial zinc to the surface.

The position of the band at about 2200 cm^{-1}, due to the weakly adsorbed carbon monoxide species, was found to be a function of the degree of surface oxidation. The band was observed at 2212 cm^{-1} on highly oxidized samples and at 2174 cm^{-1} on a poorly oxidized surface. Moreover, it was found that the integrated intensity decreased as the band was shifted to higher frequencies (Fig. 5-18). This interdependency of frequency, intensity, and surface oxidation has been attributed by Seanor and Amberg (95, 98) to changes in the dipolar nature of the adsorbed carbon monoxide caused by changes in the surface force field. These in turn are caused by different degrees of surface oxidation. A similar dependency of the frequency of this CO species upon the degree of oxidation of a number of oxides and metals has now been noted. An alternative explanation can be given in terms of unstabilized σ-bond formation between the adsorbed CO and a surface Lewis acid site (Section 6-6).

C. Carbon Dioxide Adsorption

The spectrum of carbon dioxide adsorbed on a zinc oxide sample has been obtained by Matsushita and Nakata (99). The zinc oxide used in this case was supported on a high-area silica gel. At room temperature the adsorption of carbon dioxide gave rise to two strong absorptions at 1640 and 1430 cm^{-1}. The rate of growth in intensity of these bands was similar and indicative that both bands are due to the same species. The bands are again attributed to the presence of a "carbonate" ion on the surface, and it seems likely that it is of the bidentate type.

On heating the carbon dioxide and zinc oxide to 200°C, new peaks were observed at 1570 and 1380 cm^{-1}, the previous peaks, at 1640 and 1430 cm^{-1}, being barely discernible as shoulders on the absorption curve. These bands are at frequencies similar to those reported by Amberg and co-workers for carbon monoxide adsorbed on oxidized zinc oxide surfaces (1560–1530, 1470, 1330–1342 cm^{-1}) and can probably be attributed to the same bidentate species. After the material stood for two days, however, the spectrum reverted almost to its original form, the major absorptions occcurring at 1640 and 1430 cm^{-1}. The bands at 1570 and 1380 cm^{-1} were observed only as shoulders on the other broad bands.

5-10. VANADIUM PENTOXIDE

The infrared spectra of vanadium pentoxide and V_2O_5–MoO_3 (3:1) catalysts have been reported by Terama and co-workers (*100*). The vanadium pentoxide has an infrared spectrum that shows a sharp absorption at 1025 cm^{-1} and a broad absorption at 800 cm^{-1}. The addition of molybdenum oxide to the vanadium pentoxide causes a gradual shift of the 1025-cm^{-1} band down to 1015 cm^{-1}. The band at 1025 cm^{-1} is due to a V—O stretching vibration in the lattice of the bulk material and, since this bond is located very close to the position found for the V$=$O bond in $VOCl_3$, it is assumed to have double-bond character and to be catalytically more reactive than the other vanadium–oxygen bonds. No evidence of a surface species has been obtained, however.

5-11. FERRIC OXIDE

A. Water Adsorption

A spectroscopic examination of the α-Fe_2O_3 surface has been reported by Blyholder and Richardson (*101, 102*). At room temperature, the freshly prepared ferric oxide exhibits a strong absorption at about 3500 cm^{-1} together with a band at 1615 cm^{-1}. The latter is identified as the H—O—H bending mode and shows the presence of molecular water on the surface. Prolonged evacuation at room or elevated temperatures removes the band at 1615 cm^{-1} and causes significant changes in the 3500-cm^{-1} region of the spectrum. Initially the band at 3500 cm^{-1} is reduced in intensity until two peaks can be clearly resolved: a sharp peak at 2.76 μ (3628 cm^{-1}) and a shoulder at 2.88 μ (3472 cm^{-1}). Further heating causes elimination of this shoulder and, at 475°C, a single peak is observed at 2.75 μ (3640 cm^{-1}). Analogy with the assignments made for the silica surface suggests that these bands are due to freely vibrating surface hydroxyl groups, the low-frequency asymmetry being attributable to hydrogen bonding between adjacent groups. Continued heating eventually removes all trace of surface hydroxyl groups.

Readsorption of water upon the completely dehydrated iron oxide surface causes a reversal of the dehydration process. Singly bonded hydroxyl groups are formed initially, and it is not until a considerable quantity of water vapor has been chemisorbed that the band at 1615 cm^{-1}, due to molecular water, is observed. In view of this, it seems likely that the rehydration process involves interaction of one molecule of water with a surface Fe—O species and the production of two surface hydroxyl groups. Physical adsorption of water then occurs by hydrogen bonding with these newly formed adjacent groups. When H_2S, the sulfur analog of water, is added to the ferric oxide surface, a hydroxyl band with about half the intensity of that produced by chemisorbed water is observed. This indicates that H_2S also reacts with a surface Fe—O linkage to produce one surface hydroxyl group and a SH species. In neither of these cases does the lone pair of electrons on the oxygen atom interact with the surface to give a coordinately bonded species.

The addition of water (and other adsorbents) to the completely dehydrated Fe_2O_3 also caused several interesting spectral changes in the region below 1670 cm^{-1}. The spectrum of the dehydrated samples shows the presence of bands at 6.6, 7.42, 7.75, 7.88, and 8.8 μ (1514, 1348, 1290, 1269, 1136 cm^{-1}). Adsorption of water causes the 7.42 and 7.75-μ (1348- and 1290-cm^{-1}) bands to diminish in intensity; new bands are produced at 7.62 and 8.2 μ (1313 and 1219 cm^{-1}); and the 8.87-μ band is increased in intensity. Similar changes are observed with all adsorbates. Blyholder and Richardson (*102*) eliminate the possibility of the new bands being due to OH deformation vibrations of surface hydroxyl groups and speculate that the bands are due to vibrations of surface atoms in the ferric oxide, possibly connected with defects caused by the presence of Fe^{2+} ions.

B. Ammonia on Ferric Oxide

When ammonia is added to a completely dehydrated Fe_2O_3 surface at room temperature, bands at 3.1 and 6.3 μ (3225 and 1588 cm^{-1}) are produced, together with the changes noted above. These bands are in the region characterized for N—H stretching and bending vibrations, respectively, and are so assigned. There is no trace of a band due to the formation of surface hydroxyl groups, and it must therefore be presumed that the ammonia does not decompose to form an —OH and an —NH_2 species. No bands corresponding to an NH_4^+ ion are detected, except in the presence of molecular water, and it is concluded that the ammonia retains its identity as an NH_3 species. The presence of only one band due to N—H stretching vibrations is disconcerting, because both symmetric and asymmetric vibrations would be expected. The absence of the second band is attributed to hydrogen-bonding interactions. Although this interpretation is supported by the relative intensities of the stretching and bending vibrations, it is clear that no definite assignment can be made.

REFERENCES

1. J. B. Peri and R. B. Hannan, *J. Phys. Chem.*, **64,** 1526 (1960).
2. J. B. Peri and R. B. Hannan, *Spectrochim. Acta*, **16,** 237 (1960).

3. J. B. Peri, *J. Phys. Chem.*, **69**, 211 (1965).
4. J. B. Peri, *J. Phys. Chem.*, **69**, 220 (1965).
5. E. P. Parry, *J. Catalysis*, **2**, 371 (1963).
6. M. L. Hair and I. D. Chapman, *J. Phys. Chem.*, **69**, 3949 (1965).
7. M. W. Tamele, *Discussions Faraday Soc.*, **8**, 270 (1950).
8. M. F. Lappert, *J. Chem. Soc.*, **1962**, 542.
9. D. Cook, *Can. J. Chem.*, **41**, 522 (1963).
10. I. D. Chapman and M. L. Hair, *Proceedings of the Third International Congress on Catalysis*, North-Holland, Amsterdam, 1965, p. 1091.
11. M. L. Hair and I. D. Chapman, unpublished work, 1965.
12. M. Misono, Y. Saito, and Y. Yoneda, *Proceedings of the Third International Congress on Catalysis*, North-Holland, Amsterdam, 1965, p. 408.
13. J. B. Peri, *J. Phys. Chem.*, **70**, 3168 (1966).
14. Y. Amenomiya, J. H. B. Chenier, and R. J. Cvetanovic, *Proceedings of the Third International Congress Catalysis*, North-Holland, Amsterdam, 1965, p. 1135.
15. H. A. Taylor and N. Thon, *J. Am. Chem. Soc.*, **74**, 4169 (1952).
16. J. B. Peri, *J. Phys. Chem.*, **69**, 231 (1965).
17. R. G. Greenler, *J. Chem. Phys.*, **37**, 2094 (1962).
18. A. A. Babushkin and A. V. Uvarov, *Dokl. Akad. Nauk SSSR*, **110**, 581 (1956).
19. M. L. Hair, unpublished data, 1965.
20. A. E. Hirschler and J. O. Hudson, *J. Catalysis*, **3**, 239 (1964).
21. K. Hirota, K. Fueki, K. Shindo, and Y. Nakai, *Bull. Chem. Soc. Japan*, **32**, 1261 (1959).
22. J. J. F. Scholten, P. Mars, P. G. Menon, and R. Van Hardeveld, *Proceedings of the Third International Congress on Catalysis*, North-Holland, Amsterdam, 1965, p. 881.
23. L. H. Little and C. H. Amberg, *Can. J. Chem.*, **40**, 1997 (1962).
24. N. D. Parkyns, *Proceedings of the Third International Congress on Catalysis*, North-Holland, Amsterdam, 1965, p. 914.
25. J. B. Peri, *Actes du Deuxième Congrès International de Catalyse, Paris, 1960*, Vol. 2, Editions Technip, Paris, 1961, p. 1333.
26. D. J. C. Yates and P. J. Lucchesi, *J. Chem. Phys.*, **35**, 243 (1961).
27. D. J. C. Yates and P. J. Lucchesi, *J. Phys. Chem.*, **67**, 1197 (1963).
28. P. J. Lucchesi, J. L. Carter, and D. J. C. Yates, *J. Phys. Chem.*, **66**, 1451 (1962).
29. J. L. Carter, P. J. Lucchesi, J. H. Sinfelt, and D. J. C. Yates, *Proceedings of the Third International Congress on Catalysis*, North-Holland, Amsterdam, 1965, p. 644.
30. M. L. Hair and P. L. Robinson, *J. Chem. Soc.*, **1960**, 2775.
31. T. H. Elmer and M. E. Nordberg, preprint, *VII International Congress on Glass, Brussels*, June 1965.
32. G. C. Pimentel and A. L. McClellan, *The Hydrogen Bond*, Reinhold, New York, 1960.
33. H. C. Brown and R. R. Holmes, *J. Am. Chem. Soc.*, **78**, 2173 (1956).
34. I. D. Chapman and M. L. Hair, *J. Catalysis*, **2**, 145 (1963).
35. M. R. Basila, *J. Phys. Chem.*, **66**, 2223 (1962).
36. A. Léonard, S. Suzuki, J. J. Fripiat, and C. DeKimpe, *J. Phys. Chem.*, **68**, 2608 (1964).
37. H. A. Benesi, *J. Phys. Chem.*, **61**, 970 (1957).

38. L. M. Roev, V. N. Filimonov, and A. N. Terenin, *Opt. i Spektroskopiya*, **4**, 328 (1958).

39. R. G. Haldeman and P. H. Emmett, *J. Am. Chem. Soc.*, **78**, 2922 (1956).

40. J. E. Mapes and R. P. Eischens, *J. Phys. Chem.*, **58**, 1059 (1954).

41. D. E. Nicholson, *Nature*, **186**, 630 (1960).

42. R. O. French, M. E. Wadsworth, M. A. Cook, and I. B. Cutler, *J. Phys. Chem.*, **58**, 805 (1954).

43. W. A. Pliskin and R. P. Eischens, *J. Phys. Chem.*, **59**, 1156 (1955).

44. N. W. Cant and L. H. Little, *Nature*, **211**, 69 (1966).

45. M. R. Basila and T. R. Kantner, *J. Phys. Chem.*, in press.

46. M. R. Basila, T. R. Kantner, and K. H. Rhee, *J. Phys. Chem.*, **68**, 3197 (1964).

47. M. R. Basila and T. R. Kantner, *J. Phys. Chem.*, **70**, 1681 (1966).

48. J. B. Peri, *J. Phys. Chem.*, **70**, 2937 (1966).

49. H. P. Leftin, *Proceedings of the Third International Congress on Catalysis*, North-Holland, Amsterdam, 1965, p. 1111.

50. H. P. Leftin and M. C. Hobson, *Advan. Catalysis*, **14**, 115 (1963).

51. C. Naccache, J. Bandiera, G. Wicker, and B. Imelik, *Proceedings of the Third International Congress on Catalysis*, North-Holland, Amsterdam. 1965, p. 1113.

52. J. Turkevich, F. Noraki, and D. Stamires, *Proceedings of the Third International Congress on Catalysis*, North-Holland, Amsterdam, 1965. p. 587.

53. P. B. Weisz and J. N. Miale, *J. Catalysis*, **4**, 529 (1965).

54. J. C. Frohnsdorff and G. L. Kington, *Proc. Roy. Soc. (London)*, **A247**, 469 (1958).

55. A. V. Kiselev and V. I. Lygin, *Surface Sci.*, **2**, 236 (1964).

56. V. N. Abramov, A. V. Kiselev, and V. I. Lygin, *Russ. J. Phys. Chem. English Transl.*, **39**, 60 (1965).

57. H. A. Szymanski, D. N. Stamires, and G. R. Lynch, *J. Opt. Soc. Am.*, **50**, 1323 (1960).

58. L. Bertsch and H. W. Habgood, *J. Phys. Chem.*, **67**, 1621 (1963).

59. J. L. Carter, P. J. Lucchesi, and D. J. C. Yates, *J. Phys. Chem.*, **68**, 1385 (1964).

60. C. L. Angell and P. C. Schaffer, *J. Phys. Chem.*, **69**, 3463 (1965).

61. H. W. Habgood, *J. Phys. Chem.*, **69**, 1764 (1965).

62. J. B. Uytterhoeven, L. G. Christner, and W. K. Hall, *J. Phys. Chem.*, **69**, 2117 (1965).

63. G. T. Kerr, E. Dempsey, and R. J. Mikovsky, *J. Phys. Chem.*, **69**, 4050 (1965).

64. J. L. Carter, D. J. C. Yates, P. J. Lucchesi, J. J. Elliot, and V. Kevorkian, *J. Phys. Chem.*, **70**, 1126 (1966).

65. V. N. Abramov, A. V. Kiselev, and V. I. Lygin, *Russ. J. Phys. Chem. English Transl.*, **37**, 613 (1965).

66. J. W. Ward and H. W. Habgood, *J. Phys. Chem.*, **70**, 1178 (1966).

67. R. L. Ledoux and J. L. White, *Science*, **143**, 244 (1964).

68. R. L. Ledoux and J. L. White, *J. Colloid Interface Sci.*, **21**, 127 (1966).

69. L. A. Romo, *J. Phys. Chem.*, **60**, 987 (1956).

70. J. J. Fripiat and F. Toussaint, *J. Phys. Chem.*, **67**, 30 (1963).

71. F. Toussaint, J. J. Fripiat, and M. C. Gastuche, *J. Phys. Chem.*, **67**, 26 (1963).

72. J. G. Miller, *J. Phys. Chem.*, **65**, 800 (1961).

73. B. D. Saksena, *Trans. Faraday Soc.*, **60**, 1715 (1964).

74. B. D. Saksena, *Trans. Faraday Soc.*, **57**, 242 (1961).

75. J. M. Serratosa and W. F. Bradley, *J. Phys. Chem.*, **62**, 1164 (1958).

76. J. J. Fripiat, J. Chaussidon, and R. Touillaux, *J. Phys. Chem.*, **64**, 1234 (1960).
77. M. M. Mortland, J. J. Fripiat, J. Chaussidon, and J. Uytterhoeven, *J. Phys. Chem.*, **67**, 248 (1963).
78. J. J. Fripiat, *Proceedings of the 12th National Conference on Clays and Minerals*, Macmillan, New York, 1964, p. 327.
79. V. C. Farmer and M. M. Mortland, *J. Phys. Chem.*, **69**, 683 (1965).
80. J. D. Russell, *Trans. Faraday Soc.*, **61**, 2284 (1965).
81. A. Servais, J. J. Fripiat, and A. Leonard, *Bull. Soc. Chim. France*, **1962**, 617.
82. A. Servais, J. J. Fripiat, and A. Leonard, *Bull. Soc. Chim. France*, **1962**, 625.
83. A. Servais, J. J. Fripiat, and A. Leonard, *Bull. Soc. Chim. France*, **1962**, 635.
84. J. Chaussidon, R. Calvet, J. Helsen, and J. J. Fripiat, *Nature*, **196**, 161 (1962).
85. R. W. Hoffmann and G. W. Brindley, *J. Phys. Chem.*, **64**, 1655 (1960).
86. R. W. Hoffmann and G. W. Brindley, *J. Phys. Chem.*, **65**, 443 (1961).
87. P. J. Anderson, R. F. Horlock, and J. F. Oliver, *Trans. Faraday Soc.*, **61**, 2754 (1965).
88. R. I. Razouk and R. Sh. Mikhail, *J. Phys. Chem.*, **62**, 920 (1958).
89. J. J. F. Scholten, P. Mars, P. G. Menon, and R. Van Hardeveld, *Proceedings of the Third International Congress on Catalysis*, North-Holland, Amsterdam, 1965, p. 881.
90. O. V. Krylov, M. J. Kushnerev, Z. A. Markova, and E. A. Fokina, *Proceedings of the Third International Congress on Catalysis*, North-Holland, Amsterdam, 1965.
91. D. J. C. Yates, *J. Phys. Chem.*, **65**, 746 (1961).
92. K. E. Lewis and G. D. Partfitt, *Trans. Faraday Soc.*, **62**, 204 (1966).
93. W. I. Stuart and T. L. Whateley, *Trans. Faraday Soc.*, **61**, 2763 (1965).
94. S. Matsushita and T. Nakata, *J. Chem. Phys.*, **32**, 982 (1960).
95. C. H. Amberg and D. A. Seanor, *Proceedings of the Third International Congress on Catalysis*, North-Holland, Amsterdam, 1965, p. 450.
96. G. Blyholder, *Proceedings of the Third International Congress on Catalysis*, North-Holland, Amsterdam, 1965, p. 657.
97. J. H. Taylor and C. H. Amberg, *Can. J. Chem.*, **39**, 535 (1961).
98. D. A. Seanor and C. H. Amberg, *J. Chem. Phys.*, **42**, 2967 (1965).
99. S. Matsushita and T. Nakata, *J. Chem. Phys.*, **36**, 665 (1962).
100. K. Terama, S. Teranishi, S. Yoshida, and N. Tamaru, *Proceedings of the Third International Congress on Catalysis*, North-Holland, Amsterdam, 1965, p. 282.
101. G. Blyholder and E. A. Richardson, *J. Phys. Chem.*, **66**, 2597 (1962).
102. G. Blyholder and E. A. Richardson, *J. Phys. Chem.*, **68**, 3882 (1964).
103. K. Nakamoto, *Infrared Spectra of Inorganic and Coordination Compounds*, Wiley, New York, 1963.
104. V. C. F. Holm, G. C. Bailey, and A. Clark, *J. Phys. Chem.*, **63**, 129 (1959).
105. R. M. Barrer, *Endeavour*, **23** (90), 122 (1964).
106. A. F. Wells, *Structural Inorganic Chemistry*, 3rd ed., Clarendon, London, 1962.
107. J. B. Peri, *Proceedings of the Third International Congress Catalysis*, North-Holland, Amsterdam, 1965, p. 654.
108. C. E. O'Neill and D. J. C. Yates, *Spectrochim. Acta*, **17**, 953 (1961).
109. R. P. Eischens and W. A. Pliskin, *Advan. Catalysis*, **9**, 663 (1956).
110. M. Courtois and S. J. Teichner, *J. Catalysis*, **1**, 121 (1962).

6

Adsorption on Metals and Metal Oxides

6-1. INTRODUCTION

Spectral observations of adsorbed molecules on metallic surfaces are not nearly as numerous or, in general, as well defined as those obtained on insulating and semiconducting oxides. The reasons for this are not hard to find and have already been mentioned in connection with experimental techniques. Whereas many of the precise data correlating catalytic effects with d-band properties of metals have derived from work on evaporated films, the spectroscopist is unable to use these films in transmission studies. The metal samples used in transmission experiments must be supported on an "inert" oxide by impregnation techniques, and the exact nature of the resultant product is not well known. Interaction of the metal with the support has been suggested (*1*) and there is difficulty in ensuring that the impregnated metallic salt is completely reduced to the metal. Moreover, the metallic particles sinter readily and it is difficult to ensure that their size remains less than the wavelength of the incident radiation. Consequently, scattering is an ever-present problem.

Because transition metals are commercially important in the catalytic industry, their surface properties have been most investigated. In particular, the adsorption of carbon monoxide upon metallic surfaces has been the subject of many investigations. Indeed, the main impetus for much of

217

the current activity in the spectroscopy of adsorbed molecules came from the pioneering work of Eischens and his co-workers in these systems.

6-2. CARBON MONOXIDE ADSORBED ON
NICKEL AND NICKEL OXIDE

A. Strongly Adsorbed Carbon Monoxide

The CO–Ni system has been the subject of numerous investigations, all of which agree to some extent and all of which disagree in the actual data obtained. Sample reproducibility is an obvious problem, and several interpretations have been given to account for the experimental results.

In one of the original investigations of this system, Eischens et al. (2) studied the spectral changes observed as carbon monoxide was adsorbed on a silica-supported nickel surface, and the series of spectra shown in Fig. 6-1 were obtained. The most interesting feature of these spectra is

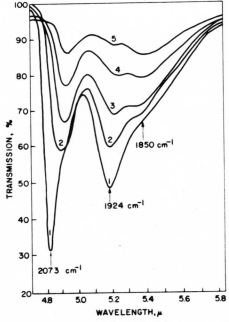

Fig. 6-1. *The adsorption of carbon monoxide on Ni–SiO₂ as a function of surface coverage.* [*Redrawn from Reference (2) by courtesy of the Journal of Physical Chemistry.*]

that the positions of the bands and their relative intensities are a function of surface coverage. Thus, the three bands that can be observed at about 4.82, 5.2, and 5.35 μ (2073, 1924, and 1870 cm^{-1}) vary in intensity as the surface coverage is altered. When CO is added to the Ni–SiO$_2$ samples at a pressure of 0.1 mm, a strong band is observed at 4.82 μ (2073 cm^{-1}) and a medium-intensity band is observed at 5.2 μ (1924 cm^{-1}). Shoulders are observed on these bands at 4.9 μ (2040 cm^{-1}) and 5.4 μ (1852 cm^{-1}), respectively. On pumping for 12 min, the 2073-cm^{-1} peak is no longer observed and the 2040-cm^{-1} shoulder becomes distinctly resolved, its intensity at this stage being equal to that of the 1924-cm^{-1} peak, which itself has been reduced to about 80% of its original value. The shoulder at 1852 cm^{-1} is also more obvious. Continued pumping causes reduction in intensity of all bands and slight changes in frequency. In the final spectrum, the 1924-cm^{-1} band is almost completely removed, the high-frequency band is observed at about 2030 cm^{-1} with a shoulder at 2040 cm^{-1}, and the shoulder at 1850 cm^{-1} is a clearly resolved band. At this stage the intensities of the 1850-cm^{-1} absorption and the 2030-cm^{-1} absorption are approximately equal.

According to data on metal carbonyl compounds available at that time, it was known that the C—O stretching frequency, observed in gaseous carbon monoxide at 2143 cm^{-1}, was shifted to between 2000 and 2100 cm^{-1} after monodentate ligand formation with transition-metal compounds of Ni, Fe, Co, Mn, and Re. Bidentate ligand formation caused a greater shift in frequency, the C—O stretch usually being observed below 2000 cm^{-1}. In view of this analogy, Eischens et al. (2) attributed the bands above 2000 cm^{-1} to a "linear" CO group on the surface (type A), and those below 2000 cm^{-1} to a "bridged" CO structure (type B).

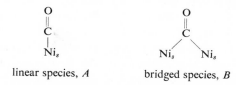

linear species, A   bridged species, B

Blyholder (3) has since reexamined these assignments on the basis of results on the CO–Ni system obtained under conditions that enabled him to get spectral data sown to 250 cm^{-1}, well beyond the range attained by other workers. The metallic nickel in this case was unsupported and was embedded in mineral oil. The carbon monoxide was adsorbed after dissolution in the mineral oil. Above 1400 cm^{-1} the results were analogous to those reported by Eischens et al. in that chemisorbed carbon monoxide was found to give strong bands at 2080 and 1940 cm^{-1}. These bands were not interrelated in any consistent manner and would therefore normally be assigned to different surface species—a linear structure and a bridged structure, respectively. Consideration of the two structures A and B shows that the linear species is of the XYZ type and should give rise to three vibrations: a C—O stretch, a Ni—C stretch, and an Ni—C—O bending mode. For the simple carbonyl sulfide molecule, S—C—O, these vibrations are observed at 2064, 859, and 224 cm^{-1}, respectively. In view of the much greater mass of the surface Ni atom, the two latter vibrations would be anticipated at much lower wave numbers in the surface complex than than those observed for S—C—O.

The bridged structure is of the ZXY$_2$ type (analogous to carbonyl chloride, Cl$_2$CO) and should give rise to six infrared-active vibrations. Most of these should be expected at low frequencies, but both the symmetric and asymmetric Ni—C stretching frequencies should have been observed in the spectral range available to Blyholder. In actuality, Blyholder was able to observe only one other band in his spectrum—at 435 cm^{-1}—and he attributed this to the single Ni—C stretching frequency expected from a linearly adsorbed species.

Most metal–carbon bonds exhibit a stretching force constant of about 2 mdynes/Å, and from this Blyholder estimated that the asymmetric stretching frequency for a bridged species should have been observed between 700 and 1000 cm^{-1}. If it is argued that the band observed at 435 cm^{-1} is the asymmetric stretching frequency, then this implies a Ni—C force constant of only 1 mdyne/Å—less than half of that reported for known metal-carbon bonds (4). The position of the band at 435 cm^{-1} is in good agreement with data obtained for nickel carbonyl, Ni(CO)$_4$, where the Ni—C stretching vibration and the Ni—C—O bending vibration have been assigned values of 422 and 466 cm^{-1}, respectively (5). The band observed by Blyholder in this region is very broad and possibly encompasses both of these absorptions. Blyholder's interpretation also receives support from the work of Kraihanzel and Cotton (6), who have now obtained inorganic complexes containing monodentate CO ligands that exhibit C—O stretching vibrations down to 1800 cm^{-1}. In view of the uncertainty regarding the existence of a bridged species, the bands above and below 2000 cm^{-1} will be referred to as type A and type B species, respectively, in the remainder of the text.

The addition of oxygen to carbon monoxide chemisorbed at the nickel-hydrocarbon oil interface gives rise to the spectra reproduced in Fig. 6-2. The bands at 2080 and 1940 cm^{-1} are removed and strong bands develop at

1560 and 1330 cm^{-1}, together with medium-intensity bands at 1040, 830, and 525 cm^{-1}. Since oxygen alone admitted to a freshly evaporated nickel surface gives rise to a similar broad band at 525 cm^{-1} and since bulk nickel oxide exhibits a broad band at 490 cm^{-1}, that absorption band is attributed to a nickel oxide species formed on the surface of the nickel metal. The positions of the bands at 1560 and 1330 cm^{-1} should be compared to the values found by other workers for CO_2 adsorption on oxides

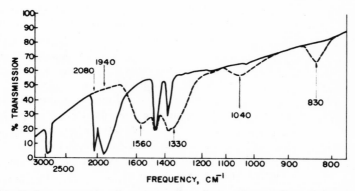

Fig. 6-2. *Carbon monoxide adsorption and surface carbonate formation on an iron surface. Solid line, CO adsorption; dashed line, after addition of oxygen. [Redrawn from Reference (3) by courtesy of North-Holland Publishing Company, Amsterdam.]*

and collected in Table 5-4. Clearly, a surface carbonate species has been formed. Discussion in Section 5-8 indicated that vibrations in these regions could probably be attributed to bidentate carbonate complexes. Blyholder's results add considerably to this assignment, because his experimental technique allows observation of the additional frequencies observed in inorganic complexes at 1030 and 834 cm^{-1} (7). The excellent agreement gives great credibility to the assignments and demonstrates the utility of Blyholder's technique.

B. Weakly Adsorbed Carbon Monoxide

In most work dealing with the adsorption of carbon monoxide on metals and oxides, a band in the region of 2200 cm^{-1} has been noted. It is due to a weakly held species, and it has been discussed by several workers. This band is also observed on nickel surfaces, and it will be considered later (Section 6-6) in a general discussion of the adsorbed carbon monoxide species.

C. Effect of the Supporting Oxide

In the work of Eischens et al. (2), their nickel sample was supported on a high-area silica substrate, and bands due to several adsorbed CO species were observed. Blyholder, with his oil-supported Ni, observed only two bands. Although these were at qualitatively similar positions in the spectrum, the exact frequencies were somewhat different than those reported in the earlier work. O'Neill and Yates (8) have examined the role of the supporting "inert" oxides on the surface properties of the nickel metal by studying the infrared spectra of carbon monoxide adsorbed on nickel samples supported on silica, alumina, and titania. The silica support apparently had little effect on the metallic nickel, but the alumina and titania supports induced gross variations both in the relative proportions of various species present and in the strength of the adsorption.

With both silica-supported nickel and alumina-supported nickel, O'Neill and Yates report spectra that are very similar to those reported by Eischens, Francis, and Pliskin. For the silica-supported samples, bands in the region of 2070–2050 and 1925–1900 cm^{-1} are reported, whereas the alumina-supported sample gave bands in the region of 2070–2040 and 1945–1958 cm^{-1}. Garland (9) reports bands at 2075–2045 and 1960–1910 cm.$^{-1}$ For titania-supported nickel, however, considerable changes in the relative intensities of the type A and type B species are noted. At low pressures a strong type A band is observed at 2080 cm^{-1}, but the type B species is only barely evident at 1925 cm^{-1}. Increasing pressure causes the 2080-cm^{-1} band to increase slightly in intensity and to broaden, owing to the appearance of a shoulder at about 2025 cm^{-1}. The 1925-cm^{-1} band also increases in intensity, but at higher pressures it is masked by the rapid appearance of a band at 1975 cm^{-1}. This band is due to an extremely weakly held species, which is completely removed by a 30-sec evacuation.

The relative rates of removal of the type A and B species on the three supports are shown in Fig. 6-3. In all three cases it is seen that the type A species is removed more rapidly than the type B species. The rate of removal of both species is greater with the titania support than with either the alumina or silica supports. In the case of the silica support, approximately 25% of the adsorbed CO is removed by a 30-min evacuation. This value is reportedly close to that observed for carbon monoxide desorption from reduced nickel powders after similar evacuation, and it tends to indicate that in this system the silica is indeed inert.

Although this work indicates that the support causes major differences in spectral observations, the actual method of sample preparation must also be of considerable importance. Thus, whereas neither O'Neill and Yates nor Eischens, Francis, and Pliskin could find any evidence of formation of nickel carbonyl, $Ni(CO)_4$, Yates and Garland (*10*) report the formation of this compound when treating an alumina-supported nickel sample with carbon monoxide at pressures of about 5 m. Indeed, these

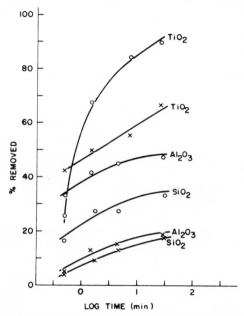

Fig. 6-3. *The rates of removal of carbon monoxide from nickel supported on silica, alumina, and titania:* ○, *type A species;* ×, *type B species.* [*Redrawn from Reference (8) by courtesy of the Journal of Physical Chemistry.*]

workers used this reaction to remove nickel from samples containing up to 25% nickel and were able to show that the relative intensities of the bands were a function of the amount of nickel deposited on the alumina surface. At full coverage, a 25% $Ni–SiO_2$ sample gave spectra almost identical with those of a 25% $Ni–Al_2O_3$ sample.

The variety of bands obtained by Yates and Garland were attributed to different crystalline, semicrystalline, and amorphous nickel sites, as shown in Table 6-1. In view of Blyholder's data, however, the assignments to bridged carbonyl groups must be considered tentative.

The complicated changes in frequency and intensity of the adsorbed CO species that are observed as surface coverage is altered have received an

TABLE 6-1[a]

Band	Frequency range, cm^{-1}	Band center, cm^{-1}	Species	Site	Strength of adsorption
A	1850–1940	1915	$\underset{\displaystyle Ni \qquad Ni}{\overset{\displaystyle O}{\underset{\displaystyle C}{\parallel}}}$ (bridged over two Ni)	Crystalline Ni	Very strong
B	1940–1990	1963	(O=C and C=O groups bridging over Ni, Ni)	Crystalline Ni	Moderately strong
C	1990–2050	2035	$\overset{\displaystyle O}{\underset{\displaystyle Ni}{\overset{\parallel}{C}}}$	Crystalline Ni	Very strong
D	2050–2070	2057	$\overset{\displaystyle O}{\underset{\displaystyle Ni}{\overset{\parallel}{C}}}$	Semicrystalline	Moderately strong
E	2070–2110	2082	$\overset{\displaystyle O}{\underset{\displaystyle Ni}{\overset{\parallel}{C}}}$	Dispersed Ni	Weak

[a] Assignment of bands to surface Ni—CO species by Yates and Garland (*10*). Reprinted from the *Journal of Physical Chemistry*, with permission.

alternative explanation fom Hammaker et al. (*11*). These workers propose that the complex results for carbon monoxide chemisorbed on silica-supported platinum can be explained on the basis of induced dipole–dipole interaction between the chemisorbed molecules. Further experimentation is required before a true explanation of these effects is obtained.

It should be noted that the data reviewed here have been obtained on supported-nickel samples. In view of the work of Peri (*12*), which has demonstrated the great difficulty of reducing such samples completely to the metallic state, there remains an element of doubt as to the nature and reproducibility of the surfaces investigated. The effect of incomplete reduction (or some dissociative chemisorption of the carbon monoxide) would be to create different adsorption sites on the metallic surface. The presence of the oxygen atoms would alter the energy of adsorption sites on adjacent nickel atoms and considerably complicate the spectrum as com-

TABLE 6-2

Effect of Reduction Treatment on the Position and Intensity of Carbon Monoxide Adsorbed on Silica-Supported Nickel[a]

Treatment	Effect at following frequencies, cm^{-1}:							
	2210	2198	2180	2140	2105	2080	2050	1960
Unreduced Ni–SiO$_2$	Small, strongly held	Intense proportional to pressure		Weak, strongly held		Very weak		—
H$_2$, 1 hr, 300°C	—	Reduced in intensity	Very weak	Very intense, strongly held	Very weak	Medium	Weak	—
H$_2$, 1 hr, 450°C	—	As before	—	Decrease in intensity		Medium– strong		Medium

[a] Data taken from Reference (*12*).

pared with that of the pure metal. Clearly, a reproducible sample must be the primary requisite in future experimentation.

The difficulty of achieving complete reduction and therefore, by inference, the effect of remaining oxygen on the nature of the adsorbed species are shown by the data given in Table 6-2. The data are taken from Peri's work on the nature of the Ni–SiO$_2$ surface (*12*). It can be seen that the effect of increased reduction is to cause the type *A* species to be observed at lower frequencies. The type *B* species is not observed until a well-reduced surface has been obtained.

D. Nickel Metal Films

In an effort to examine the infrared spectra of carbon monoxide chemisorbed on metallic nickel, several workers have used reflectance techniques on evaporated films or transmission through specially prepared porous films. The high-resolution reflectance spectra of Pickering and Eckstrom

(*13*) revealed the presence of two strong bands at 2060 and 2050 cm^{-1} together with a weak band at 2030 cm^{-1}. No bands attributable to a bridged CO species were observed. Indeed, no other bands were observed in the region 2300–750 cm^{-1}. Gardner and Petrucci (*14*) similarly report only a single band at 2060 cm^{-1}. Sardisco (*15*), however, from a transmission study, reports bands at 2020 and 1980 cm^{-1}.

In an attempt to explain the apparent differences in the position of the absorption peaks of CO on nickel, Garland et al. (*16*) developed a new experimental technique in which nickel films were prepared by evaporation of nickel in the presence of carbon monoxide gas at pressures ranging from 10^{-3} to 44 mm. The attraction of this technique is that spectra can be recorded from 4000 to 300 cm^{-1}. The results obtained by using this method are in general agreement with those of previous workers in that strong absorption bands of variable frequency and intensity were produced at about 2080 and 1900 cm^{-1}. However, these workers did note a new band of medium intensity that occurred at about 1620 cm^{-1}. The intensity and position of this band were very dependent upon the method of preparation of the film, particularly on the time that elapsed between the preparation of the sample and the recording of the spectrum. Addition of oxygen to the sample did not cause an increase in the intensity of the 1620-cm^{-1} band. It was argued therefore that this band was not caused by decomposition of the carbon monoxide and subsequent formation of a carbonyl compound on an oxide surface. The authors ascribed this band to a bridged carbonyl-type structure in which the carbon of the CO molecule was attached to two surface nickel atoms. The low frequency at which the band occurs was attributed to an interaction of the carbonyl oxygen with a third nickel atom, as shown.

$$\begin{array}{c} Ni_s \\ \diagdown \\ C{=}O \cdots Ni_s \\ \diagup \\ Ni_s \quad \textbf{(1)} \end{array}$$

This type of structure is analogous to that obtained for ketones adsorbed on Lewis acid sites on alumina. There the $>C{=}O$ stretching frequency is known to be shifted to about 1625 cm^{-1} from its normal position at 1780 cm^{-1} (Fig. 5-7). Diketones chelated to metal atoms also typically absorb in this region (*17*). In the assignment of the band to the species (**1**), however, the arguments of Blyholder regarding the presence of bridged CO species should be recalled. Garland et al. were unable to detect any bands attributable to the asymmetric Ni—C vibration that might be expected in the 400–1000-cm^{-1} region.

The addition of oxygen at room temperature to the adsorbed CO on Ni caused extensive removal of CO from the surface. This was evidenced by the complete disappearance of the type A band and considerable reduction in the intensity of the doublet observed for the type B species. Concomitantly the 1620-cm^{-1} band was slightly reduced in intensity and new bands appeared at 1530 and 1363 cm^{-1}. The two new bands are characteristic of surface carbonates and are so assigned.

A band at 1620 cm^{-1} has also been noted by Eckstrom (19) in a multiple-reflection study. This particular study is of note in that Eckstrom reports no fewer than 23 separate bands in the 1200–750-cm^{-1} region. Either this was a very complicated surface or the experimental data were subject to alternative explanation.

E. Adsorption on Nickel Oxide

The adsorption of carbon monoxide and carbon dioxide on nickel oxide surfaces was first described spectroscopically by Eischens and Pliskin (19). No adsorption was noted in the case of carbon monoxide, but the dioxide was adsorbed, giving bands at about 6.45 and 7.1 μ (1550 and 1408 cm^{-1}) with small shoulders at 6.1 and 7.27 μ (1640 and 1374 cm^{-1}). A later investigation on this system by Courtois and Teichner (20) employed a nickel oxide prepared from precipitated Ni(OH)$_2$, and it was found that the spectra recorded were somewhat dependent upon the pretreatment of the nickel oxide. The adsorption of carbon monoxide gave bands at 2005, 1965, 1615 or 1575, and 1425 cm^{-1}. The first two bands correspond to the type A and type B species found with nickel metal and suggest the presence of some metal in their sample. This could have been present initially or formed by partial reduction of the oxide surface during the adsorption. The two latter bands are due to surface carbonates, as already discussed. Adsorption of carbon dioxide on the nickel oxide gave bands at 1620 and 1370 cm^{-1}.

F. Nickel Carbonyl

In all the work on the Ni–CO system, the formation and observation of Ni(CO)$_4$ is an ever-present possibility. This compound may be identified spectroscopically by two infrared-active vibrations at 2057 and 422 cm^{-1} [ν (CO) and ν (Ni—C), respectively]. Few workers have reported the formation of this compound, though many have specifically analyzed for it. In this connection, Parkyns' (21) results on the adsorption of Ni(CO)$_4$ on alumina are of interest. Parkyns found that nickel carbonyl readily adsorbed on the alumina to give an infrared spectrum characteristic of the physically adsorbed species. Desorption of the $Ni(CO)_4$, however, revealed the presence of a surface species exhibiting bands at 2090 and 1832 cm^{-1}. These correspond to the type A and type B species already ascribed to carbon monoxide chemisorbed on nickel, and they indicate that the nickel carbonyl is dissociatively adsorbed on alumina to give finely dispersed nickel particles that, in turn, chemisorb the carbon monoxide produced by the decomposition. It should be noted that here again only two bands are reported. With yet another preparative method, the frequencies of the adsorbed CO species are different from those observed by other workers, and in this case the type B species vibrates at the lowest frequency yet reported.

6-3. THE NATURE OF THE Ni–SiO$_2$ SURFACE

A. Surface Hydroxyl Groups

The miscellany of results obtained for carbon monoxide adsorption on supported nickel can be taken as an indication of surface heterogeneity and sample nonhomogeneity. Despite this, however, there has been little attempt to define the nature of this surface. In view of this, the recent results of Peri (*12*) are of some importance. Peri observed that the addition of metallic nickel to the silica caused the appearance of a second type of surface hydroxyl group at about 3620 cm^{-1}, which is in addition to the group normally found on the pure silica surface at 3750 cm^{-1}. The band was prominent on the oxidized samples and was little affected by the subsequent reduction. Both of these surface hydroxyl groups underwent isotopic exchange at the same rate with deuterium gas at 500°C, and they were relatively unaffected by either oxidation or steaming. The new group, however, could be removed more rapidly from the surface than the 3750-cm^{-1} group by evacuation at 800°C following either a preoxidation or a steaming treatment. This new surface hydroxyl group was equated to a surface silanol group perturbed by a nearby surface nickel ion. The surface envisioned is thus somewhat analogous to a silica–alumina surface, and it is possible that the nickel ions create an inductive effect on the silanol group sufficient to cause this hydroxyl group to become more acidic than the normal Si—O—H. Ammonia adsorption, however, produced no evidence of an NH_4^+ species.

B. Ammonia Adsorption

Uchida and Imai (*22*) had previously noted (1962) that the surface of Ni–SiO$_2$ was acidic, and, in view of this, the spectrum of ammonia adsorbed on a Ni–SiO$_2$ surface is of some interest. Peri found that ammonia was strongly adsorbed by his Ni–SiO$_2$ surface, and the resultant spectrum showed major bands near 3400, 3300, and 1630 cm^{-1}. In conformity with previous interpretations, these are attributed to an NH$_3$ species coordinately bonded to surface Lewis acid sites, presumably incompletely coordinated nickel ions. Preadsorption of ammonia onto the Ni–SiO$_2$ surface prevented the adsortion of all carbon monoxide except the species that gave rise to the adsorption near 2050 cm^{-1}. Progressive removal of ammonia from the surface by evacuation at elevated temperatures enabled further adsorption of carbon monoxide to take place, the band at 2140 cm^{-1} reforming first, followed by the band at 2198 cm^{-1} (Table 6-2).

C. HCl Adsorption

In accord with his work on other Lewis acid surfaces, such as alumina and silica–alumina, Peri found that hydrogen chloride reacted with active

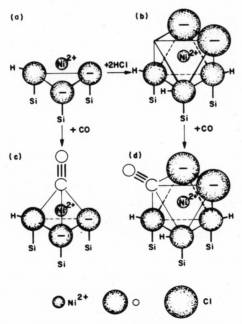

Fig. 6-4. *Peri's view of HCl and CO adsorption on Ni–SiO$_2$: (a) "acidic" tetrahedral Ni^{2+} ion; (b) after HCl adsorption; (c) after CO adsorption; (d) after HCl and CO adsorption. [Redrawn from Reference (12) by courtesy of the Faraday Society.]*

surface oxide ions to produce a surface chloride and additional hydroxyl groups (23). In this case, the spectrum in the 3000–3800-cm^{-1} region indicated the presence of a considerable number of hydrogen-bonded hydroxyl groups and the formation of some molecular water. Preadsorption of hydrogen chloride greatly affected the spectrum observed upon addition of carbon monoxide. The band normally observed on the untreated sample at 2198 cm^{-1} was suppressed, whereas a band at 2135 cm^{-1} was greatly increased in intensity. This result is interpreted as an interconversion of sites in the manner of Fig. 6-4.

6-4. CARBON MONOXIDE ADSORPTION ON OTHER METALS

A. Carbon Monoxide on Platinum

The infrared spectrum of carbon monoxide adsorbed on a platinum surface was first measured by Eischens et al. (2). Both silica- and alumina-supported samples were used. Adsorption of carbon monoxide on the silica-supported platinum led to the appearance of only one adsorbed species, which was shown by a spectral band at 4.82 μ (2073 cm^{-1}). Adsorption on the alumina-supported sample gave rise to two bands at 4.9 and 5.5 μ (2040 and 1820 cm^{-1}). In the case of the silica-supported sample, only one band was observed at all surface coverages. Although its position and intensity were functions of surface coverage, the absence of secondary bands makes it impossible to deduce whether the surface is homogeneous or heterogeneous. Eischens and co-workers speculated that the changes in frequency and intensity of the band due to the adsorbed carbon monoxide could be due to coupling interactions between two adsorbed molecules. In an endeavor to differentiate between these two possibilities, Eischens and his co-workers measured the relative intensities of the bands due to adsorbed $C^{12}O$ and $C^{13}O$ molecules as a function of surface coverage. If the intensity effects observed with the single isotopic species are due to surface heterogeneity, then it would be exected that both the $C^{12}O$ and $C^{13}O$ species would be affected equally and that their *relative* intensities would be unchanged as the surface coverage was altered. If, however, the adsorbed carbon monoxide molecules interact with each other, the relative intensities will no longer be linearly related. As can be seen from Figs. 6-5(a) and 6-5(b), the addition of mixtures of $C^{12}O$ and $C^{13}O$ to the silica-supported platinum gives rise to two bands at about 2060 and 2000 cm^{-1}, which are attributed to the respective isotopic species. The actual positions and intensities of the bands, however, are dependent on both the isotopic ratio and the degree of surface coverage.

Thus, in Fig. 6-5(a) at $\theta = 1$, a mixture containing 63 % C^{12}O (isotopic ratio 1.7) gives bands at 2060 and 1990 cm^{-1} (intensity ratio 4.2), whereas a mixture containing 36 % C^{12}O (isotopic ratio 0.56) gives bands at 2055 and 2000 cm^{-1} (intensity ratio 1.1). Theoretically, of course, the intensity ratio should be equal to the isotopic ratio. Desorption of carbon monoxide from the surface in the case of the 63 % C^{12}O mixture caused the intensity ratio to decrease. However, even at very low coverage, it was still as high as 2.2, compared with the theoretical value of 1.7.

Isotopic shifts can normally be used to determine the bond force constants and, by using the values obtained at the lowest coveages, Eischens et al. calculated values of 4.5×10^5 dynes/cm for the Pt—C bond and 16×10^5 dynes/cm for the C—O bond. In their original paper (2), these values are interpreted as indicating a single bond between the

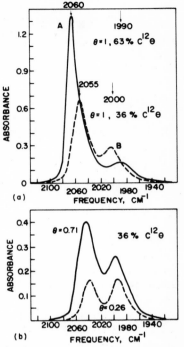

Fig. 6-5. The dependence of frequency and intensity of bands due to adsorbed (a) C^{12}O and (b) C^{13}O on surface coverage θ and isotopic ratio. [Redrawn from Reference (25) by courtesy of Spectrochimica Acta (Pergamon Press).]

platinum and carbon and a triple bond between the carbon and oxygen. Reference to Table 6-3, however, suggests that both bonds have considerable double-bond character. The actual values obtained for the two force constants are in good agreement with those obtained by Garland et al. (24) from observations of both stretching and bending vibrations.

In order to explain the apparently anomalous intensities, it is necessary to consider the coupling effects that can occur when two CO molecules are adsorbed close to each other on surface sites. Let us consider the four species shown next and the possible fundamental vibrations of the

TABLE 6-3

Force Constants of Some C—O and M—C Bonds Compared with Those of Some Adsorbed Species[a]

Molecules	Bond order	k	Bond	k
CO	Triple	18.5		
CO_2	2–3	15.5		
$R_2C{=}O$	Double	12.1		
$CH_3{-}O{-}CH_3$	Single	4.87		
$Fe(CO)_5$			Fe—C	3.36
$Ni(CO)_4$			Ni—C	2.1
$Zn(CH_3)_2$			Zn—C	2.4
$CO–Pt_s$		16		4.5
$CO–Fe_s$		14		4

[a] The force constants are given in millidynes per angstrom. After Blyholder (*4*).

adsorbed C—O species.

$$
\begin{array}{cccc}
\uparrow O \quad O \uparrow & \uparrow O \quad O \downarrow & \uparrow O \quad O \uparrow & O \uparrow O \downarrow \\
| \quad\quad | & | \quad\quad | & | \quad\quad | & | \quad\quad | \\
C^{12} \;\; C^{12} & C^{12} \;\; C^{12} & C^{12} \;\; C^{13} & C^{12} \;\; C^{13} \\
| \quad\quad | & | \quad\quad | & | \quad\quad | & | \quad\quad | \\
Pt_s{-}Pt_s & Pt_s{-}Pt_s & Pt_s{-}Pt_s & Pt_s{-}Pt_s \\
(1) & (2) & (3) & (4) \\
\text{active} & \text{inactive} & \text{active} & \text{active}
\end{array}
$$

It is clear that the vibrations of the adjacent carbon monoxide molecules can be either in phase with each other (**1, 3**) or out of phase (**2, 4**) with each other. If these species then interact via a coupling mechanism, the effect will be to produce two vibrations that have frequencies higher (**1**) and lower (**2**) than the original single vibration. For a single isotopic species the out-of-phase vibration (**2**) will not cause a change in the dipole moment perpendicular to the surface and will thus be inactive in the infrared. The observed C—O vibration will appear at higher frequencies. When a mixture of $C^{12}O$ and $C^{13}O$ is used, however, the out-of-phase vibration will no longer be inactive, and, because of the small change in dipole moment that occurs, the net effect is to reduce the intensity of the $C^{13}O$ vibration and increase the intensity of the $C^{12}O$ vibration.

A mathematical treatment of this effect has been given in a recent paper by Hammaker et al. (*25*). A dipole–dipole coupling interaction between the chemisorbed CO molecules is assumed, and, following the method of

Decius (*26*), values are calculated for the intensity ratios and frequencies of the adsorbed isotopic species. Comparison with experimental data is good at coverages less than $\theta = 0.6$. Essentially this explanation predicts that:

1. The dipole–dipole interaction will be greatest at the highest surface coverages.

2. The higher the $C^{12}O$–$C^{13}O$ isotopic ratio, the greater will be the intensity ratio of the respective bands.

3. As the surface coverage is decreased, the intensity ratio of $C^{12}O$ to $C^{13}O$ will decrease.

4. As the surface coverage is decreased, the $C^{12}O$ vibration will be observed at lower frequencies.

The spectra reproduced in Figs. 6-5(a) and 6-5(b) clearly demonstrate the qualitative correctness of these predictions and add a new dimension, however troublesome, to our interpretations of the spectra of adsorbed molecules.†

A further point of interest and importance arises from the results of Hammaker et al. and is interpreted in terms of dipole–dipole interaction. These workers found that when an isotopic mixture of carbon monoxide was adsorbed on silica-supported platinum at 30°C, heated to 200°C, and then cooled to 30°C, the spectrum obtained after the heat treatment was completely different from that observed after the first addition of carbon monoxide. The intensity ratio was reduced from 1.1 to 0.6, and the total integrated intensity increased from 3.36 to 5.16 cm^{-1}. Various arguments advanced by those authors show that this effect was due to the fact that in the initial adsorption there was a certain clustering of the carbon monoxide molecules on the platinum particles near the surface of the disc, and the consequent dipolar interactions produced an anomalous spectrum. Heating to 200°C allowed the carbon monoxide to desorb and distribute itself more evenly over the platinum surface.

Garland et al. (*24*) have also examined the infrared spectrum of carbon monoxide adsorbed on a porous platinum surface. In this case the platinum was not supported and was prepared by evaporation of the metal in the presence of a small pressure of gaseous carbon monoxide. The results are in general agreement with data obtained for alumina-supported platinum samples, in that two bands were observed in the C—O stretching region at 2053 and 1840 cm^{-1}. The type *B* band is sensitive to sample preparation and is considerably weaker ($\simeq \frac{1}{20}$) than the high-frequency

† Dr. Eischens has pointed out that the interpretation of the spectra of adsorbed species would be even more troublesome if this predicted interaction was not observed!

band. Very interestingly, however, these authors were able to observe bands at 570 and 477 cm^{-1}, which can be attributed to the C—O bending and Pt—C stretching vibrations, respectively, of a linearly adsorbed species. Calculation of the force constants, using a valence-force approach, led to values of 15.6 and 4.1 mdynes/Å for the C—O and Pt—C bonds, respectively. These are in good agreement with the values of 16 and 4.5 mdynes/Å obtained by Eischens and co-workers from their isotopic ratio experiments. Comparison with Table 6-3 indicates that both bonds exhibit considerable double-bond character, i.e., the surface species might be written

$$Pt_s{=}C{=}O$$

B. Carbon Monoxide on Palladium

The spectrum of carbon monoxide chemisorbed on a silica-supported palladium surface at 25° has been obtained by Eischens et al. (2). The results are very similar to those obtained for the Ni–CO system, and two distinct types of band are again observed; the high-frequency bands that appear at about 4.8 μ (2085 cm^{-1}) are attributed to a type A CO species, and the low-frequency bands, below 2000 cm^{-1}, are attributed to a type B CO species. As the surface coverage is slowly increased, a band at 5.45 μ (1834 cm^{-1}) is the first to appear, followed by bands at 5.2 and 4.85 μ (1924 and 2060 cm^{-1}). The bands due to the type B species are much more intense than those due to the type A species. On evacuation, the bands are removed in the reverse order of their appearance. This, together with the fact that the number of bands is a function of surface coverage, is taken as an indication of surface heterogeneity, possibly associated with different crystal faces. Garland et al. (24) have observed similar spectra for an evaporated palladium sample; they observed bands at 2085, 1970, and 1840 cm^{-1}. The relative intensities of these bands were found to be somewhat variable. These workers were unable to detect any bands in the 600–300-cm^{-1} region due to bending modes or Ni—C stretching vibrations.

C. Carbon Monoxide on Ruthenium

The infrared spectra of carbon monoxide chemisorbed on ruthenium supported on both alumina and silica has been reported by Lynds (27). For the alumina-supported metal, bands were observed at 2125 and 2060 cm^{-1}, whereas for the silica-supported sample (0.8 % Ru), bands occurred at 2151 and 2083 cm^{-1}. When the amount of ruthenium impregnated in the silica was increased to 1.5 %, the 2151 cm^{-1} band shifted to 2143 cm^{-1}.

In all cases the intensities of the bands appeared to be independent of the degree of coverage.

D. Carbon Monoxide on Iridium

For CO adsorption on iridium, only one band is observed (27). This occurs at 2070 cm^{-1} when an alumina support is used and at 2074 cm^{-1} when a silica-supported sample is used.

E. Carbon Monoxide on Rhodium

The infrared spectrum of carbon monoxide adsorbed on rhodium metal has been studied by Garland et al. (24). The rhodium sample was prepared by flash evaporation in 3 to 12 mm of carbon monoxide. The spectra obtained follow the pattern disclosed by investigations on the adsorption of carbon monoxide on other metals, in that two distinct areas of band formation were observed. The major band appears at about 2058 cm^{-1}, together with a broader band in the 1850–1900 cm region. Again, the relative intensities of these bands are very sensitive to the nature of sample preparation and, presumably, to the amount of surface coverage. In some spectra, a small sharp band was observed at 2111 cm^{-1} and the broad band in the 1900 cm^{-1} region was often resolved into three absorptions at 1905, 1852, and 1817 cm^{-1}. In the bending region of the spectrum there were indications of a weak absorption between 575 and 400 cm^{-1}, but no definite assignment could be made.

Prior to this work the spectrum of carbon monoxide adsorbed on rhodium supported on alumina had been obtained by Yang and Garland (22). The results on the supported metal differed in many respects from those reported above for an evaporated sample. Adsorption of carbon monoxide at room temperature onto a fresh 2% Rh sample gave a spectrum that showed two peaks appearing as a doublet at 2095 and 2027 cm^{-1}. The positions of these bands was not a function of surface coverage, and their intensities were almost equal. At low coverages, a band at 2045 cm^{-1}, sensitive to sample preparation, was sometimes observed. For a 16% Rh sample, this intermediate band (2062 cm^{-1}) was the most intense.

Sintering of the 2% Rh sample, or increasing the quantity of Rh present, caused the 2045 cm^{-1} band to be more pronounced and led to the observation of a new band between 1905 and 1925 cm^{-1}. Both of these bands were sensitive to surface coverage. A further effect of the sintering process was to cause the bands at 2095 and 2027 cm^{-1} to be moved to 2108 and 2040 cm^{-1}. This effect, however, was shown to be due to the elimination of adsorbed water during the sintering process and not to the change in particle size of the metal. Readsorption of water caused the adsorbed CO species to vibrate at the original frequencies.

In an effort to properly identify the surface species giving rise to these absorptions, Yang and Garland examined the spectrum of rhodium carbonyl chloride $Rh_2(CO)_4Cl_2$. This compound probably has the structure

$$OC\diagdown\underset{OC}{\overset{}{Rh}}\diagup\underset{Cl}{\overset{Cl}{\diagdown}}Rh\diagup\underset{CO}{\overset{CO}{\diagdown}}$$

in which two CO ligands are attached to each rhodium atom. Both asymmetric stretching modes would occur and are observed at about 2030 and 2090 cm^{-1}. Thus, the bands observed at these positions in the spectrum of carbon monoxide adsorbed on rhodium are attributed to a species in which two carbonyl groups are attached to a single rhodium atom. Single bands occurring about halfway between 2030 and 2090 cm^{-1} are attributed to linear CO groups (type A) in conformity with other explanations.

Oxygen reacts with the chemisorbed carbon monoxide on rhodium at 170°C. The 2095- and 2027-cm^{-1} bands decrease in intensity during the oxidation and are replaced by a new band at 2127 cm^{-1}. This was attributed to the reaction scheme

$$\overset{O}{\underset{}{C}}\diagdown\underset{}{\overset{}{}}\underset{-Rh_s-}{\overset{O}{\underset{}{C}}}\diagup + O_2(g) = \overset{O}{\underset{}{C}}\diagdown\underset{-Rh_s-}{\overset{O}{\diagup}} + CO_2(g)$$

in which the effect of the oxygen on the metal surface is to cause the C—O vibration to occur at higher frequencies. This result is in agreement with Peri's observations on the CO–Ni(SiO$_2$) system (12).

Water vapor also reacted with the adsorbed CO in a complicated fashion. Thus, whereas a 16% Rh sample originally exhibited bands at 2095, 2027, 2055, and 1900 cm^{-1}, the addition of water to this system caused complete removal of the 2095- and 2027-cm^{-1} bands and replacement of the 1900-cm^{-1} band with a strong band at about 1875 cm^{-1}. The reaction, however, had almost no effect on the band at 2055 cm^{-1}.

F. Carbon Monoxide on Copper

Smith and Quets (29, 30) have investigated the infrared spectrum of carbon monoxide adsorbed on a copper surface over the temperature range −196° to 500°C. Their spectra were recorded in conjunction with thermodesorption studies, and the results indicate that carbon monoxide is adsorbed on copper in a complex manner and in two different states.

At the lowest temperature, at least five bands can be observed in the spectrum: two very weak bands at 2250 and 1990 cm^{-1} and three bands in the region between 2100 and 2150 cm^{-1}. Of these, the bands at 2130 and 2150 cm^{-1} are due to carbon monoxide adsorbed on silica and are removed slowly as the temperature is raised. The remaining bands at 2100 and 2120 cm^{-1} are thus due to carbon monoxide adsorbed on the copper. The band at 2100 cm^{-1} is asymmetric at $-70°C$, and a shoulder can be observed at about 2070 cm^{-1}. On warming of the sample to about 0°C this shoulder disappears and, at 40°C, the final spectrum shows only a single band, at 2120 cm^{-1}, due to adsorbed carbon monoxide. This band persists even on prolonged evacuation at room temperature. In the presence of gaseous carbon monoxide, a band at 2100 cm^{-1} can still be observed at 200°C.

Spectra obtained as a function of surface coverage are of interest in as much as they show that adsorption of carbon monoxide on silica occurs first (band at 2125 cm^{-1}). This is followed by adsorption on the metal (band at 2100 cm^{-1}). On increase of the surface coverage, bands at 2070 (CO on Cu) and 2150 cm^{-1} (CO on SiO_2) begin to appear. The resolution of the bands in this region is possible only at the low temperatures involved. At higher temperatures, all the bands are broadened and overlap so that only a single band at 2100 cm^{-1} is observed.

For an alumina-supported sample, a spectrum similar to that for the silica-supported copper was obtained. In this case, however, the band observed at room temperature occurred at 2110 cm^{-1} rather than 2120 cm^{-1}. In view of the fact that the actual position of this band appeared to depend somewhat upon the particle size of the copper, it seems unlikely that any of these effects can be attributed to the chemical nature of the supports.

From an earlier study, Eischens and Pliskin (31) report similar results for the adsorption of carbon monoxide on copper and show that the addition of oxygen to this system causes the band at 2100 cm^{-1} to shift to 2120 cm^{-1}. Smith and Quets noticed that hydrogen causes the same effect and, in view of the fact that they observed two bands in this region, they suggest that the effect of both the oxygen and the hydrogen is to cause depression of one absorption and enhancement of the other.

Amberg and Seanor (32) also note that the position of the CO band is a function of the degree of reduction and note that the band position in their sample moves from 2143 to 2130 cm^{-1} as the surface becomes progressively more reduced.

Thermodesorption experiments on metallic copper show that the two types of adsorbed carbon monoxide are characterized by thermodesorption energies of 10 and 20 Kcal/mole. These are correlated by Smith and Quets with the bands at 2070 cm^{-1} and 2100–2120 cm^{-1}, respectively.

Surface-potential measurements of CO adsorbed on copper as a function of surface coverage have been made by Siddiqui and Tompkins (33), who have shown that the surface potential of copper becomes more positive when the metal is exposed to carbon monoxide at $-183°$C. The surface potential increases until the surface coverage is about 0.25, at which point the surface potential starts to decrease. At a surface coverage of about 0.5, the potential is about half its maximum value. Smith and Quets suggest that these results should be explained on the basis of two different surface species rather than in terms of an inductive effect acting upon adjacent molecules. Although inductive effects cannot be ruled out, the linear relationship Smith and Quets observe between the frequencies of the adsorbed CO species and their desorption energies would seem to argue in favor of the dual-site interpretation.

G. Carbon Monoxide on Iron

The spectrum of carbon monoxide chemisorbed on iron was first reported by Eischens and Pliskin (31). For a silica-supported iron sample at room temperature, adsorbed carbon monoxide was observed to give a peak at 1960 cm^{-1} that, at higher CO pressures, showed the presence of a shoulder at 4.95 μ (2019 cm^{-1}). The simplest carbonyl compound containing iron, $Fe(CO)_5$, has only linear CO groups, and these exhibit their fundamental stretching vibration at 2028 cm^{-1}. The compound $Fe_2(CO)_9$ contains bridged carbonyl groups, and these have been assigned a CO stretching frequency of 1847 cm^{-1}. In view of this, Eischens and Pliskin concluded that carbon monoxide chemisorbed on iron to give a linear species. No supporting evidence was available, and the assignment was considered somewhat uncertain, because bands below 2000 cm^{-1} had at that time normally been assigned to bridged carbonyl species. However, in view of the discussions already presented, it is realized that the original skepticism was unwarranted. Confirmation of the assignment has been provided by Blyholder (34), who has examined the spectrum of carbon monoxide on iron by using the evaporation-mull technique described previously and who obtained spectral data down to 270 cm^{-1}. Only two absorption bands were observed—at 1950 and 580 cm^{-1}—the position of the high-frequency band corresponding closely to that observed by Eischens and Pliskin for a silica-supported sample.

The presence of only two bands is indicative of a linear species rather than a bridged species, and the bands observed by Blyholder were therefore attributed to C—O and Fe—C stretching vibrations, respectively. The experimental frequencies of the adsorbed CO species were calculated to correspond to force constants for the C—O and Fe—C bonds of about 14 and 4 mdynes/Å, respectively. Comparison with the values obtained by other workers (Table 6-3) indicates that the bond order of both the C—O and Fe—C bonds is close to 2. In view of this, the surface species can be written

$$Fe_s = C = O$$

Calculation of the Fe—C distance by application of Paulings electronegativity data (35) led to a value of 1.67 Å, and the bond was estimated to have about 12 % ionic character.

In an extension of this work Blyholder and Neff (36) reported spectral studies on the adsorption of carbon monoxide on a silica-supported iron sample. Two peaks attributable to chemisorbed carbon monoxide were observed at 20°C. The major band occurred at 4.95 μ (2019 cm^{-1}), and the second absorption appeared as a shoulder at 5.01 μ (1998 cm^{-1}). On heating to 150°C the bands retained the same shape and the same relative intensities as in the original spectrum, but they were shifted to lower wave numbers. At room temperature, the size of the chemisorbed peak was independent of the pressure of the gaseous carbon monoxide, but at 180°C the amount of CO chemisorbed became dependent on the pressure. The lack of intensity dependence on surface coverage led Blyholder and Neff to speculate that the two bands observed were due to adsorption on two different types of site, probably different crystallographic faces. It should be noted that whereas Eischens and Pliskin observed a strong band at 5.1 μ (1959 cm^{-1}) with a shoulder at 4.95 μ (2018 cm^{-1}), Blyholder and Neff reported a strong band at 4.95 μ and a shoulder at 5.1 μ. This reversal of intensities tends to support the conclusion of two different adsorption sites, the relative numbers of each being determined by the different methods of preparation.

The addition of oxygen at room temperature to a silica-supported iron sample (36) does not give rise to changes in the spectrum of the sample. At 180°C, however, bands are observed at 4.75, 5.5, and 6.6 μ (2105, 1820, and 1514 cm^{-1}), and they are attributed to iron oxide formation. It is of interest to note that although the addition of oxygen to Fe–SiO$_2$ at room temperature causes no spectral changes, the oxygen will cause the removal of preadsorbed CO, presumably by preferential adsorption.

On the heating of carbon monoxide and oxygen together with the iron sample at 180°C, or on the addition of carbon dioxide to the sample at that temperature, a band is observed at 6.42 μ (1560 cm^{-1}). This band is characteristic of the carbonate structures discussed previously and is so assigned.

The addition of CO_2 to a freshly reduced iron-on-silica sample is reported by Blyholder and Neff to give rise to a peak at 5.1 μ (1959 cm^{-1}). The intensity of this band is approximately half that observed when carbon monoxide is admitted to a clean iron surface. Since its frequency corresponds to the frequencies found for adsorbed CO species, it is interpreted as being due to that species. The CO_2 is dissociatively adsorbed, even at 20°C, to give an adsorbed CO species and adsorbed oxygen. It is of interest to note that the band on this sample occurs at 5.1 μ (1959 cm^{-1}) rather than at 4.95 μ 2018 cm^{-1}). The band is observed at the latter position when carbon monoxide is adsorbed directly on the sample. This could be due to an effect of the adsorbed oxygen on the strength of the Fe adsorption site, and, in view of the fact that the band originally reported by Eischens for CO adsorbed on Fe was also observed at 5.1 μ, it is possible that the sample in that case was contaminated with oxygen. Supported oxides are notoriously difficult to reduce completely to the metal.

The interaction of carbon monoxide and hydrogen on an iron surface is of practical importance in that it is the basis of the Fischer-Tropsch synthesis. Several mechanisms have been postulated for this reaction; they include the formation of adsorbed intermediates such as carbides (37) and oxygenated alcoholic-type compounds (38, 39). Eischens and Pliskin (31) have investigated the effect of hydrogen on chemisorbed carbon monoxide on a silica-supported iron sample and found no spectral evidence of interaction at room temperatures. Blyholder and Neff (40) confirmed this finding, but observed an interaction at 180°C. These workers obtained spectra that were somewhat complicated and nondefinitive, but their results show that, at 180°C, three bands appear in the C—H stretching region of the spectrum (3.3 μ, 3030 cm^{-1}), in addition to bands due to chemisorbed CO. Moreover, a permanent increase in the intensity of the surface hydroxyl vibration at 2.8 μ (3569 cm^{-1}) was observed. The three bands observed at about 3.3 μ (3030 cm^{-1}) were due to gaseous methane formed in the reaction, and they were removed from the system by pumping. At 180°C a band due to a chemisorbed species was observed at 3.4 μ (2943 cm^{-1}), and this was attributed to the C—H stretching vibration of a saturated hydrocarbonlike species. Since unsaturated alcoholic species have been proposed as intermediates in the Fischer-Tropsch reaction, the absence of a band at 3.3 μ (3029 cm^{-1}), characteristic of an unsaturated =C—H grouping may be of some significance. The infrared evidence is in accord with the presence of species of the type

$$
\begin{array}{ccc}
\text{H} \quad \text{R} \quad \text{OH} & & \text{H} \quad \text{R} \quad \text{H} \\
\diagdown \mid \diagup & & \diagdown \mid \diagup \\
\text{C} & \text{and} & \text{C} \\
\mid & & \mid \\
\text{M} & & \text{M}
\end{array}
$$

Since the intensity of the chemisorbed CO peak is approximately 75% of that formed in an analogous experiment in which hydrogen was not present, it seems likely that most of the surface is free and not covered with the species proposed above.

6-5. PREDICTION OF CATALYTIC ACTIVITY

A. Concept of Matching Vibrations

Catalytic chemists have long been in need of a tool that would enable them to define the "active sites" at which the reactions proceed. The number of the active sites, however, is very small compared to the total number of surface atoms; consequently, definitive observations are difficult to make. Although infrared spectroscopy gives a great deal of information regarding the major portions of the surface, only the work of Peri and his definition of "α sites" on silica-alumina (41) can be considered at this stage to be specific to catalytically active sites. In the absence of definitive measurements, numerous correlations have been made between catalytic activities and solid-state parameters such as conductivity type and bond strength. One of the best-known examples of this type of approach is the early correlation between the bond lengths of adsorbing hydrocarbons and metal–metal distances assumed to exist on certain active surfaces. Few of these approaches are theoretically well founded, but until they are disproved, they lead to at least an "empirical understanding" of the processes involved and serve to suggest directions for research.

Myers (42) has proposed an interesting approach based on the correlation of the vibrational frequencies of reactant and catalyst. Essentially, it is argued that if the vibrational frequency of the bond that must be broken to initiate the catalytic reaction is the same as that of the bond formed between the catalyst and the molecule, then a transfer of energy can take place easily and catalytic activity is observed. The transfer of energy is assumed to be quantized, and overtones of fundamental vibrational frequencies are also considered. In particular, Myers considered the reactions of ethylene. This compound can undergo the catalytic reactions shown in Fig. 6-6. The vibrations of the ethylene molecule have been discussed previously and are shown in Fig. 2-14. Twelve vibrational modes are possible.

In the presence of nitrogen dioxide, ethylene is oxidized by molecular oxygen to formaldehyde. After considering the interatomic vibrations of the ethylene molecule, Myers argued that the ν_2 mode (C=C stretch) was

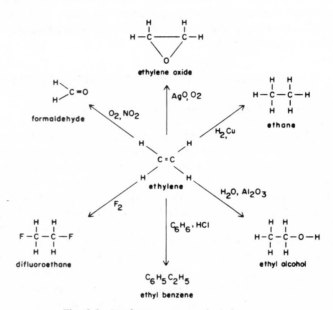

Fig. 6-6. Catalytic reactions of ethylene.

the vibration most likely to cause the necessary preliminary fracture into an H_2C species. This vibration is observed at 1623 cm^{-1}. The NO$_2$ molecule is a nonlinear, XY$_2$-type species similar to H$_2$O (Fig. 2-8). It exhibits three vibrational modes ν_1, ν_2, and ν_3 at 1321, 648, and 1621 cm^{-1}. The loss of oxygen from the NO$_2$ molecule is most likely to proceed via the ν_3 vibration, and thus it is seen that, for both the NO$_2$ and the C$_2$H$_4$, the vibrations most likely to cause the "correct" fragmentation have almost identical frequencies. Similar arguments have been applied by Myers for the other reactions shown in Fig. 6-6. By suitable manipulation and argument, the corresponding frequencies between catalyst and ethylene have been proposed as in Table 6-4.

TABLE 6-4

Correlation between Ethylene Frequency and Catalyst Frequency[a]

Reaction product	Ethylene frequency, cm^{-1}	Catalyst	Frequency, cm^{-1}
Formaldehyde	1625	NO$_2$	1621
Ethylene oxide	950	AgO	962[b]
Ethane	1625	CuH	1611
Difluorethane	1100	F$_2$	1102
Ethyl benzene	2990	HCl	2978[b]
Ethanol	950	AlO	964

[a] As proposed by Myers (*42*).
[b] First overtone.

B. Intermedions

This type of approach has been considerably amplified and put on a more quantitative basis by Gardner and his co-workers. Initially, Gardner and Petrucci (*14, 43*) investigated the adsorption of carbon monoxide on copper oxide, nickel, and cobalt and observed bands at the frequencies given in Table 6-5.

The observation that the two highest-frequency bands on cobalt and the highest-frequency band on copper oxide occurred at frequencies *higher* than the frequency of the free CO molecule led Gardner and Petrucci to propose that these adsorbed species might be intermediate in electronic structure between the free CO molecule and the CO$^+$ ion, the latter exhibiting a vibrational mode at 2184 cm^{-1}.

TABLE 6-5

Frequencies of Some Adsorbed CO Species[a]

System	Wave number, cm^{-1}		
CuO–CO	2173	2127	2000
Ni film–CO	2174	2115	2060
Co–CO	2179	2160	2091
CO gas		2143	
CO$^+$		2184	

[a] As determined by Gardner and Petrucci.

In solid-state approach to chemisorption and catalysis, Wolkenstein (44) had previously postulated that atoms could be adsorbed on surfaces by an electron-transfer mechanism in which the adsorbate could have several forms, each form being associated with a whole number of electrons i.e.,

$$X \rightarrow X_{ads}^{\pm 1}, X_{ads}^{\pm 2}, X_{ads}^{\pm 3}, \text{ etc.} \qquad (6\text{-}1)$$

Gardner and Petrucci modified this concept by assuming that the adsorbed species could contain nonintegral numbers of electrons, but that the

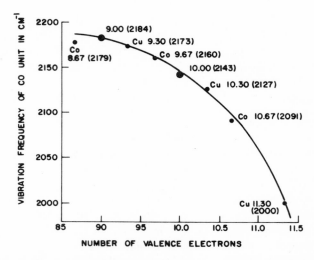

Fig. 6-7. *The relationship between vibrational frequency of some adsorbed* CO *species and the number of valence electrons.* [*Redrawn from Reference (14) by courtesy of the Journal of the American Chemical Society.*]

different species resulting from the adsorption of a single adsorbent would differ from each other by an integral number of electrons, i.e.,

$$X \rightarrow X_{ads}^{n \pm 1}, X_{ads}^{n \pm 2}, X_{ads}^{n \pm 3}, \text{ etc.} \qquad (6\text{-}2)$$

where n is a fraction less than 1.

Gardner and Petrucci then assumed that the vibrational frequencies reported in Table 6-5 could have a single relation to the number of valence electrons. Only two points (CO and CO$^+$) were known with certainty, but it proved possible to construct the curve shown in Fig. 6-7. This curve is close to a right hyperbola passing through the points:

$$\nu\,(CO)^+ = 2183.90\ cm^{-1} \qquad E\,(CO) = \quad 9$$
$$\nu\,(CO) \ \ = 2143.27\ cm^{-1} \qquad\qquad\quad = 10$$
$$\nu\,(CO)^{2-} = 0\ cm^{-1} \qquad\qquad\qquad\quad = 12$$

where $E\,(CO)$ is the number of valence electrons, and $\nu\,(CO)$ is the vibrational frequency of the CO species. The proposed relationship has the exact form

$$[2269.96 \pm \nu\,(CO)][12.1182 - E\,(CO)] = 268.31\ cm^{-1} \qquad (6\text{-}3)$$

Application of this equation to the data presented in Table 6-5, together with additional data obtained for carbon monoxide adsorbed on metallic copper, copper fluoride, iron, iron oxide, and silver (45, 46) led to the results shown in Table 6-6. From this table it is seen that the observed vibrations have been divided into two groups. In the first group the number of electrons contained in the absorbed CO species varies by an integral number, whereas in the other group no such relationship

TABLE 6-6

Vibrational Frequencies of Some Adsorbed CO Species and the Calculated Number of Valence Electrons[a]

	Intermedions		Carbonyls	
Adsorbent	Band, cm^{-1}	Number of electrons	Band, cm^{-1}	Number of electrons
Copper metal			2095	10.59
Copper(I) fluoride			2146	9.95
Copper(II) oxide	2173	9.35	2127	10.24
	2121	10.32	2000	11.12
Cobalt	2160	9.68	2179	9.17
	2091	10.62		
Iron oxide	2127	10.24	2020	11.04
Iron	1960	11.25		
Silver	2165	9.56		
	2099	10.55		
Chromium oxide	2203	8.11		
	2181	9.10	2129	10.21
	2134	10.14	2056	10.86
Platinum	2063	10.82	2081	10.71
Nickel	2058	11.85	2030	11.00
	1230	11.86	1965	11.24

[a] Data taken from References (45) and (46).

exists. The species in the first group have been termed *intermedions*, and they are assumed to be the species responsible for chemical reactivity. The second group of surface species are designated as *carbonyls*. The latter are usually the more stable surface species, whereas the intermedions tend to be easily formed and just as easily removed.

One of the interesting postulates of this approach is that the position of a band attributable to an intermedion is not affected by the nature of the substrate, but is affected only by the cation involved. Thus, for example,

TABLE 6-7

Polarization Fractions of Metals and Variation with Atomic Number[a]

24	25	26	27	28	29
Cr	Mn	Fe	Co	Ni	Cu
0.099		0.257	0.635	0.856	0.315
			45	46	47
			Rh	Pd	Ag
			0.778	0.810	0.544
			77	78	
			Ir	Pt	
			0.798	0.817	

[a] Reproduced from Reference (*47*), courtesy of the *Journal of Catalysis.*

CO species that can be called intermedions will always occur at 2173 and 2121 cm^{-1} on copper-containing surfaces, and absence of these bands on carbon monoxide adsorption would, presumably, mean an absence of catalytic activity. In this respect, it is of interest to consider the bands observed when CO is adsorbed on copper fluoride (*45*) (Table 6-6). When the carbon monoxide is adsorbed on the copper fluoride surface, a single species is formed and is evidenced by the appearance of a CO stretching frequency at 2146 cm^{-1}. The displacement of this value from that observed for a pure copper metal film (2095 cm^{-1}) is attributed to the electronegativity of the fluorine atoms. Oxygen, which is less electronegative than the fluorine, causes a smaller shift, the surface carbonyl formed on copper oxide exhibiting a vibration at 2127 cm^{-1}.

The fractional part of the nonintegral number of valence electrons associated with the intermedions has been termed the *polarization fraction*. It is thought to be a unique property of the metal adsorbent. Polarization fractions for a series of metals have now been obtained (*47*), and they are shown in Table 6-7. A certain periodicity can be observed, and one is reminded of the similarity between this approach and the highly useful concept of "electronegativity" as originally formulated by Pauling.

A recent note by Gardner (48) indicates that the polarization fraction may be related to contributions of low-lying energy levels of the electronic configuration of the metal ion under consideration. This also implies that the polarization fraction will be dependent upon ionic charge.

C. The Adsorption Process

One of the interesting features of Table 6-6 is that bands attributable to intermedions have been detected only when carbon monoxide has been adsorbed on metals that contain partially vacant d orbitals. Thus, in the case of copper, they are found only with the divalent oxide.

Conventionally, we could write the chemisorption of carbon monoxide on cupric ions by the equations

$$CO + Cu_s^{2+} = Cu_s^+ + CO^+ \tag{6-4}$$

or

$$CO + Cu_s^{2+} = Cu_s^{3+} + CO^- \tag{6-5}$$

In terms of intermedions possessing nine or eleven electrons, these equations are written

$$CO^{10} + Cu_s^9 = Cu_s^{10} + Co^9 \tag{6-6}$$

$$CO^{10} + Cu_s^9 = Cu_s^8 + Co^{11} \tag{6-7}$$

However, since the polarization fraction of copper is 0.32, the presence of intermedions containing 9.32 and 10.32 valence electrons is implied. The possible electron transfers are written

$$CO^{10} + Cu_s^{8.32} = Cu_s^{10} + CO^{8.32} \tag{6-8}$$

$$CO^{10} + Cu_s^{9.32} = Cu_s^{10} + CO^{9.32} \atop (2173 \text{ cm}^{-1}) \tag{6-9}$$

$$CO^{10} + Cu_s^{8.32} = Cu^8 + CO^{10.32} \atop (2121 \text{ cm}^{-1}) \tag{6-10}$$

$$CO^{10} + Cu_s^{9.32} = Cu_s^8 + CO^{11.32} \tag{6-11}$$

Only two of the four possible intermedions have been observed on copper; they correspond to vibrations at 2173 and 2121 cm^{-1}. All other species observed are thus surface carbonyls and are considered to be more stable and not catalytically active.

D. Prediction of Catalytic Activity (47)

With this semiempirical background, it is now possible to produce a mathematical interpretation of catalytic activity by using the concept of matching vibrations. Thus, if we consider the equation

$$\text{H—H} + \text{:C}\equiv\text{O:} \rightleftharpoons \text{H—}\ddot{\text{C}}\text{—O—H} \tag{6-12}$$

it must be assumed that this reaction will occur on a catalyst that, by virtue of its specific polarization fraction, will cause the molecules to be chemisorbed in such a manner that their vibrational frequencies are equal.

The frequency of the hydrogen molecule intermedion has been calculated in a manner analogous to that described for the carbon monoxide intermedion. The vibration frequency is given by the equation

$$\nu_{H_2} = 2080.57 E_{H_2} \tag{6-13}$$

where E_{H_2} is again the number of valence electrons. Mathematical manipulation of Eqs. (6-3) and (6-13) shows that the optimum polarization fractions for the above reaction must be either 0.256 or 0.641. Reference to Table 6-7 shows that these fractions respectively correspond to iron and cobalt—metals that are well known for their catalytic activity in this hydroformylation reaction.

Similar calculations have been made for the reactions

$$2H_2 + O_2 \rightleftharpoons 2H_2O$$
$$CO + \tfrac{1}{2}O_2 \rightleftharpoons CO_2$$
$$HC\equiv CH + H_2 \rightleftharpoons H_2C\!\!=\!\!CH_2$$

and the percentage difference between frequencies of adsorbed intermedions has been used to forecast and explain a kinetic isotope effect that occurs in the oxidation of $H_2 + D_2$ over copper (43). The interested reader is referred to the original articles for further details.

6-6. THE NATURE OF CARBON MONOXIDE ADSORPTION

In the previous discussions of the adsorption of carbon monoxide on metals (and metal oxides) it has become clear that the exact positions and intensities of the bands due to adsorbed carbon monoxide are a function of both the surface coverage and the method of sample preparation. In general, the metal surfaces have been found to exhibit two types of sites of completely different energies that have been referred to as type A and B sites. These were formerly considered to be due to linear and bridged carbon monoxide species, respectively. Although it has not been unequivocally proved, the current evidence indicates that both species are probably of the linear type. The possibility of two carbon monoxide molecules attached to a single metal site (e.g., on Rh) also cannot be ignored, but formation of this type of species appears to be the exception rather than the rule. All in all, the range of frequencies that has been observed varies all the way from a weakly held species, observed at about 2200 cm^{-1} on oxidic surfaces, to the type B species, which are observed down to 1800 cm^{-1}—a spectral range of 400 cm^{-1}. One adsorption mechanism that would account for this range of frequencies has already been fully discussed in connection with the prediction of catalytic activity. In this, the adsorbed carbon monoxide is presumed to be adsorbed in an ionic form, positive ions giving rise to frequencies above 2143 cm^{-1} and negative ions giving rise to frequencies below 2143 cm^{-1}.

The close analogy between the stable carbon monoxide complexes of transition-metal compounds reported in the literature of inorganic chemistry and the surface complexes reported in this text suggests that the nature of the bonding in the two series of complexes should be similar. In the inorganic complexes, the bonding is essentially covalent and the stability of these complexes is attributed to a "back-donation" or interaction between the filled d-orbitals of the metal and antibonding orbitals of the carbon monoxide. This has been discussed by Orgel (*49*) and many other authors.

The carbon monoxide molecule has three fully occupied σ orbitals that give rise to a σ bond between the carbon and oxygen atoms and a free pair of unshared electrons on both of these atoms. The four remaining electrons occupy a doubly degenerate π orbital, leaving a strongly antibonding σ orbital and a strongly antibonding π orbital. Conventionally, therefore, the carbon monoxide molecule has a strong, triple bond between the atoms. Complex formation takes place primarily via the lone pair of electrons on the carbon atom, a covalent σ bond being formed with electron acceptors of the Lewis acid type. This bond is very weak, and typical Lewis acids, such as the boron halides, form only weak, unstable complexes with carbon monoxide. In the presence of a Lewis acid possessing filled d orbitals, however, interaction between the metallic d orbitals and the antibonding π orbital on the carbon monoxide molecule can take place, and the original

σ bond is considerably strengthened. Thus, the metal carbonyls, such as $Ni(CO)_4$, and the carbonyl halides, such as $PtCl_2 \cdot 2CO$, are relatively stable materials.

The effect of the initial σ-bond formation between the donor carbon atom and the acceptor metal ion would be expected to have little effect on the vibrational frequency of the carbon monoxide molecule. If anything, the transfer of charge from the less electronegative carbon atom to the metal will cause an increase in the order of the carbon-oxygen bond, and thus the C—O vibration will be observed at slightly higher frequencies than in the free gaseous molecule. Such an observation has been made: the weak $H_3B \leftarrow CO$ complex exhibits a stretching frequency at 2164 cm^{-1} as compared with the carbon monoxide frequency, which is observed at 2143 cm^{-1} (50). Stronger Lewis acids might be expected to give even greater shifts, and it is of interest to note that Peri (12) has correlated the presence of a band at 2198 cm^{-1} for carbon monoxide adsorbed on Ni–SiO$_2$ with the strongest of the surface Lewis acid sites (as evidenced by ammonia adsorption) observed on that material.

Conversely, the transfer of charge from the metal to the carbon monoxide ligand during the back-donation process must considerably reduce the strength of the C—O bond. This is evident in the data obtained for inorganic carbonyls, where the C—O frequencies are observed in the range 1800–2140 cm^{-1}, but generally are seen around 2000 cm^{-1}.

Orgel points out that d orbitals are always available in transition metals, but that their number is dependent on the particular stereochemistry under consideration. Thus, in tetrahedral compexes all the d orbitals can partake in the double bonding, but in an octahedral complex only the d_{xy}, d_{yz}, and d_{xz} orbitals are available. Clearly, at the surface of a metal, the stereochemical configuration is liable to be complicated and dependent on the method of preparation. Furthermore, it will be affected by heat treatment (sintering), poisoning, preadsorption, and the surface coverage of the carbon monoxide. Small wonder that a miscellany of results have been obtained!

Blyholder (51) has discussed the adsorption of carbon monoxide on metal surfaces from "a molecular orbital view" and arrived at conclusions similar to those given above. In particular, he has commented on the effect of edges, corners, and dislocations on the stereochemistry of the surface atoms. Some of his conclusions have been criticized by Yates (52). However, it should be noted that, at this stage in the study of surface chemistry, there is no adequate means of determining the arrangement of surface atoms except by the utilization of low-energy electron scattering

techniques under the most stringent conditions—conditions not encountered in the infrared studies of supported metals. A general increase in the
crystallinity of a sample cannot necessarily be taken as evidence of an
increase in the coordination number of the surface atoms.

In general, the d-orbital considerations predict that the lower the
coordination number of the surface atoms, the greater is the possibility of
back donation by the d orbitals, the lower is the vibration frequency of the
adsorbed CO, and the stronger is the metal–carbon bond. From the mass
of experiental data collected thus far it can be seen that these predictions are
qualitatively observed.

The effect of oxygen preadsorption onto a surface must be to reduce the
availability of the d orbitals. More effective reduction procedures, therefore, will lower the frequency of vibration of the adsorbed CO. This effect
has been noted by several workers, and, in particular, the reader is referred
to Peri's work on Ni–SiO$_2$ (12). It is also possible for the carbon monoxide
to be dissociatively chemisorbed, and it is almost impossible to guarantee
a metal surface completely free of oxygen. The analogous nitric oxide
molecule has been shown to be adsorbed dissociatively on nickel (53).

Coordination of carbon monoxide to a metal surface by σ-bond formation alone would not be expected to cause a drastic change in the intensity
of the C—O vibration. The effect of back donation and overlap of the
metal d-orbitals with the antibonding π orbital of the carbon monoxide,
however, will be to produce gross changes in intensity. Like the frequency,
these will depend on the amount of orbital overlap. This effect is illustrated
by the data collected by Amberg and Seanor (32), which are reproduced in
Fig. 5-18. For the adsorption of carbon monoxide on a Cu,CuO–SiO$_2$
sample, it can be seen that the intensity of the adsorbed C—O vibration
is increased by a factor of 7 as the sample becomes more reduced, the
frequency shifting from 2140 to 2132 cm^{-1} during the reduction process.
Amberg and Seanor interpret these effects in terms of small changes in the
internuclear distance [intensity $\alpha (d\mu/dr)^2$] rather than in terms of donor–
acceptor complexes.

The band observed at high frequency ($\simeq$2200 cm^{-1}) when carbon monoxide is weakly adsorbed on a highly oxidized zinc oxide sample has also
received an alternative explanation from Amberg and Seanor (54).
These workers note the correlation between the degree of preoxidation and
the vibrational frequency of the adsorbed species and provide arguments for
considering that the carbon monoxide is adsorbed via an ion–dipole interaction with surface oxide ions. The positive end of the C—O dipole is on
the carbon atom. This atom, therefore, interacts with the negative surface

oxide ions to give a species of the form

$$\diagdown \overset{}{\underset{\diagup}{O^{2-}_s}} \cdots \overset{\delta+ \ \ \delta-}{C-O}$$

Such a proposal accounts for both the weakness of the bond and the intensity changes that are observed. In the absence of further data, it is impossible to distinguish between this type of species and the σ-bond proposal. The only advantage of the latter is that it provided one explanation for all the observed species. Oxide ion activity, however, cannot be ignored.

A weak band at about 2200 cm^{-1} was also observed for carbon monoxide adsorbed on NiO–SiO$_2$ (*19*). This was ascribed by Eischens and Pliskin to a structure speculatively attributed to an active intermediate in the oxidation of carbon monoxide. Schematically it was written in the form

$$Ni_s \cdots O \cdots C \cdots O$$

6-7. SOME MISCELLANEOUS ADSORPTION STUDIES

A. Nitric Oxide on Nickel and Iron

Nitric oxide, NO, is an interesting ligand that has a structure derived from carbon monoxide by the addition of one extra electron to the antibonding π orbital. It can, therefore, form a series of stable complexes in the same manner as carbon monoxide, and the nature of its adsorption on metal surfaces is of some interest. Nitric oxide itself exhibits a stretching vibration at 1843 cm^{-1}, and the vibrational frequency of the NO$^+$ ion has been determined to be 2220 cm^{-1}. The vibrational frequency of the NO$^-$ ion is probably below 1000 cm^{-1}. Lewis and co-workers (*55*) have examined a series of inorganic complexes containing nitric oxide as a ligand, and they concluded that the cationic NO$^+$ stretching frequency falls in the 1940–1575-cm^{-1} range, whereas the anionic NO$^-$ frequency occurs between 1200 and 1040 cm^{-1}. From this it is seen that it is possible to interpret the spectra of adsorbed nitric oxide in terms of ionic species, just as Gardner did for carbon monoxide adsorption. The concept of σ-bond formation stabilized by back donation of d electrons may also be invoked.

Terenin and Roev (*56, 57*) have obtained the infrared spectra of nitric oxide adsorbed on a variety of metals, oxides, and sulfates. A wide variety of bands were observed, indicating a miscellany of adsorption sites. The major species are collected in Table 6-8. A variety of assignments are given in the original papers but, in the absence of bands due to bending vibrations, these assignments must be considered highly speculative. Blyholder and Allen (53) have reported much simpler spectra for nitric oxide adsorbed on oil-supported nickel and iron. Certain differences in relative intensities of the bands are noted when the results are compared with those of Terenin and Roev, but this is to be expected in view of the different preparative techniques. Blyholder and Allen have observed

TABLE 6-8

Position of Major Bands Due to Nitric Oxide Adsorbed on Metals, Oxides, and Sulfates[a]

Element	Metal	Oxide	Sulfate
Fe	2008, 1735	1927, 1805, 1735	1850, 1735
Cr	2010, 1905, 1830, 1735	2093, 2028, 1842, 1735	2010, 1920, 1830, 1735
Ni	1830, 1735	1805, 1735	1850, 1735
Co			2035, 1900, 1805, 1735
Mn			2000

[a] From Reference (57).

bands in the 600–700-cm^{-1} region that are attributable to the M—N and M–N–O stretching and bending vibrations of a nitric oxide species adsorbed linear with and perpendicular to the surface, in the same manner as carbon monoxide. In particular, the adsorption of nitric oxide on nickel gave bands at 1840, 650, and 625 cm^{-1}, which, in conformity with the above assignment, suggests force constants of 13.0 and 5.7 mdynes/Å for the N—O and Ni—N bonds respectively. These figures agree well with values obtained for the same bonds in the $Co(CO)_3NO$ molecule (14.0 and 3.87 mdynes/Å).

On both iron and nickel the nitric oxide is partially decomposed to give

$$2NO(g) \rightarrow N_2(g) + 2O_{ads}$$

Blyholder and Allen have observed the spectrum of the nickel oxide formed by this process, and Sachtler (58) has shown that at this stage the surface potential is negative, owing to the adsorbed oxygen. Adsorption of more nitric oxide gives rise to a positive surface potential that has been interpreted as due to the presence of NO_{ads}^+. Also at this stage the reaction

$$NO(g) + NO_{ads} \rightarrow N_2O(g) + O_{ads} \qquad (6\text{-}14)$$

further complicates the spectral interpretations. Neither hydrogen nor oxygen at room temperature reacts with the adsorbed species (53).

The nitric oxide is more strongly adsorbed than carbon monoxide and will displace the latter from the surface. It is also more strongly adsorbed than carbon dioxide, though the two species can exist together on the surface for a short time. In this case, the bands due to the carbon dioxide species are shifted by the coadsorption.

B. Nitrogen Dioxide Adsorption

Nitrogen dioxide also adsorbs on nickel and iron in a manner that is similar in some respects to carbon dioxide adsorption. At low pressures of NO_2, the gas is dissociatively adsorbed and a spectrum characteristic of nitric oxide on the metal oxide is obtained. At higher pressures an oxidized surface "nitrate" is obtained. Again the spectra are difficult to interpret, because it appears that more than one surface species is formed. The spectrum in general resembles that of a bidentate NO_3 complex (59).

$$
\begin{array}{c}
O \\
| \\
N \\
\diagup \quad \diagdown \\
O \qquad\qquad O \\
\diagdown \quad \diagup \\
M_s
\end{array}
$$

In view of the close analogy with the surface "carbonate" formation, this assignment seems very reasonable.

C. Oxygen-Containing Compounds Adsorbed on Iron

The structure of some surface compounds formed by various alcohols aldehydes, ketones, and organic oxides with iron supported in oil at 25°C have been reported by Blyholder and Neff (60). All these organic compounds react to give the same type of surface species, namely, a surface alkoxide. No trace of OH, $>C=O$, or $>C=C<$ groups was observed, and only in the case of the ethyl alcohol adsorption was there any evidence at all for the formation of decomposition products. In order to determine the degree of surface covered by these species, Blyholder and Neff used the adsorption of carbon monoxide as an indicator. They found that the addition of alcohol to the iron caused almost complete elimination of the sites responsible for carbon monoxide adsorption. Slightly more carbon monoxide adsorption was noted in the case of the secondary alcohol adsorption, and some of the adsorbed species was desorbed during this addition. Even more carbon monoxide was adsorbed on the acetone surface, and, in the case of the ether adsorption, a strong band at 1950 cm^{-1} due to chemisorbed carbon monoxide was noted.

D. Sulfur Compounds Adsorbed on Nickel

Sulfur compounds such as thiophene, H_2S, and organic sulfides are notorious for their ability to poison the catalytic activity of metal surfaces. These compounds are well-known ligands in inorganic chemistry and might be expected to chemisorb on metal surfaces by donation of their lone-pair electrons and to form a strong covalent linkage with the d orbitals of the metal. Various infrared studies on the addition of sulfur compounds to nickel surfaces are of interest. Garland (61) studied the effects of carbon disulfide addition to a nickel surface and reported that no peaks were observed in the infrared spectrum. In view of this, it was concluded that the molecule did not adsorb as such. However, preaddition of carbon disulfide to the nickel surface caused considerable changes in the spectrum of adsorbed carbon monoxide. The changes are dependent upon the amount of preabsorption of CS_2 and the method of preparation of the original samples. In general, as the amount of poison is increased, the bands below 2000 cm^{-1}, which are ascribed to the type B CO species, decrease in intensity until eventually they can no longer be observed. At the same time, the relative intensity of the bands at about 2050 and 2090 cm^{-1} is altered, the 2050-cm^{-1} band becoming weaker and the 2090-cm^{-1} band stronger. In heavily poisoned samples only one band can be observed (2094 cm^{-1}), although there are indications of a shoulder at about 2050 cm^{-1}. The implication from this work is that the catalytically active sites are probably those associated with the formation of the type B CO species. Mercury vapor, another well-known catalyst poison, causes similar changes in the spectrum of carbon monoxide adsorbed on nickel (62).

Blyholder and Bowen (63) similarly report that addition of H_2S at either 20° or 165°C to a silica-supported nickel surface gives a spectrum that shows no evidence of an adsorbed species. After removing the gaseous H_2S, these workers then showed that adsorption of carbon monoxide at 20°C gave a spectrum similar to that obtained by addition of CO to a freshly reduced surface. However, after treatment with the H_2S at 165°C, only a small peak due to chemisorbed CO could be observed. Thus, whereas at 20°C the H_2S had little effect on the nickel, at 165°C it poisoned the surface, at least as far as the sites responsible for carbon monoxide adsorption are concerned. This extremely useful approach—using molecules such as CO for indicator purposes—has received comparatively little attention to date.

The addition of methyl hydrogen sulfide to a supported-nickel sample at room temperature gives a spectrum in which only one band can be attributed to an adsorbed species. This occurs at 2910 cm^{-1}. Since CH_3SH itself does not give rise to an absorption at that frequency, it can be concluded that the molecule does not adsorb by the coordination of the sulfur atom with the metal surface.

Examination of Table 2-4 shows that CH_3 bands give rise to a characteristic vibration at 2962 cm^{-1}, whereas $>CH_2$ bands give a characteristic vibration at 2926 cm^{-1}. In view of this, Blyholder and Bowen assign the band at 2910 cm^{-1} to a surface $>CH_2$ species. This assignment is consistent with any of the following surface species:

$$
\begin{array}{ccc}
\text{SH} & \text{H}\quad\text{H} & \text{H}\qquad\text{H} \\
| & \quad/ & \diagdown\quad\diagup \\
\text{CH}_2 & \text{H---C---S} & \text{C} \\
| & |\quad| & \diagup\quad\diagdown \\
\text{Ni}_s & \text{Ni}_s\ \text{Ni}_s & \text{Ni}_s\qquad\text{Ni}_s
\end{array}
$$

Ethyl hydrogen sulfide adsorbs on the silica-supported nickel sample and gives an infrared spectrum with absorptions at 2960, 2915, 2860, 1447, and 1371 cm^{-1}, together with a very weak absorption at 1406 cm^{-1}. The band at 2915 cm^{-1} is easily the strongest in the spectrum and is again attributed to the CH vibration of a $>CH_2$ group. The band at 2860 cm^{-1} is also assigned to this grouping. The bands at 2962 and 1370 cm^{-1} can be attributed to vibrations of a —CH_3 group. However, since the bands due to the $>CH_2$ vibration are much more intense than those due to the —CH_3 grouping, it is evident that at least two species are present on the surface. The spectral data are consistent with the assumption that one of the species contains no CH_3 group and has one of the following structures:

$$
\begin{array}{cccc}
\text{S---H} & & \text{H}_2 & \text{H} \\
| & & \text{C} & | \\
\text{CH}_2 & & \diagup\ \diagdown & \text{S} \\
| & \text{CH}_2\text{---CH}_2 & \text{H}_2\text{C}\quad\text{S} & | \\
\text{CH}_2 & |\qquad| & |\qquad| & \text{H}_2\text{C---C---H} \\
| & \text{Ni}_s\quad\text{Ni}_s & \text{Ni}_s\ \cdot\text{Ni}_s & |\quad| \\
\text{Ni}_s & & & \text{Ni}_s\ \text{Ni}_s
\end{array}
$$

The second species is present in a relatively small amount and could have one of the following types of structure:

$$
\begin{array}{cccc}
\text{CH}_2 & & & \\
| & & \text{CH}_3 & \\
\text{CH}_2 & \text{H} & | & \text{H} \\
| & | & \text{CH}_2 & | \\
\text{S} & \text{HS---C---CH}_3 & | & \text{S---C---CH}_3 \\
| & | & \text{Ni}_s & |\quad| \\
\text{Ni}_s & \text{Ni}_s & & \text{Ni}_s\ \text{Ni}_s
\end{array}
$$

Diethyl sulfide, $(C_2H_5)_2S$, adsorbed on Ni gives a spectrum closely related to that observed in the previous system. The adsorption again occurs apparently by rupture of the C—S bond, and no evidence for covalent bonding through the S atom is obtained. The relative intensities of the bands attributed to $>CH_2$ and —CH_3 groups show the presence of more adsorbed —CH_3 species than would be expected from the interpretation of the $(C_2H_5)HS$ spectra. They argue in favor of the presence of yet another surface species.

Thiophene,

$$
\begin{array}{cc}
\text{H—C}\!\!\!-\!\!\!-\!\!\!-\!\!\!\text{C—H} \\
\text{H—C} \qquad \text{C—H} \\
\diagdown \quad \diagup \\
\text{S}
\end{array}
$$

also adsorbs on a Ni surface with decomposition rather than by bond formation through the sulfur atom (63).

Gaseous thiophene exhibits two bands of interest in discussion of the nature of the adsorbed species. These are the strong C—H stretching frequency that occurs at 3096 cm^{-1} and the ring vibration that occurs at 1590 cm^{-1}. Upon adsorption at room temperature, the ring vibration is completely absent from the spectrum and the 3096-cm^{-1} band is replaced by bands at 2940 cm^{-1} and a shoulder at 2885 cm^{-1}. Both of these bands are characteristic of C—H vibrations in which the carbon atom is fully saturated, but their positions are such that no definite assignments can be made. Blyholder and Bowen argue that the low carbon–hydrogen ratio in the parent molecule favors the presence of CH_2 rather than CH_3, but in either case some self-hydrogenation is implied. The loss of the ring vibration during adsorption implies that the adsorbed species has a more linear configuration, the formation of the surface complex invoking the formation of either two or four Ni—C bonds, and possibly a Ni—S bond. The relative intensities of the C—H vibrations suggest the presence of more than one species.

E. Nitrogen on Nickel

Because of the wide use of nitrogen adsorption techniques in the determination of surface areas, the nature of the bond formed between adsorbent and adsorbate during this process is of fundamental importance to our understanding of surface interactions. The free nitrogen molecule has no infrared-active vibrations because of its symmetry, but, as has already been discussed, on its adsorption on silica at $-100°C$, the Raman vibration at 2331 cm^{-1} is activated and is observed in the infrared spectrum of the adsorbed gas.

Prior to the advent of infrared techniques in the study of surface chemistry, the adsorption of nitrogen on nickel had been examined by conventional means. At low temperatures it was acknowledged that nitrogen could be chemically adsorbed on both nickel films and on silica-supported nickel surfaces, whereas at normal temperatures this chemi-

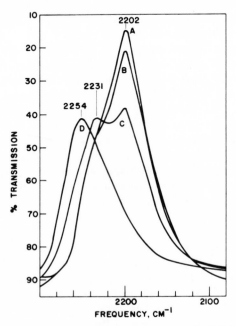

Fig. 6-8. *The addition of hydrogen to nitrogen adsorbed on Ni–SiO₂ at −100°C: A, N₂ adsorption; B to D. Increasing hydrogen pressure. [Reproduced from Reference (64) by courtesy of North-Holland Publishing Company, Amsterdam.]*

sorption was not observed. In order to identify the nature of chemisorbed nitrogen, Eischens and Jacknow (64) examined the infrared spectrum of nitrogen adsorbed upon a silica-supported nickel surface at temperatures ranging from −180° to 30°C.

These workers report that a chemisorbed species can be observed on the Ni–SiO₂ surface at room temperature, provided a nitrogen pressure of at least 0.01 torr is employed. Only when the gas pressure reaches several centimeters does the band approach its maximum intensity. The chemisorbed species is readily observed at −100°C, when it is evidenced by the presence of a strong band at 2202 cm⁻¹ (Fig. 6-8). The considerable shift from the gaseous nitrogen vibration frequency ($\Delta \nu = 129$ cm^{-1}) is confirmation of the "chemical" nature of the bonding. Adsorption of the isotopic species N_2^{14}, N_2^{15}, or $N^{14}N^{15}$ gives rise to separate distinctive bands in the spectrum (2195, 2123, 2160 cm^{-1}) and provides positive evidence that dissociation of the nitrogen molecule does not take place during the adsorption process. The isotopic shifts thus obtained were utilized by Eischens and Jacknow to determine the force constants for the N—N and Ni—N bonds, and these were calculated to be 19.1×10^{-5} and 3×10^{-5} dynes/cm, respectively. These values suggest that the Ni—N bond order is about 1, whereas the N—N bond order is about 3. The nitrogen molecule ion, N_2^+, has been calculated to have a vibrational frequency of 2207 cm^{-1}. This is close to the value observed for the surface species, which is written

$$-\mathrm{Ni}_s\!-\!\mathrm{N}\!\equiv\!\mathrm{N}^+$$

The infrared evidence in itself does not justify the assignment to a positive ion. However, Gundry and his co-workers (65) had already shown that the nickel surface became positively charged during nitrogen chemisorption, and this, together with the close correspondence of the vibration frequencies of the adsorbed species and the molecule ion, is satisfactory evidence for the formulation.

Eischens and Jacknow also determined the extinction coefficient of the adsorbed nitrogen to be 0.2×10^{-17} cm^2/molecule. This value is extremely high and similar to that observed for chemisorbed carbon monoxide. It is indicative of a highly polarized species.

The frequency of vibration of the N—N atom does not in itself permit distinction between the species in which the $N\!\equiv\!N^+$ molecule ion lies perpendicular to the surface or parallel with the surface. In the latter case, however, a high extinction coefficient would not be expected, and thus the linear species seems most probable. In truth, the adsorbed species cannot be a true molecule ion, because the species would be completely symmetrical and have no infrared-active vibrations. Moreover, an absorption induced by the surface asymmetry would not give rise to such an intense vibration, and thus the species must be considered close to, but not exactly, that illustrated.

When hydrogen was added to the chemisorbed nitrogen–nickel system at $-100°C$, the spectra reproduced in Fig. 6-8 were obtained. Clearly, the effect of adding hydrogen is to decrease the intensity of the band at 2202 cm^{-1} with the concurrent formation of a band at 2231 cm^{-1}. Addition of excess hydrogen causes this band to shift to 2254 cm^{-1}. The decrease in intensity of the 2202-cm^{-1} band, measured as a function of hydrogen addition, indicates a 1:1 relationship between the nitrogen and hydrogen during this process. This relationship suggests the formation of a surface species that can be formulated as

$$
\begin{array}{ccc}
\text{H} & & \text{H} \qquad\quad \text{H} \\
| & & \diagdown \qquad \diagup \\
\text{N} & \text{or} & \text{N}\!-\!\text{N} \\
\diagup \;\; \diagdown & & \diagup \qquad\quad \diagdown \\
\text{Ni} \quad \text{Ni} & & \text{Ni} \qquad\quad \text{Ni}
\end{array}
$$

Unfortunately, Eischens and Jacknow were unable to detect any band due to the nitrogen-hydrogen vibration. This, however, is not indicative, because N—H bands are generally very weak and difficult to detect. The final shift of the absorption peak from 2231 to 2254 cm^{-1}, which occurs on addition of excess hydrogen, is difficult to explain. Eischens and Jacknow speculate that at this stage the hydrogen is adsorbed as a hydride, H^-, ion upon the same nickel atom as that to which the nitrogen is attached. The shift to higher frequencies is attributed to an inductive effect on the nitrogen-nitrogen triple bond caused by the electronegative H^- ion, i.e.,

$$
\begin{array}{c}
\overset{+}{\text{N}} \\
||| \\
\text{H}^- \qquad\qquad \text{N} \\
\diagdown \qquad\qquad \diagup \\
\text{Ni}_s
\end{array}
$$

It should be noted, from Fig. 6-8, however, that there is no major change in the intensity of the band, despite the frequency shift. An inductive effect such as illustrated above might be expected to cause a change in the intensity of the absorption due to a change in the dipole moment.

At 30°C, hydrogen, ammonia, and hydrocarbons all cause the 2202-cm^{-1} band to shift to 2254 cm^{-1}. Oxygen, carbon monoxide, and nitrous oxide completely remove the band, but no prior shift is noted. At -50°C, ammonia addition to the bare nickel surface gives rise to a spectrum that shows a band at 2202 cm^{-1} due to adsorbed nitrogen. Clearly, under these conditions the ammonia has decomposed upon adsorption into nitrogen and hydrogen. It is not clear, however, why the hydrogen produced does not cause a shift of the N_2^+ vibration to 2231 cm^{-1}. This shift occurs when hydrogen is separately added to the chemisorbed nitrogen.

Little information is available on the nature of the sites that chemisorb nitrogen. Whereas adsorbed carbon monoxide is distributed uniformly over a nickel surface, with nitrogen, a maximum coverage of 30% is indicated by the chemisorption experiments. The results of Peri (*12*) on carbon monoxide and ammonia adsorption on Ni–SiO$_2$ are of interest in this connection. Peri was able to show that a large number of Lewis acid sites exist on the Ni–SiO$_2$ surface. The ability of surfaces containing such sites to form radical ions, when contacted with hydrocarbons of low ionization potential, suggests a possible analogy between those reactions and the formation of the nitrogen molecule ion. For example, the overall reactions

$$\overset{|}{\underset{|}{-Al}} + perylene = \overset{|}{\underset{|}{-Al^{\ominus}}} perylene^{\oplus}$$

can be compared with

$$Ni_s + N_2 = Ni_s^- N_2^+$$

Obviously, a great deal of work must be carried out with these systems before a true understanding can be reached.

Hardeveld (*66*) has commented that he has been able to observe the band due to chemisorbed nitrogen only on nickel samples prepared by decomposition of nickel nitrate. Nakata and Matsushita (*67*), however, report observation of a band at 2202 cm^{-1} on a nickel sample prepared from nickel acetate as well as from nickel nitrate, and so the formation of the species is well authenticated, even if the exact nature of the species is not defined. In any chemisorption process it is to be expected that preparative techniques will influence surface properties. The ease with which the catalytic activity of a surface can be destroyed serves as a permanent reminder of this effect.[†]

F. Formic Acid on Nickel (Oxide)

Surface formates have been proposed as active intermediates in the decomposition of formic acid. The nature of the surface species formed when formic acid is adsorbed on a silica-supported nickel surface has been investigated spectroscopically by Eischens and Pliskin (*69*) following earlier work by Hirota (*70*) and Fahrenfort and Hazebroeck (*71*).

Eischens and Pliskin showed that at least two forms of the chemisorbed acid can be distinguished. The addition of small amounts of formic acid to a completely reduced Ni–SiO$_2$ sample at −60°C gave a spectrum that was reminiscent of the formate ion, but, on the basis of the relative

---

[†] Hardeveld and Montfoort (*68*) have recently provided evidence that the band due to chemisorbed nitrogen is observed only when the metal crystallites are between 15 and 70 Å in diameter. If this qualification was fulfilled, then chemisorbed nitrogen was observed on platinum and palladium in addition to nickel.

intensities of the C—H and C—O bands, it could not be traced to this species. Instead, Eischens and Pliskin assign the bands to a covalent surface formate as represented in (**1**).

$$
\begin{array}{cc}
\underset{\text{Ni}_s \quad \text{Ni}_s}{\underset{O \diagup\quad\diagdown O}{\underset{C}{\overset{H}{|}}}} & \underset{\text{Ni}^{+}_s}{\underset{O \diagup\quad\diagdown O}{\underset{C}{\overset{H}{|}}}} \\
(1) & (2)
\end{array}
$$

When this system is allowed to warm to room temperature, the formate partially decomposes to carbon monoxide. This in turn chemisorbs on the exposed metal surface to give both type A and type B CO species.

Addition of formic acid to nickel oxide gives rise to the ionic surface formate (**2**), which has a spectrum analogous to that of the metal formates. The addition of excess formic acid to a reduced nickel surface also gives the ionic surface formate, owing to reduction of the formic acid and consequent formation of an oxide surface.

Addition of formic acid to platinum causes complete decomposition even at $-60°C$. Bands due to adsorbed CO are again formed, but in this case only the type A species appears to be produced (*69*).

G. Ethylene Adsorption on Metal Surfaces

The adsorption of ethylene and other unsaturated hydrocarbons on metal and metal oxides has been studied spectroscopically in an endeavor to determine the nature of the adsorbed species. Studies of ethylene adsorbed on nickel–silica (*12,31,72*), palladium–porous glass (*73*), and NiO–, CuO–, PdO–porous glass (*74*) have been reported. The spectra reported in these investigations are similar and show that the nature of the adsorbed species is dependent upon the temperature at which adsorption takes place and, more particularly, on the presence or absence of hydrogen in the system. In the case of the porous glass supports, the slight acidity of the support has some bearing on the results and is difficult to dissociate from the effect of the metal.

According to Eischens and Pliskin, the spectrum of adsorbed ethylene obtained in the absence of hydrogen is characteristic of a species in which the ethylene has been dissociatively chemisorbed. The carbon atoms appear to be fully saturated, but the intensities of the C—H vibrations are so weak that the number of hydrogen atoms attached to each carbon atom must be considered small. Eischens and Pliskin suggest that this surface species is probably of variable composition. The dissociated complex is readily hydrogenated to a saturated butane-like species. Peri's more recent results for ethylene adsorbed on $Ni-SiO_2$ suggest that the ethylene first dimerizes on adsorption to give a butene. This is readily hydrogenated to butane. Saturated species are also observed when hydrogen is adsorbed on the metal surface prior to addition of ethylene. The surface species in this case is possibly initially of the type

$$
\begin{array}{cc}
\text{H} & \text{H} \\
| & | \\
\text{H}-\text{C}-\text{C}-\text{H} \\
| & | \\
\text{M}_s & \text{M}_s
\end{array}
$$

Hydrogenation of this associated species gives rise to a polymeric surface complex apparently of the type $M_s-(CH_2)_n-CH_3$. A measurement of the relative intensities of the bands due to the CH_2 and CH_3 groups enables an estimate of n to be made. It is probably about 3.

H. Acetylene Adsorption on Metal Surfaces

Eischens and Pliskin (*31,72*) have reported that the adsorption of acetylene on a nickel–silica surface gives rise to the formation of surface ethyl groups. A self-hydrogenation mechanism is presumably involved.

$$
\text{M}_s + 2\tfrac{1}{2}\text{C}_2\text{H}_2 \rightarrow
\begin{array}{c}
\text{H} \\
| \\
\text{H}-\text{C}-\text{H} \\
| \\
\text{H}-\text{C}-\text{H} \\
| \\
\text{M}_s
\end{array}
+ 3\text{C}_s
$$

Addition of hydrogen causes hydrogenation of the surface carbide with the formation of a saturated species in which the $CH_2:CH_3$ ratio is apparently greater than 1. The use of deuterium rather than hydrogen in this experiment showed that the ethyl groups formed initially were unaffected by the further hydrogenation and that the new bands observed in the spectrum were derived wholly by reaction with the surface carbide. Similar results are reported by Nash and DeSieno (*75*) and Dunken et al. (*76*).

Little et al. (*73*) report that the spectrum of acetylene on copper, palladium, and nickel shows evidence of an olefinic species (bands at 3090 and 3030 cm^{-1}). After addition of hydrogen, these bands are replaced and a saturated hydrocarbon is produced (bands at 2910 and 2850 cm^{-1}). These results differ from those of Eischens and Pliskin in the initial formation of the unsaturated species. At the other extreme of surface reactivity, Nash and DeSieno (75) found that acetylene immediately reacted with an unsupported copper sample to give a species analogous to that obtained after the hydrogenation of ethylene chemisorbed on nickel. The production of large amounts of carbide in this adsorption was evidenced by a fivefold increase in the intensity of the bands due to the adsorbed species, following a hydrogenation treatment.

I. Paraxylene on Transition Metals: Isotopic Exchange

Hirota and Ueda (77) have examined the isotopic exchange of deuterium for hydrogen in paraxylene and its related compounds at 100°C over a number of transition-metal catalysts. Deuteration of the paraxylene molecule can occur by exchange with either a methyl-hydrogen or a ring-hydrogen atom. In the first case, the C—D vibration is identified at 2118 cm^{-1}; in the latter case the C—D vibration occurs at 2252 cm^{-1}. On nickel, there is no evidence of ring substitution of D for H, but, when the catalysts are changed along the series Ni, β-Co, α-Co, Rh, Ru, Ir, Pd, Pt, both the relative proportions of the band at 2252 cm^{-1} to the band at 2118 cm^{-1} and the catalytic activity increase. This selectivity ratio is in accord with a mechanism proposed by Hirota and Ueda on independent kinetic measurements.

REFERENCES

1. G. C. A. Schuit and L. L. Van Reijen, *Advan. Catalysis*, **10**, 242 (1958).
2. R. P. Eischens, S. A. Francis, and W. A. Pliskin, *J. Phys. Chem.*, **60**, 194 (1956).
3. G. Blyholder, *Proceedings of the Third International Congress on Catalysis*, North-Holland, Amsterdam, 1965, p. 657.
4. G. Blyholder, *J. Chem. Phys.*, **36**, 2036 (1962).
5. L. H. Jones, *J. Chem. Phys.*, **28**, 1215 (1958).
6. C. S. Kraihanzel and F. A. Cotton, *Inorg. Chem.*, **2**, 533 (1963).
7. K. Nakamoto, *Infrared Spectra of Inorganic and Coordination Compounds*, Wiley, New York, 1963.
8. C. E. O'Neill and D. J. C. Yates, *J. Phys. Chem.*, **65**, 901 (1961).
9. C. W. Garland, *J. Phys. Chem.*, **63**, 1423 (1959).
10. J. T. Yates, Jr., and C. W. Garland, *J. Phys. Chem.*, **65**, 617 (1961).
11. R. M. Hammaker, S. A. Francis, and R. P. Eischens, *Spectrochim. Acta*, **21**, 1295 (1965).
12. J. B. Peri, *Discussions Faraday Soc.*, **41**, 121 (1966).
13. H. L. Pickering and H. C. Eckstrom, *J. Phys. Chem.*, **63**, 512 (1959).
14. R. A. Gardner and R. H. Petrucci, *J. Am. Chem. Soc.*, **82**, 5051 (1960).
15. J. B. Sardisco, *Perkin-Elmer Instr. News*, **15**, 13 (1963).
16. C. W. Garland, R. C. Lord, and P. F. Troiano, *J. Phys. Chem.*, **69**, 1195 (1965).
17. L. J. Bellamy, *The Infrared Spectra of Complex Molecules*, Methuen, London, 1958.
18. H. C. Eckstrom, *J. Phys. Chem.*, **70**, 594 (1966).

19. R. P. Eischens and W. A. Pliskin, *Advan. Catalysis*, **9,** 662 (1956).

20. M. Courtois and S. J. Teichner, *J. Catalysis*, **1,** 121 (1962).

21. N. D. Parkyns, *Proceedings of the Third International Congress on Catalysis,* North-Holland, Amsterdam, 1965, p. 914.

22. M. Uchida and T. Imai, *Bull. Chem. Soc. Japan*, **35,** 989, 995 (1962).

23. J. B. Peri, *J. Phys. Chem.*, **70,** 3168 (1966).

24. C. W. Garland, R. C. Lord, and P. F. Troiano, *J. Phys. Chem.*, **69,** 1188 (1965).

25. R. M. Hammaker, S. A. Francis, and R. P. Eischens, *Spectrochim. Acta*, **21,** 1295 (1965).

26. J. C. Decius, *J. Chem. Phys.*, **23,** 1290 (1955).

27. L. Lynds, *Spectrochim. Acta*, **20,** 1369 (1964).

28. A. C. Yang and C. W. Garland, *J. Phys. Chem.*, **61,** 1504 (1957).

29. A. W. Smith and J. M. Quets, *J. Catalysis*, **4,** 163 (1965).

30. A. W. Smith, *J. Catalysis*, **4,** 172 (1965).

31. R. P. Eischens and W. A. Pliskin, *Advan. Catalysis*, **10,** 1 (1958).

32. C. H. Amberg and D. A. Seanor, *J. Chem. Phys.*, **42,** 2967 (1965).

33. M. M. Siddiqui and F. C. Tompkins. *Proc. Roy. Soc. (London)*, **A268,** 452 (1962).

34. G. Blyholder, *J. Chem. Phys.*, **36,** 2036 (1962).

35. L. Pauling, *Nature of the Chemical Bond*, Cornell Univ. Press, Ithaca, N.Y., 1960.

36. G. Blyholder and L. D. Neff, *J. Phys. Chem.*, **66,** 1464 (1962).

37. F. Fischer and H. Tropsch, *Brennstoff-Chem.*, **7,** 97 (1926).

38. H. H. Storch, N. Golumbic, and R. B. Anderson, *The Fischer-Tropsch and Related Syntheses*, Wiley, New York, 1951.

39. R. J. Kokes, W. K. Hall, and P. H. Emmett, *J. Am. Chem. Soc.*, **79,** 2989 (1957).

40. G. Blyholder and L. D. Neff, *J. Phys. Chem.*, **66,** 1664 (1962).

41. J. B. Peri, *Proceedings of the Third International Congress on Catalysis*, North-Holland, Amsterdam, 1965, p. 1100.

42. R. R. Myers, *Ann. N.Y. Acad. Sci.*, **72,** 339 (1958).

43. R. A. Gardner, *J. Phys. Chem.*, **64,** 1120 (1960).

44. Th. Wolkenstein, *Advan. Catalysis*, **9,** 807 (1957).

45. R. A. Gardner and R. H. Petrucci, *J. Phys. Chem.*, **67,** 1376 (1963).

46. R. A. Gardner, *J. Catalysis*, **3,** 22 (1964).

47. R. A. Gardner, *J. Catalysis*, **3,** 7 (1964).

48. R. A. Gardner, *J. Catalysis*, **3,** 105 (1964).

49. L. E. Orgel, *Transition-Metal Chemistry*, Wiley, New York, 1960.

50. L. H. Little, quoted by J. B. Peri (*12.*)

51. G. Blyholder, *J. Phys. Chem.*, **68,** 2772 (1964).

52. J. T. Yates, Jr., *J. Phys. Chem.*, **68,** 2777 (1964).

53. G. Blyholder and M. C. Allen, *J. Phys. Chem.*, **69,** 3998 (1965).

54. C. H. Amberg and D. A. Seanor, *Proceedings of the Third International Congress on Catalysis*, North-Holland, Amsterdam, 1965, p. 450.

55. J. Lewis, R. J. Irving, and G. Wilkinson, *J. Inorg. Nucl. Chem.*, **7,** 32, 38 (1958).

56. A. Terenin and L. Roev, *Spectrochim. Acta*, **1959,** 946.

57. A. Terenin and L. Roev, *Actes du Deuxième Congrès International de Catalyse, Paris, 1960*, Editions Technip, Paris, 1961, p. 2183.

58. W. M. H. Sachtler, *Actes du Deuxième Congrès International de Catalyse, Paris, 1960*, Editions Technip, Paris, 1961, p. 2197.

59. G. Blyholder and M. C. Allen, *J. Phys. Chem.*, **70,** 352 (1966).

60. G. Blyholder and L. D. Neff, *J. Phys. Chem.*, **70**, 893 (1966).
61. C. W. Garland, *J. Phys. Chem.*, **63**, 1423 (1959).
62. J. T. Yates, Jr., and C. W. Garland, *J. Phys. Chem.*, **65**, 618 (1961).
63. G. Blyholder and D. O. Bowen, *J. Phys. Chem.*, **66**, 1288 (1962).
64. R. P. Eischens and J. Jacknow, *Proceedings of the International Congress on Catalysis*, North-Holland, Amsterdam, 1965, p. 627.
65. P. M. Gundry, J. Haber, and F. C. Tompkins, *J. Catalysis*, **1**, 1363 (1962).
66. R. V. Hardeveld, *Proceedings of the Third International Congress on Catalysis*, North-Holland, Amsterdam, 1965, p. 638.
67. T. Nakata and S. Matsushita, *J. Catalysis*, **4**, 631 (1965).
68. R. V. Hardeveld and A. V. Montfoort, *Surface Sci.*, **4**, 396 (1966).
69. R. P. Eischens and W. A. Pliskin, *Actes du Deuxième Congrès International de Catalyse, Paris, 1960*, Vol. 1, Editions Technip, Paris, 1961, *p.* 789.
70. K. Hirota, K. Kuwata, and Y. Nakai, *Bull. Chem. Soc. Japan*, **31**, 861 (1958).
71. J. Fahrenfort and H. L. Hazebroek, *Z. Physik. Chem. (Frankfurt)*, **20**, 105 (1959).
72. W. A. Pliskin and R. P. Eischens, *J. Phys. Chem.*, **60**, 482 (1956).
73. L. H. Little, N. Sheppard, and D. J. C. Yates, *Proc. Roy. Soc. (London)*, **A259**, 242 (1960).
74. L. H. Little, *J. Phys. Chem.*, **63**, 1616 (1959).
75. C. P. Nash and R. P. DeSieno, *J. Phys. Chem.*, **69**, 2139 (1965).
76. H. Dunken, K. Schmidt, and H. Hobert, *Z. Chem.*, **4**, 312 (1964).
77. K. Hirota and T. Ueda, *Proceedings of the Third International Congress on Catalysis*, North-Holland, Amsterdam, 1965, p. 1238.

7

Some Miscellaneous Surfaces

7-1. NICKEL SULFATE

The surfaces of many metal sulfates show an ability to change the color of Hammett indicators. They appear to form a series of solid acids analogous to the alumina and silica–alumina materials widely used in catalysis. Moreover, experiments with nickel sulfate show a correlation between the surface acidity as measured by the indicator method and the catalytic activity of the material in polymerization and hydration reactions. This observation is of special interest in view of the correlation between Brönsted acidity and propylene polymerization (1) that has been found for a series of silica–alumina catalysts of varying compositions (Fig. 5-8). The catalytic activity of the nickel sulfate is dependent upon the temperature at which the sulfate has been heat-treated; maximum activity occurs after a heat treatment at about 360°C. At this point the total acidity as measured by the Benesi method (2) is about 10^{-4} mole/g, whereas the Lewis acidity measured in a similar fashion is approximately 3×10^{-7} mole/g.

As it is normally obtained, nickel sulfate contains six molecules of water of crystallization that can be removed by heating to 550°C. At this temperature the material is in the anhydrous form. During the heating process, important changes occur in the infrared spectrum. Obviously the bands due to the water molecules are slowly removed, but in addition, the loss of water causes a loss in the degeneracy of the sulfate vibrations, which split and appear at different frequencies. Thus, whereas at room temperature only one band due to the asymmetric sulfate stretching vibration is observed at 1090 cm^{-1}, on heating between 150° and 350°C, three bands are observed at 1020, 1090, and 1150 cm^{-1}. Above 350°C a sudden change is observed in the position of these three bands, and at 400°C they are observed at 1235, 1160, and 1030 cm^{-1}. These infrared

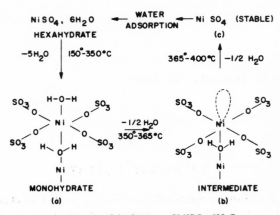

Fig. 7-1. *The dehydration of* $NiSO_4 \cdot 6H_2O$.

spectra, in conjunction with X-ray diffraction data, show that, between 150° and 350°C, the hexahydrate, $NiSO_4 \cdot 6H_2O$, is converted into the monohydrate $NiSO_4 \cdot H_2O$ [Fig. 7-1(a)]. At 400° the stable dehydrated nickel sulfate has been produced [Fig. 7-1(c)]. This dehydration is shown schematically in the illustration. At 365°C (the temperature corresponding to the maximum catalytic activity), the infrared spectrum shows the presence of both of these forms, and Takeshita et al. (*3*) suggest that an intermediate [Fig. 7-1(b)] is formed by the removal of one molecule of water of crystallization.

Comparison of this species with the Lewis acid sites postulated on the alumina surface shows that there is indeed a strong similarity. Thus, whereas the sites on the alumina surface are presumably due to a vacant *p* orbital, the unstable nickel sulfate species has a vacant sp^3d^2 orbital.

Addition of water to a sample previously heated to 550°C causes direct conversion back to the hexahydrate. The intermediate [Fig. 7-1(b)] is not detected during this process. Presumably the water vapor is initially physically adsorbed on the surface of the stable nickel sulfate and the conversion to the hexahydrate takes place directly. Further work on this system should be of great interest, because it provides the surface chemist with a material that can be readily identified by X-ray analysis.

7-2. ALKALI HALIDES

A. Water Adsorption

Although studies of alkali halide surfaces are not subject to the limitations of most oxides with respect to the amount of infrared transmission,

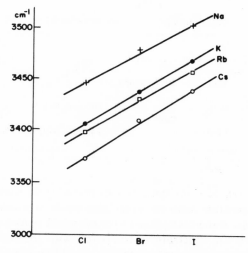

Fig. 7-2. *Position of* O—H *stretching frequencies of water adsorbed on various alkali halide surfaces.* [*Redrawn from Reference (4) by courtesy of the Royal Society.*]

little work on the infrared spectra of molecules adsorbed on these substrates has been published. This is presumably due both to the lack of commercial interest in these surfaces and to the low surface area associated with the materials. The spectrum of molecular water adsorbed on pressed discs formed from finely powdered alkali halides, however, has been obtained by Price et al. (4). These data show that the frequency of the strongest OH vibration observed in the 3000–3500-cm^{-1} region is directly related to the electronegativity of both the cation and the anion. Thus, from Fig. 7-2 it can be seen that, as the cation is varied from Na$^+$ to K$^+$ to Rb$^+$ to Cs$^+$, the vibrational frequency is decreased along the series.

Similarly, in going from I⁻ to Br⁻ to Cl⁻, the vibrational frequency is also decreased. The fact that the greatest shift is produced by the most electronegative anion and the most electropositive cation is taken as an indication that the water is attached to the surface by hydrogen bonding to the negative ions. The small, positive ions are buried inside the structure and are relatively inaccessible.

B. HCN Adsorption

The infrared spectra of both HCN and CO_2 adsorbed on evaporated alkali halide films have been published by Kozirovsky and Folman (5).

TABLE 7-1

HCN Adsorption on Sodium Chloride[a]

	ν_1, cm^{-1}	ν_3, cm^{-1}	ν_2, cm^{-1}	Orientation to surface
Gas	3311	2097 (weak)	712	
Adsorbed Species				
(i)	3145		800 (singlet)	Perpendicular, major species
		2095		
(ii)	3040		746 (doublet)	Parallel, minor species

[a] Data taken from Reference (6).

This work, although of a preliminary nature, indicates that on many of the alkali halide surfaces there exist two adsorption sites, and the relative intensities of many of the bands due to the adsorbed species are considerably altered when the spectrum is compared with that of the gaseous molecules. Further work on these surfaces should be of great interest in studies of physical adsorption, because the spectral range available can allow a complete identification of the adsorbed species. As an example of this, the frequencies observed for HCN adsorbed on sodium chloride are shown in Table 7-1. These can be compared with the frequencies reported for adsorption on a porous glass surface (Section 4-F6), where considerable polymerization was noted.

Thus, when HCN is adsorbed on a high-area film of sodium chloride, the adsorbed material shows five distinct bands. This is to be compared with the gaseous spectrum, which normally exhibits only two of the three infrared active bands owing to the extreme lack of intensity of the ν_3 (C≡N) vibration. On adsorption, this band is increased in intensity and is clearly observable at 2095 cm^{-1}. The two bands at 3145 and 3040 cm^{-1}

are attributed to the ν_1 (C—H) vibrations of two different surface species. The two bending modes at 800 and 746 cm^{-1} are also due to these different forms. The HCN molecule is highly polar, the hydrogen atom constituting the positive end of the dipole. The adsorption process is, therefore, presumed to occur via interaction of the hydrogen atom with the negative chloride ions in the surface of the sodium chloride, the specific interaction accounting for the large shift observed in the frequency of the C—H vibrations ($\Delta\nu = 170, 270$ cm^{-1}). The two species that occur are thought to be due to parallel and perpendicular orientations. The resolution of the 746-cm^{-1} band into a doublet implies a splitting due to a change in symmetry, and thus this band can be attributed to the species held parallel to the surface.

Kozirovsky and Folman (6) have calculated the shifts in frequency that might be expected for the C—H vibration, and they obtained values of between -119 and -178 cm^{-1} when they assumed distances of 3.0 and 3.2 Å for the Cl$^-$ . . . (HCN) distance. The theoretical calculation was based on a model in which the physically adsorbed HCN is held perpendicular to the surface. Experimentally, this type of species is found to constitute the major proportion of the adsorbed HCN. The observed frequency shift is -166 cm^{-1}, which is in good agreement with the theoretical calculation.

REFERENCES

1. V. C. F. Holm, G. C. Bailey, and A. Clark, *J. Phys. Chem.*, **63**, 129 (1959).
2. H. A. Benesi, *J. Phys. Chem.*, **61**, 970 (1957).
3. T. Takeshita, R. Ohnishi, T. Matsui, and K. Tanabe, *J. Phys. Chem.*, **69**, 4077 (1965),
4. W. C. Price, W. F. Sherman, and G. R. Wilkinson, *Proc. Roy. Soc. (London)*, **A247**, 467 (1958).
5. Y. Kozirovsky and M. Folman, *J. Chem. Phys.*, **41**, 1509 (1964).
6. Y. Kozirovsky and M. Folman, *Trans. Faraday Soc.*, **62**, 808 (1966).

8

Emission, Reflection, and Raman Spectra

8-1. EMISSION SPECTRA

In Chapter 2 it was pointed out that, whenever the equation

$$\Delta E = h\nu$$

is satisfied, either a discrete absorption or an emission of energy can occur. Every material, therefore, gives a chracteristic spectrum. The *emission spectrum* is the inverse of the absorption spectrum. For most materials, the amount of radiation emitted at room temperature is comparatively small, and in order to detect this radiation, wide spectral slit widths must be employed in the spectrometer. As was seen from Chapter 3, this effect leads to a poorly resolved spectrum. For the surface chemist, however, the technique offers many potential advantages, because it provides a method of studying the surfaces of materials that are normally opaque to infrared radiation.

Eischens and Pliskin (*1*) were the first investigators to explore the emission spectra of chemisorbed molecules, but the poor resolution of their spectra emphasized the experimental difficulties inherent in this technique. In recent years, however, the experimental problems have been tackled again by Low and his co-workers (*2-4*). The problems involved in determining the emission spectra of surface species have been reviewed.

Successful spectra of fatty acids adsorbed on steel surfaces have been obtained, and evidence for the formation of oxidized species has been published (3). The emission spectra of several pieces of paint, paper, rubber, and grease have also been reported (4). The considerable improvement in resolution that was achieved in Low's work came from the use of both multiple scanning and inferometric techniques (2). The first technique vastly increases the signal-to-noise ratio and enables spectra to be obtained that are almost comparable in quality with many obtained in transmission work. Further developments can be expected in this field, and the interested experimenter is referred to Low's original papers for further details.

8-2. REFLECTION SPECTRA

A. Specular Reflection

In studying the infrared spectra of materials, most workers have employed transmission spectroscopy and have gone to considerable lengths to reduce light losses caused by reflection at the sample surface. The spectrum of the reflected light is as unique to the material under investigation as the transmission spectrum. However, the interpretation is much more difficult, owing to the variability of the spectrum with varying angle of incidence and the fact that a phase change occurs during the reflection process. The true reflectance spectrum, therefore, bears no resemblance to the transmission spectrum. This type of true reflection is known as *specular reflection*. Further details on this effect can be obtained from Reference (5).

B. Ellipsometry

The phase change that the incident light undergoes during the reflection process is different for the two components of the radiation that are parallel with and perpendicular to the surface. An elliptic polarization of the reflected radiation is thus produced. This phenomenon in itself provides a potentially useful tool, known as ellipsometry, for surface studies. It promises to be particularly useful in the study of electrodes under operating aqueous conditions (6), and it has been used to study monolayers of oxygen adsorbed on low-surface-area silicon surfaces (7).

C. Refraction and Critical Angle

When a beam of monochromatic light is incident upon the interface between two transparent materials a and b at an angle i, the transmitted light is refracted at an angle r to the normal to the surface (Fig. 8-1).

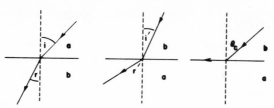

Fig. 8.1. *The refraction of a beam of monochromatic light. Two materials are represented by a and b, the density of b being greater than that of a. θ_c is the critical angle.*

The relationship between i and r is given by the equation

$$\frac{\sin i}{\sin r} = \frac{c_a}{c_b} = n \tag{8-1}$$

where c_a and c_b are the velocities of the light in phases a and b and b is assumed to be the more dense material. When phase a is a vacuum, the constant n is known as the *refractive index* of the material. Since the velocity in phase b is dependent upon the wavelength of the incident radiation, the refractive index of the material also varies with the wavelength. In the absence of strong absorption bands, the refractive index decreases as wavelength increases. In the region of strong absorptions, very sharp changes in index occur (Fig. 8-2). This phenomenon is of

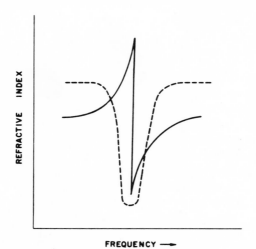

Fig. 8-2. *The change in refractive index of a material in the neighborhood of an absorption band. The solid line represents the refractive index, the dashed line the absorption.*

importance in the practical application of internal reflection spectroscopy.

From Eq. (8-1) it is seen that as long as $c_a > c_b$, for every angle of incidence there must be a refracted ray. If, however, the light is passed from phase b with a higher index of refraction to the phase a of lower index, there is an angle of incidence beyond which there is no refracted ray. This limiting angle is called the *critical angle*. It is the angle of incidence for which the angle of refraction r is $90°$ and $\sin r = 1$, the maximum possible value. When the critical angle is exceeded and no refracted ray can exist, the light is totally reflected. If n_b and n_a are the refractive indices of phase b and phase a, respectively, and i is the critical angle of incidence into phase a, $\sin i = n_a/n_b$. When phase a is a vacuum, $\sin i = 1/n_b$.

D. Internal Reflection

Even when the angle of incidence exceeds the critical angle, some radiation penetrates the second phase. The depth of penetration is of the order of a wavelength of the radiation and depends upon the refractive indices of both phases and the angle of incidence. A schematic plot of

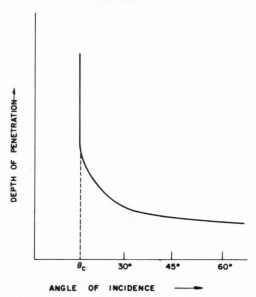

Fig. 8-3. *Schematic plot showing typical variation of depth of penetration as a function of the angle of incidence.*

the depth of penetration against the angle of incidence is shown in Fig. 8-3. This effect has been used to provide an attractive analytical tool, and the phenomenon is known as *internal reflection* or ATR (attenuated total reflection) spectroscopy.

The spectrum that is recorded approximates the normal transmission spectrum, and thus the method provides a valuable means of examining materials that are too opaque for transmission experiments. In one of the techniques presently employed, a series of reflections is obtained by placing two samples on an internal reflection element (Fig. 8-4) and using a *multiple internal reflection* effect. If the refractive index of the reflector material is sufficiently high, the spectra obtained approximate those obtained by transmission spectroscopy. If the refractive index of the reflector material is lower than the refractive index recorded at the peak maximum (Fig. 8-2), then anomalous band shapes and band broadening are observed. Also, differences in the relative intensities

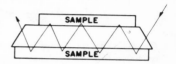

Fig. 8-4. *The multiple internal reflection effect.*

of bands can sometimes be observed when ATR and transmission spectra are compared.

The theory of the internal reflectance method has been discussed by Fahrenfort (*8*) and Harrick (*9,10*), but a full understanding has not yet been achieved. From a practical point of view, the method works well and gives some amazingly reproducible spectra. It is exceedingly useful as a qualitative technique and is especially valuable for looking at macroscopic surface properties (paints, plastics, tin cans, wood, paper) and for the analysis of bulk surface impurities and surface coatings (Fig. 8-5). Applications to monolayer studies are limited, although a commercial unit that enables ATR spectra to be obtained in an evacuated system (*11*) is now available.

From a practical point of view it should be remembered that intimate contact between sample and reflector is essential, because the effect can be observed only where absolute contact is achieved. Increasing the number of internal reflections serves to increase the chance of the light interacting with a point of contact, the total effect being identical with increasing the sample thickness in transmission spectroscopy. In the study of monolayer properties, it is the ratio of surface layer to bulk material in the path of the radiation that is the most important parameter. The shallowest penetration is therefore desired, and this is achieved by varying the angle of incidence (Fig. 8-3). This problem has recently been tackled

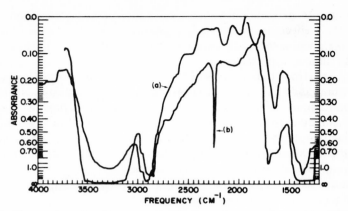

Fig. 8-5. The spectra of polymer-coated cellophane by transmission (a) and internal reflection (b). The polymer coat shows only in the internal reflection curve. [Spectra obtained and reproduced by courtesy of Wilks Scientific Corporation.]

by Greenler (*12*), who has examined the relationship between the angle of incidence and extinction in the case of reflection spectra of mono-molecular layers adsorbed on bulk metal surfaces.

E. Some Reflectance Studies

In one of the earliest reflectance studies, Francis and Ellison (*13*) reported the spectra of monolayers of barium stearate adsorbed on steel mirrors. These workers argued that in a reflection spectrum, when the dipole moment change was parallel with the incident radiation, the vibrational modes would appear only weakly in the resultant spectrum, whereas when the dipole moment change was perpendicular to the radiation, strong interaction with the incident light would be observed. In the case of barium stearate monolayers, the methylene C—H stretching and deformation vibrations are parallel with the surface, and they would therefore be expected to be very weak. This prediction was indeed confirmed and the vibrations of these groups were barely observable. Certain differences in the spectra were also noted, depending on whether the films were one or more layers in thickness.

The adsorption of carbon monoxide and hydrogen on nickel and rhodium mirrors has been studied by Pickering and Eckstrom (*14*) by using a multiple reflection technique. These workers found that the reflectivity of their metal films changed considerably during the adsorption and desorption process and that this feature in itself could be used to demonstrate that a surface interaction was occurring. Thus, when carbon monoxide at 1 mm pressure was added to a rhodium film, a band at 4.854 μ (2060 cm^{-1}) was observed together with a band at 4.785 μ (2091 cm^{-1}). Following the assignments discussed earlier, these bands are assigned to vibrations of linear M—C—O species. During the desorption step, the latter band showed an increased reflectivity, but its frequency was not altered, whereas the first band moved to 4.914 μ (2034 cm^{-1}). Conversely, the addition of hydrogen to the rhodium film caused a decrease in reflectivity that was not reversible. Twenty-three absorption bands were distinguished and attributed to hydrogen-rhodium species. This result is somewhat surprising, because multiple M_s—H vibrations have never been observed by using transmission spectroscopy (15).

The adsorption of hydrogen on silicon has also been shown to give rise to a recognizable Si—H species. Becker and Gobelli (16), using a multiple internal reflection technique, report formation of a broad band centered at 4.85 μ (2060 cm^{-1}) during the chemisorption of hydrogen on single crystal silicon. Since SiH_4 exhibits an Si—H stretching vibration at 4.57 μ (2188 cm^{-1}) the assignment seems reasonable.

Undoubtedly this technique shows great promise as a qualitative tool. However, much experimental and theoretical work needs to be done before the method can be quantitatively applied to surface studies.

8-3. RAMAN SPECTRA

Although light scattering is abhorred in most spectroscopic work, an analysis of the light scattered by a material provides considerable information about the vibrational and rotational energy levels in the material. It is thus a useful adjunct to infrared spectroscopy.

If a molecule is irradiated by monochromatic light of frequency ν_0, then two types of light scattering can occur. In the first, the scattered light has the same frequency, ν_0, as the incident radiation. This effect is known as Rayleigh scattering. Some of the incident light, however, can be absorbed by the molecule and re-emitted as scattered light at a different frequency. This is known as the Raman effect. The frequency of this scattered light, ν_s, can be either higher or lower than that of the incident light ν_0. The difference $\nu_0 - \nu_s$ is known as the Raman frequency. It corresponds to a vibrational frequency, and thus the Raman spectrum gives information similar to that given by the infrared spectrum. The exciting radiation ν_0 is usually so selected that the resultant spectrum is observed in the ultraviolet region. Since the Raman frequency can be either positive or negative, the actual spectrum consists of a series of lines symmetrically displayed on both sides of the incident frequency. Positive shifts are known as Stokes lines, negative shifts as anti-Stokes lines. Raman shifts are observed whenever the vibration of the molecule under observation gives rise to a change in polarization. Since a change in polarizability can often occur without a change in dipole moment, (i.e., in a symmetrical molecule), the Raman effect is complementary to infrared spectroscopy.

Although Raman spectroscopy has been used very successfully in many areas, it has had limited application to surface studies. Karagounis and Issa (17) have used the technique to study the spectra of a series of aromatic compounds adsorbed on silica. They found that the scattering intensity was exceptionally sensitive to the thickness of the irradiated layer of powder. The Raman lines observed were generally displaced only slightly as a result of adsorption. However, the intensities of the lines in the spectrum of the adsorbed species were considerably affected. On comparing the relative intensities of these lines with those in the spectrum of the free molecule, it was found that the lines due to the adsorbed species were all more nearly equal in intensity.

REFERENCES

1. R. P. Eischens and W. A. Pliskin, *Advan. Catalysis*, **10**, 51 (1958).
2. M. J. D. Low and I. Coleman, paper presented at *16th Annual Mid-America Symposium on Spectroscopy, Chigago, 1965.*
3. M. J. D. Low and H. Inoue, *Can. J. Chem.*, **43**, 2047 (1965).
4. M. J. D. Low and H. Inoue, *Anal. Chem.*, **36**, 2399 (1964).
5. I. Simon, *J. Opt. Soc. Am.*, **41**, 336 (1951).
6. J. O'M. Bockris, M. A. V. Devanathan, and A. K. N. Reddy, *Proc. Roy. Soc. (London)*, **279**, 327 (1964).
7. R. J. Archer and G. W. Gobelli, *Phys. Chem. Solids*, **26**, 343 (1965).
8. J. Fahrenfort, *Spectrochem. Acta*, **17**, 698 (1961).
9. N. J. Harrick, *Ann. N.Y. Acad. Sci.*, **101**, 928 (1963).
10. N. J. Harrick, *J. Opt. Soc. Am.*, **55**, 851 (1965).
11. Wilks Scientific Corp., South Norwalk, Conn., 1965.
12. R. G. Greenler, *J. Chem. Phys.*, **44**, 310 (1966).
13. S. A. Francis and A. H. Ellison, *J. Opt. Soc. Am.*, **49**, 131 (1959).
14. H. L. Pickering and H. C. Eckstrom, *J. Phys. Chem.*, **63**, 512 (1959).
15. R. P. Eischens, *Z. Physik. Chem. (Frankfurt)*, **24**, 12 (1960).
16. G. E. Becker and G. W. Gobelli, *J. Chem. Phys.*, **38**, 2942 (1963).
17. G. Karagounis and T. M. Issa, *Z. Elektrochem.*, **66**, 874 (1962).

9

New Applications of Infrared to Surface Studies

9-1. INTRODUCTION

From the work discussed in the preceding chapters it is seen that much of the initial development work on the application of infrared spectroscopy to the study of surface species has derived from an endeavor to determine the nature of the surface sites that are responsible for catalytic reactivity. Although little of the information derived is of direct application to catalytic theory, the results of these experiments have revealed a great deal about the nature of oxide and metal surfaces. This information is of great potential use to workers in other areas. Up to the time of writing, the infrared technique has not been utilized very much by workers in other areas of surface chemistry, but a start has been made in many new directions. Introductory studies have been made that have particular application to solid–solid interactions, thin-film work, flotation experiments, corrosion, glass and plastic surfaces, glass electrodes and membrane technology. Since it is anticipated that the future expansion of the subject will contribute greatly to knowledge in these areas, a few examples of some recent studies will be presented in order to indicate avenues of potential future research.

9-2. CORROSION

The chemistry of the corrosion process is imperfectly understood. The corrosion of a metal is known to be an electrochemical process in which the corroding metal leaves the metallic state at the anode to give metal ions that dissolve in the solution, e.g.,

$$Fe(metal) - 2e \rightarrow Fe^{2+}(aq)$$

Alternatively, the metal may be converted to a solid compound at the anode.

The reaction that takes place at the cathode depends upon the pH of the solution and the availability of oxygen and proceeds via one of the two reactions:

$$2H^+(aq) + 2e(metal) \rightarrow H_2(g)$$
$$\tfrac{1}{2}O_2 + H_2O + 2e(metal) \rightarrow 2OH^-(aq)$$

The corrosion can be controlled by negating either the anodic or the cathodic reaction. Poling and Eischens (1) have pointed out that the corrosion of iron and steel can often be prevented by inhibitors that contain NO groupings. The exact function of the nitrogen oxide inhibitors is not known, but it has been suggested their success is due to one or more of the following:

1. Their ability to promote the growth of protective oxide films (2–4).
2. A chemisorption of the inhibitors on the metal surface that prevents access by other molecules (5,6).
3. A chemisorption of the inhibitors on a metal-oxide surface that reduces the chemical gradient across the oxide layer (7). The rate of transport of the metal ions to the external solution is thus reduced and the corrosion is inhibited.

It was with this background in mind that Poling and Eischens undertook their investigation of the adsorption of nitric oxide and butyl nitrite on an iron surface. In view of the experimental difficulties involved in examining bulk metals by transmission spectroscopy, these workers used silica-supported iron samples, and, in common with many other workers, they experienced great difficulty in reducing these samples. Their spectroscopic results and interpretations are in general agreement with those of other workers in the $NO-Fe-SiO_2$ system (Section 6-7). Adsorption of nitric oxide onto bulk Fe_3O_4 or onto a preoxidized iron sample gave rise to a single band between 1820 and 1830 cm^{-1}. Following the assignments of Terenin and Roev (8), this band is attributed to the formation of a surface nitrosyl species that may be written formally as

$$Fe_s^{2+}:N{=}O^-$$

On the reduced iron surface, a band at 1750 cm^{-1} was observed in addition to the band at 1820 cm^{-1}. The 1750-cm^{-1} band was ascribed to an NO species chemisorbed on reduced parts of the surface; the 1820-cm^{-1} band was ascribed to a species chemisorbed on the nonreduced portions of the surface. In order to examine the applicability of their data to conditions more appropriate to the normal corrosive environment, Eischens and Poling observed the spectral changes that took place when oxygen and water were added to the NO–Fe–SiO$_2$ system. The main effect of these additions was to cause elimination of the 1750-cm^{-1} band. The 1820-cm^{-1} band was only slightly reduced in intensity, which indicates that if an adsorbed species is important in preventing corrosion, it is likely to be the species associated with the 1820-cm^{-1} band, in other words, the species associated with the *oxidized* surface.

Butyl nitrite was found to be dissociatively adsorbed on the reduced iron surface. Bands were produced at 1815, 1750, 1465, and 1370 cm^{-1}. The first two bands correspond to those found when nitric oxide was added to the sample and are assigned to NO groups adsorbed on oxidized and reduced portions of the surface, respectively. The bands at 1465 and 1370 cm^{-1} correspond to C—H bands found at the same frequency in gaseous butyl nitrite and indicate that the adsorbed butyl radical remains essentially intact. The nitric oxide species were removed at a lower temperature (100°C) than the hydrocarbons (200°C). At the latter temperature the hydrocarbons were partially oxidized to a surface carboxylate species. The separate removal of the NO and C—H bands provides further proof that the butyl nitrite had dissociated during adsorption. It is of interest that when butyl nitrite was added to a surface containing a monolayer of water, it displaced the water from the surface and produced a strongly adsorbed, dissociated species similar to that produced when the water was not present.

These results clearly show that NO-containing inhibitors have a strong affinity for the iron oxide surface and provide at least preliminary evidence that the effect of these corrosion inhibitors is to adsorb on the surface oxide layer and thereby alter the diffusion rate of the metal ion through the oxide layer.

9-3. POLYMER SURFACES

Apart from studies on their adsorptive properties, the surfaces of polymers have received very little attention in the literature. The adhesion of polymers to other materials, however, is a serious technological problem that in the present state of the art, contains a great deal of cookery. The process involves an interaction between two surfaces, and, in order to increase the adhesion activity of the polymer surfaces, many activating processes have been tried. Irradiation of the polymers has proved a useful technique, and chemical modification of polytetrafluorethylene surfaces has been tried. Treatments with metallic sodium in liquid ammonia, with a sodium–naphthalene complex, and with potassium acetate have been successful. The nature of the resultant surfaces, however, is not known.

Borisova and his colleagues have now investigated the infrared spectrum of polytetrafluorethylene that has received these various chemical treatments (9). In all cases it was found that the surface became more hydrophylic after the treatment and the adhesive property of the polymer was increased. All three treatments gave rise to a multitude of spectral changes, the most obvious of which was the appearance of a strong band at about 1600 cm^{-1}. This was attributed to the formation of a conjugated double bond in the surface layer of the material, but exact identification is not possible. Carbonyl, hydroxyl, $>CH_2$, and $—CH_3$ groups were all formed during the reaction. The carbonyl and hydroxyl groups were removed by heating to 200°C in vacuo, but the $>CH_2$ and $—CH_3$ groups were not completely removed until a temperature of 300° had been reached. At this stage the $>C{=}C<$ double bonds were still visible in the spectra of the treated polytetrafluorethylene.

9-4. FLOTATION STUDIES

Flotation is a process of ore concentration (separation). In principle, impure minerals are crushed so that each particle consists of only one material, and these particles are suspended in water. In the original process air was blown through the suspension and it was found that some species adhered to the gas bubbles and could be removed as a froth. The other species were wet by the water and could be removed by filtration or sedimentation. In the early 1900s it was found that small amounts of nonfrothing oils could be used instead of gases, and the use of xanthates

$$R—O—C{\overset{\displaystyle S}{\underset{\displaystyle S—M}{\big\backslash}}} \qquad R = \text{alkyl},\ M = \text{metal}$$

for this purpose was patented in 1924. The xanthates are especially useful for the separation of sulfides, the hydrophilic sulfide surface being converted into a partially hydrophobic surface via an adsorption process. The actual mechanism of adsorption from solution and the nature of the adsorbed species, however, have been in some dispute. Infrared studies on this system have helped to clarify the details of the process, and spectral data have been published by Little et al. (*10*). These authors showed that in aqueous solution, and in the presence of oxygen, the xanthate was adsorbed onto copper, lead sulfide, and nickel surfaces as a multilayer coating of the corresponding heavy-metal xanthate. Exactly the same species was observed when the reaction was carried out in the vapor phase, and the reaction occurred whether the surfaces had been previously oxidized or sulfided. The majority of the adsorbed xanthate layers could be washed off by many organic solvents, but a very thin film, probably of molecular dimensions, was always left tenaciously adsorbed on the metal.

In a later paper (*11*), Poling and Leja described the application of multiple internal reflectance spectroscopy to their study and were able to show that in the absence of uncombined oxygen the xanthate anions did not absorb on either copper or lead sulfide even though the surfaces contained preadsorbed oxygen. On the other hand, dixanthogen,

$$
R-O-C \overset{\displaystyle S}{\diagdown} \quad \overset{\displaystyle S}{\diagup} C-O-R
$$
$$
S-S
$$

an oxidation product of the xanthate, did adsorb on the surfaces from non-oxygen-containing solutions. Readdition of oxygen to the xanthate–metal systems resulted in the formation of the metal xanthate multilayers observed in the previous investigations. These experiments show that the role of oxygen in the adsorption process is not one of preadsorption, but rather indicate that dissolved oxygen oxidizes xanthate ions in solution to dixanthogen. It is this molecule that is the active adsorbate and chemisorbs dissociatively to give the adsorbed metal xanthate spectra.

9-5. SOLID–SOLID INTERACTIONS

A. Titanium Dioxide and Silver Nitrate

When titanium dioxide and silver nitrate are mixed intimately together, it is found that the mixture is darkened by ultraviolet radiation. The reaction is particularly rapid in the presence of water vapor, and the near-white mixture achieves a heavy black coloration. There has been some disagreement as to whether the black product is silver or silver oxide, and the role of the titanium dioxide is not fully known, although it is assumed to be that of photocatalyst. In any event, the surface of the titania plays a major role in this solid-state interaction. Infrared techniques, both reflection and transmission, have recently been applied to this system by Clark and Vondjidis (12). Samples of the TiO_2–$AgNO_3$ mixture were compared before and after irradiation. The infrared spectra obtained show that a broad adsorption band is produced between 1100 and 5000 cm^{-1} by the irradiation process. This band cannot be attributed directly to the formation of colloidal silver and is interpreted as being due to the formation of donor impurity levels at the TiO_2 surface. Admission of air or oxygen to the sample restores the transmittance to its original level, and it is therefore proposed that the effect of the ultraviolet irradiation is to desorb oxygen from the titania surface and thereby increase the concentration of electrons at the surface. It is postulated that these excess electrons can then attract a silver ion from its environment in the $AgNO_3$ crystal. If the silver ion associated with the trapped electron interacts with light similarly to a silver atom, we have an explanation for the reversible darkening that is observed.

B. The Gold–Silica Interface

The interaction between a vacuum-deposited gold film and the silica surface has been investigated by Guerra and coworkers (13). The extent of the interaction between the gold and the silica surface was found to depend upon the temperature at which the system had been heated. The reaction was followed by observing the changes that occurred in the shape of the 1100-cm^{-1} Si—O—Si stretching vibration. As the temperature was increased from 25° to 800°C, it was observed that this band changed in intensity, becoming more symmetrical and narrowing only on the high-frequency side. This result is interpreted as being caused by the formation of an O_s—Au bond at the silica–gold interface. The interaction causes a delocalization of the Si—O vibrational level and causes the asymmetrical narrowing of the absorption band.

9-6. ANODIC STAINING

When p-type silicon is anodically polarized in hydrofluoric acid solutions, yellowish films are formed at the surface of the semiconductor crystal. The exact nature of these films has been the subject of several communications (*14–16*), and it has been variously suggested that they consist of pure silicon, silicon monoxide, and crystalline silica. Beckmann (*17*) has recently investigated the transmission spectra of several films produced electrochemically in HF solution and has concluded that the films consist chiefly of silicon hydrides. The isotopic shifts produced by deuteration of the surface hydride provide conclusive evidence for the assignment. Quantitative application of the spectroscopic data enabled an estimate of the overall composition of the films to be made. This varied between H_2SiO and $HSiO_{1.5}$. These results once again show the efficiency of the infrared technique in determining the true nature of surface layers and surface species.

9-7. ELECTRODE PROCESSES:
CHARGE, DISCHARGE REACTIONS

The nature of the adsorbed intermediates that are produced during many electrode processes are imperfectly understood, as is the structure of the electrode surface. A recent infrared study of a sintered nickel oxide electrode in both the charged and the discharged state has been made by Kober (*18*) and is of some interest. The spectral data shows that in the discharged state the electrode consists primarily of an $Ni(OH)_2$ species in which the hydroxyl groups are parallel with the c axis of the crystal [Fig. 9-1(a)]. Hydrogen bonding is completely absent. A small amount of crystalline lattice water can be seen in the spectrum, and this is found to be associated with the preparative techniques. On charging of the electrode, considerable changes can be seen in the infrared spectrum [Fig. 9-1(b)]. The hydroxyl groups are considerably perturbed and are

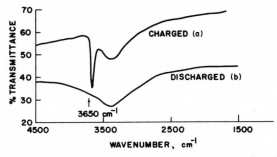

Fig. 9-1. Spectrum of a charged nickel oxide electrode compared with a discharged electrode. [Redrawn from Reference (18) by courtesy of the Journal of the Electrochemical Society.]

moved by 200 to 3450 cm^{-1}. Changes are also seen in the 300–700-cm^{-1} region of the spectrum. During discharge, the process is reversed. The hydrogen bonds are broken and the structure transforms back to the free hydroxyl configuration.

9-8. THE GLASS SURFACE

The nature of flat glass surfaces are of importance to the many investigators who use glass for laboratory ware, vacuum systems, biological reactions, glass–plastic composites, etc. In preceding chapters the nature of the porous glass surface has been discussed and its similarities with and differences from alumina and silica surfaces have been indicated. Whenever a glass surface is used, it should be remembered that it has always undergone some degree of weathering and that, on an atomic scale, it has a porous surface. Most scientists clean their glassware in acid or other aqueous solutions before use, and here again some degree of surface leaching must have taken place. The glass surface that the scientist uses, therefore, will bear little relationship to the composition of the glass. If the glass under consideration is a borosilicate glass, the exposed surface can be expected to approximate that of the porous glass surface already discussed and will probably be acidic in nature.

In general, any silica glass containing group II, III, or V ions will leach to give a surface containing Lewis acid sites. Hydroxyl groups will, of course, occur on all siliceous surfaces, and if some sort of gelatinous residue is formed during the leaching process, it may contain strong acid sites. The presence of these types of site can account for many of the anomalies noted by workers in various fields. Thus, abnormal activity of a Pyrex® borosilicate glass surface has been noted in physical adsorption studies (19), and leached soda-lime glasses are found to give much poorer chromatographic separations than the parent glasses (20). It is clear that the surface chemist who is interested in atomic or molecular interactions must treat his glassware with great care. In particular, the more soluble glasses and those containing group III cations should be washed little, if at all, prior to investigation.

9-9. CONSOLIDATION OF POROUS GLASS

In Chapter 4 it was seen that the dehydration of porous glass at temperatures up to 800°C leads to removal of surface hydroxyl groups. The OH vibration becomes more symmetric and shifts to 3750 cm^{-1} as the dehydroxylation proceeds. Above 800°C the porous glass starts to consolidate and the infrared spectrum approximates that of fused silica. A symmetrical band is observed at 2.73 μ (3663 cm^{-1}). This corresponds to the position of the OH band found in fused silica. The OH band in the consolidated glass is shifted by about 90 cm^{-1} from its free vibrational frequency and remains fairly symmetric. The shift of only 90 cm^{-1} is indicative of weak hydrogen bonding. If a linear —O—H $\cdots$ O type of bond is assumed, it can be seen from Fig. 4-14 that this perturbation corresponds to an O $\cdots$ O distance of about 3·1 Å. Two interesting questions can now be asked. Does the glass really consolidate, or are there still micropores throughout the structure? Do all glasses have micropores throughout their structure?

These questions are of some interest in the light of recent results on the ion selectivity of glass electrodes. After aging, the hydrated surface layer on the glass is undoubtedly important in establishing the origin of the electrode potential.

Eisenman has brought attention to the close analogy that exists between glass electrodes and living membranes (*21*). Acknowledgement of the importance of biological surfaces is comparatively recent, and these surfaces have not yet been subjected to infrared techniques. It might be expected that this will provide a major field of endeavor for future workers.

All in all, it can be seen that infrared spectroscopy has shown itself to be one of the most potent tools available to surface chemists. The application of this technique to new areas of endeavor will contribute greatly toward our knowledge of the chemistry of surfaces. It is anticipated that many of the readers will be inspired to help in the attainment of this knowledge.

REFERENCES

1. G. W. Poling and R. P. Eischens, *J. Electrochem. Soc.*, **113**, 218 (1966).

2. M. Cohen, *Can. J. Chem.*, **37**, 286 (1959).

3. J. Kruger, *J. Electrochem. Soc.*, **110**, 654 (1963).

4. J. L. Ord and J. H. Bartlett, *J. Electrochem. Soc.*, **112**, 160 (1965).

5. H. H. Uhlig, *Ann. N.Y. Acad. Sci.*, **58**, 843 (1954).

6. Y. M. Kolotyrkin, *Z. Elektrochem.*, **62**, 664 (1958).

7. Yung-Fang Yu Yao, *J. Phys. Chem.*, **68**, 101 (1964).

8. A. N. Terenin and L. M. Roev, *Spectrochim. Acta*, **16**, 274 (1959).

9. F. K. Borisova, G. A. Galkin, A. V. Kiselev, A. Ya. Korolev, and V. I. Lygin, *Kolloidn. Zh.*, **27**, 320 (1965).

10. L. H. Little, G. W. Poling, and J. Leja, *Can. J. Chem.*, **39**, 745, 1783 (1961); *Trans. Inst. Mining Met.*, **72**, 407, 414 (1963).

11. G. W. Poling and J. Leja, *J. Phys. Chem.*, **67**, 2121 (1963).
12. W. C. Clark and A. G. Vondjidis, *J. Catalysis*, **4**, 691 (1965).
13. C. R. Guerra, T. W. Healy, and D. W. Fuersteneau, *Nature*, **207**, 519 (1965).
14. D. R. Turner, *The Electrochemistry of Semiconductors* (P. J. Holmes, ed.), Academic, New York, 1962.
15. E. A. Efimov, J. G. Erusalimchik, and G. P. Sokolova, *Russ. J. Phys. Chem. English Transl.*, **36**, 645 (1962).
16. M. M. Koltun, *Russ. J. Phys. Chem. English Transl.*, **38**, 381 (1964).
17. K. H. Beckmann, *Surface Sci.*, **3**, 314 (1965).
18. F. P. Kober, *J. Electrochem. Soc.*, **112**, 1064 (1965).
19. J. R. H. Ross and M. W. Roberts, *J. Catalysis*, **4**, 620 (1965).
20. R. W. Ohline and R. Jojola, *Anal. Chem.*, **36**, 1681 (1964).
21. G. Eisenman, *Biophys. J.*, **2**, 259 (1962).

Appendix A

The Positions of
Characteristic Infrared Absorption Bands†

† Redrawn from N. B. Colthup, *J. Opt. Soc. Am.*, **40**, 398, 399 (1950), by courtesy of the society.

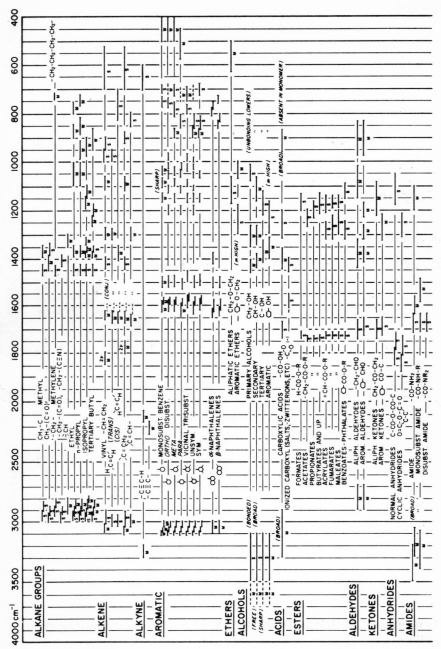

Fig. A-1a

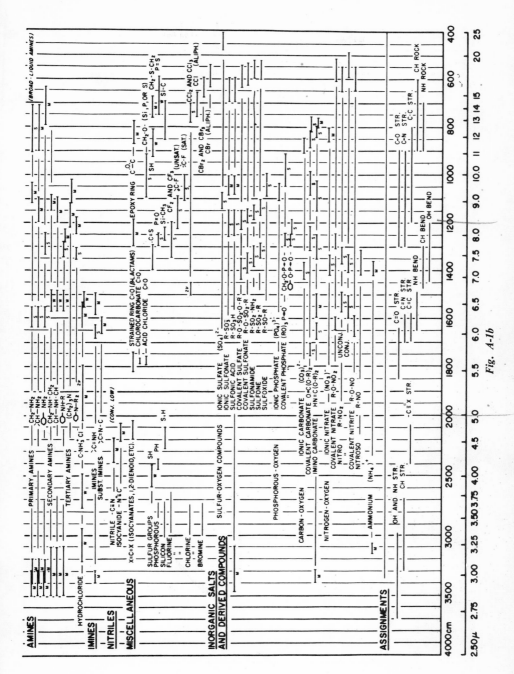

Fig. A-1b

293

Appendix B

Reciprocal Table for the Conversion
of Microns (μ) to Wave Numbers (cm^{-1})

λ, μ	$\bar{\nu}$, cm^{-1}	λ, μ	$\bar{\nu}$, cm^{-1}	λ, μ	$\bar{\nu}$, cm^{-1}
2.50	4000	2.87	3484	3.48	2873
2.51	3984	2.88	3472	3.50	2857
2.52	3968	2.89	3460	3.52	2841
2.53	3952	2.90	3448	3.54	2824
2.54	3937	2.91	3436	3.56	2809
2.55	3921	2.92	3424	3.58	2793
2.56	3906	2.93	3412	3.60	2778
2.57	3891	2.94	3401	3.62	2762
2.58	3875	2.95	3389	3.64	2747
2.59	3861	2.96	3378	3.66	2732
2.60	3846	2.97	3367	3.68	2717
2.61	3831	2.98	3355	3.70	2703
2.62	3816	2.99	3344	3.72	2688
2.63	3802	3.00	3333	3.74	2674
2.64	3788	3.02	3311	3.76	2660
2.65	3773	3.04	3289	3.78	2646
2.66	3759	3.06	3267	3.80	2632
2.67	3745	3.08	3246	3.82	2618
2.68	3731	3.10	3225	3.84	2604
2.69	3717	3.12	3205	3.86	2591
2.70	3703	3.14	3184	3.88	2577
2.71	3690	3.16	3164	3.90	2564
2.72	3676	3.18	3144	3.92	2551
2.73	3663	3.20	2135	3.94	2538
2.74	3649	3.22	3105	3.96	2525
2.75	3636	3.24	3086	3.98	2513
2.76	3623	3.26	3067	4.00	2500
2.77	3610	3.28	3048	4.04	2475
2.78	3597	3.30	3030	4.08	2451
2.79	3584	3.32	3012	4.12	2427
2.80	3571	3.34	2994	4.16	2404
2.81	3558	3.36	2976	4.20	2381
2.82	3546	3.38	2958	4.24	2358
2.83	3533	3.40	2941	4.28	2336
2.84	3521	3.42	2923	4.32	2314
2.85	3508	3.44	2906	4.36	2293
2.86	3496	3.46	2890	4.40	2273

λ, μ	$\bar{\nu}$, cm^{-1}	λ, μ	$\bar{\nu}$, cm^{-1}	λ, μ	$\bar{\nu}$, cm^{-1}
4.44	2252	6.30	1587	10.00	1000
4.48	2232	6.40	1563	10.20	980
4.52	2212	6.50	1538	10.40	962
4.56	2193	6.60	1515	10.60	943
4.60	2174	6.70	1492	10.80	926
4.64	2155	6.80	1471	11.00	909
4.68	2137	6.90	1449	11.20	893
4.72	2119	7.00	1429	11.40	877
4.76	2101	7.10	1408	11.60	862
4.80	2083	7.20	1389	11.80	847
4.84	2066	7.30	1370	12.00	833
4.88	2049	7.40	1351	12.20	820
4.92	2033	7.50	1333	12.40	806
4.96	2016	7.60	1316	12.60	794
5.00	2000	7.70	1299	12.80	781
5.05	1980	7.80	1282	13.00	769
5.10	1960	7.90	1266	13.40	746
5.15	1942	8.00	1250	13.80	725
5.20	1923	8.10	1235	14.20	704
5.25	1905	8.20	1220	14.60	685
5.30	1887	8.30	1205	15.00	666
5.35	1869	8.40	1190	15.40	649
5.40	1851	8.50	1176	15.80	633
5.45	1835	8.60	1162	16.20	617
5.50	1818	8.70	1149	16.60	602
5.55	1802	8.80	1136	17.00	588
5.60	1876	8.90	1124	17.50	571
5.65	1770	9.00	1111	18.00	556
5.70	1754	9.10	1099	18.50	541
5.75	1739	9.20	1087	19.00	526
5.80	1724	9.30	1075	19.50	513
5.85	1709	9.40	1064	20.00	500
5.90	1695	9.50	1052		
5.95	1681	9.60	1042		
6.00	1667	9.70	1031		
6.10	1639	9.80	1020		
6.20	1613	9.90	1010		

Indexes

AUTHOR INDEX

Numbers in parentheses are reference numbers and indicate that an author's work is referred to although his name it not cited in the text. Numbers in italics show the page on which the complete reference is listed.

SUBJECT INDEX

A

Absolute intensity, 57
Absorbance, definition of, 54
Absorption, 2
  integrated, 66
Acidity, *see* Lewis acidity, Surface hydroxyl groups
Adsorbate, definition of, 2
Adsorbent, definition of, 2
Adsorption
  chemical, 5
    electron transfer in, 15, 244
  definition of, 2
  heat of, 2
    dependence on surface coverage, 14
  physical, 4
    charge transfer in, 14
  polarization fraction and, 247
Adsorption isotherms, 6
$AgNO_3$, reaction with TiO_2, 285
Alkali halides, 269–270
  CO_2 adsorption on, 270
  HCN adsorption on, 270
  water adsorption on, 269
α sites, 158, 167, 180, 241
  in polymerization, 159
  number of, 158
  on alumina, 158
  on SiO_2—Al_2O_3, 180
  reaction with HCl, 159
Alumina, 141–169
  effect of pretreatment, 154
  hydration-dehydration of, 142
  Lewis acidity of, 145
  oxidative properties of, 150, 155
Alumina, adsorption on
  of acetone, 150
  of acetylene, 160

of alcohols, 155
of aldehydes, 156
of Benzaldehyde, 150, 155
of benzylnitrile, 150
of butene, 159
of carbon dioxide, 158
of cyclohexanone, 150
of ethylene, 162
of hexachloroacetone, 149
of HCl, 159
of NH_3, 146, 153
of $Ni(CO)_4$, 165, 228
of pyridine, 146
of substituted acetylenes, 161
Alumina, surface hydroxyl groups on, 141–145
  deuteration of, 142, 161
  number of, 143
  reaction of, 142
Al_2Cl_6, 45
Aluminum formate, decomposition of, 157
Anatase, *see* TiO_2
Angular momentum, 32
Anharmonicity constant, 30, 31, 34
Anodic staining, 286
Asymmetrical-top molecules, 33
Attenuated total reflectance, ATR, 276–279
Au, SiO_2—Au interface, 286

B

Back-donation, 251
Background, 58
Badger's rule, 49
Band shape, 65
Barium stearate, on steel, 278
Beam, heating effect of, 73
Benzaldehyde, on alumina, 150